# Papa Was a Farmer

## American Places of the Heart

*Sea Island Yankee*
by Clyde Bresee

*The Blessed Town: Oxford, Georgia, at the Turn
of the Century*
by Polly Stone Buck

*Grandmother's House*
by Frances Clausen Chapman

*Papa Was a Farmer*
by Brenda Weisberg Meckler

# Papa Was a Farmer

.:.     .:.       .:.

*Brenda Weisberg Meckler*

*with illustrations by*
*Marcia Erickson*

Algonquin Books of Chapel Hill
1988

published by

**Algonquin Books of Chapel Hill**
Post Office Box 2225
Chapel Hill, North Carolina 27515-2225

in association with

**Taylor Publishing Company**
1550 West Mockingbird Lane
Dallas, Texas 75235

Illustrations by Marcia H. Erickson.

LIBRARY OF CONGRESS CATALOGING-IN-PUBLICATION DATA
Meckler, Brenda Weisberg, 1900–
Papa was a farmer.
(American places of the heart)
1. Meckler, Brenda Weisberg, 1900–      . 2. Jews—Ohio—Dunham's Hill—
Biography. 3. Farmers, Jewish—Ohio—Dunham's Hill. 4. Immigrants—Ohio—
Dunham's Hill—Biography. 5. Dunham's Hill (Ohio)—Biography.
I. Title.   II. Series.
F499.D86M436      1988      977.1 [B]      88-3463
ISBN 0-912697-83-0

In loving memory of my parents who tilled the soil and of Evelyn and Laurie and of my beloved husband and to the beautiful family with which he endowed me.

# Contents

# Contents

# *Acknowledgments*

My warmest thanks to Joseph Stocker, my son-in-law, editor and preparer of this manuscript and unflinching in his crusade to cure me of my addiction to semicolons; to Mary Carnes, fellow graduate from New Richmond High School, Class of '16, for her assistance in finding photographs for the illustrator, and, with gratitude and affection, to my agent, Ms. Lynn Seligman, for her unshakable belief in the value of this book.

# 1904—1909

# *Genesis*

I was four years old, a child only three months and six days younger than the new century, and already I was engaged, together with my parents, in a criminal act.

The year was 1904, the time late on a summer night—a dark and starless night. The place: a point on Russia's border with Germany. (Today it would be Poland's border with Germany.) The darkness was essential to the success of the crime; also necessary was the discreet distribution of a few rubles to a pair of co-conspirators. One was the peasant who had brought us to a safe section of the border; the other, our contact on the other side, a second peasant in whose cabin we would sleep, on pallets of straw, until daybreak. We were, in short, "stealing the border." It was the only way we and countless others could have left Russia at that time.

In 1904 the dogs of war were howling throughout the land. Papa had served his time, as a young and single man, in the army of Nicholas II; he had no desire to repeat the experience, especially at this time when war with Japan might explode at any time. He was a family man now, and he had no feeling of allegiance to the Czar. And so he decided to get us out of the country—by stealth, of course—and take us to America.

Our destination was Boston, Massachusetts, where we would make a new life, a better life, surrounded by relatives and friends— and freedom.

We did make it to Boston, but in less than three years Papa's vision of the future was to be drastically changed. I was not destined to grow up in the historic city after all. Instead, my true American experience was to be rooted on a sixty-acre farm on Dunham's Hill in Ohio, twenty-five miles from Cincinnati. The radical transplant took place because of two unrelated events.

The first was the discovery that Papa's sixteen-year-old sister had become involved in the short-lived but bloody revolution of 1905 in Russia. The second was the fact that my mother's older brother, Michael, in Boston, was inspired to begin a new life as a farmer.

Uncle Mike had become friendly with some young Jewish men and women who had joined a movement committed to "returning to the land." They believed that the destiny of the Jewish people lay in that commitment: to till the soil, grow their own food, breathe clean air, and live in peace together all the days of their lives.

There was a song popular with these young idealists, most of whom wanted to till not just any soil but the soil of Palestine. They were the *chalutzim*, the pioneers. My uncle's enthusiasm stopped short of such a commitment; land in the United States was enough to satisfy his dream. Yet his dream took shape when he heard their song. Freely translated, it went something like this:

> In the good earth lies your richest blessing;
> 'Tis the fortune of your life—you'll want for naught;
> You'll know no sighs nor sorrow;
> You'll neither beg nor borrow;
> Today provides for tomorrow;
> Joy and honor is your portion and lot.

Thus, because of the revolutionary zeal of my young aunt, and the vision of an agrarian paradise that illumined the drab world of my uncle's sweatshop existence, the direction of our lives took a sharp turn.

The America in which I would grow up would not be along the crowded eastern seaboard but amid the cornfields and red clover, the buckeyes and the dogwoods which have been celebrated, over years long remembered, at every Fourth of July picnic in the American heartland.

# I

## *We Take Our Leave*

Papa had no relatives in the United States when we left Rowne, the city of my birth. There were boyhood friends living in Boston or New York—boys who had emigrated much earlier, with parents, and with whom he had kept up occasional contact—but no relatives. He left them all behind. For Papa, then, the leave-taking must have been painful.

His mother had died some years before. His father, a gentle, self-effacing little man, ran a smithy—living proof that not all blacksmiths had "large and sinewy hands." His place was also a rest-and-refresher way station for those of the Czar's cavalry who came that way.

There were five girls and two boys in my father's family. The oldest daughter was Tzivia, the wealthy one, married to an attorney. She was a deeply religious woman, but her life was darkened by her failure to bear children. God, she felt, had rejected her, for reasons she could not fathom but which she did not challenge. Like Job, she bowed to God's will and lavished her substance and her love on the children of her siblings.

Rahel, the mother of a son and daughter, was the next oldest. She supported her family by running a small grocery store while her husband, Chaim, studied Talmud. Then came Leah, mother of three sons and one daughter.

Herschel, the older of the two sons, was, I believe, the next sibling; he learned a good trade, watch-repairing, and was given a religious education as well. Of all Papa's family he was the only one who eventually followed us to America, where he became Uncle Harry. As was the custom, he set forth alone, leaving behind his wife and five children until he could earn and save enough money to send for them.

Rivka, the fourth daughter, unmarried at the time of their mother's death, assumed responsibility for keeping house for her father and the youngest daughter.

My father, the next-to-youngest sibling, had begged for and was given a secular education, from which he emerged a "free-thinker"—a socialist and an agnostic. This last must have been a sorrow to his grief-laden sister, Tzivia. How she took his marriage to a girl who had been her servant, I never knew. I do know that Papa supported his wife and child by tutoring young men who hoped to get into a university under the inequitable quota system that limited the number of Jews admitted. He also taught Russian reading and writing to less ambitious aspirants, who hoped only for jobs where literacy would be of use. But Aunt Tzivia probably financed the migration to America.

Which brings me to the youngest of the lot, my Aunt Braindele, whose name I would later adapt for my own use as "Brenda," when I discarded "Goldie," my given name. She was sixteen at this time of our leave-taking—spirited, beautiful, with bright, blue eyes and a close-cropped mass of dark curls. It was she who would some day be responsible for the first of a series of events that would land us in rural Ohio, the heartland of a new country.

My mother's family had emigrated to America many years before we did. All her family was there: her parents, her younger sister, her two brothers, plus numerous aunts, uncles, and cousins. They were already established in Boston and considered themselves, if not out-and-out Yankees, at least no longer greenhorns.

My mother's father had been the first to leave Krippa, their *shtetl*,

for America. When he left for America, his wife and their four children, of whom my mother was the oldest, remained in the village where my mother had been born. They lived with my mother's grandfather, who operated a tannery and a tavern. His customers were the peasants who dwelt in the village and whose land holdings surrounded their cluster of dwellings and fanned out beyond them in every direction. These peasants ran amok one Easter Sunday and burned down his tavern, sending him into a state of depression from which he never recovered. The family's only source of income while my mother's father was in America was wiped out. It then fell to Brucha, the oldest girl, the girl who would one day be my mother, to become the provider.

Her father's letters from America became less and less frequent; the money orders dribbled to zero. Finally months went by with nothing—no letters, no money orders, almost no hope.

Brucha, at fourteen, had stood on an upturned box to reach the counter on which she kneaded the family bread. Now, at fifteen or sixteen, she was packed off to Rowne, a sizable city, to become a very young but excellent cook for a lady named Tzivia, who would one day become her sister-in-law.

It was not uncommon in those days for the head of the family to leave for America to make his fortune and, in the course of time, to forget about those left behind, waiting. The children's mother had by now come to the bitter conclusion that this was to be her fate. Almost a year later, miracle of miracles, a letter arrived with *shiff's carten*—the tickets for passage to America for herself and the three youngest children. Brucha, wrote her father, would have to wait a little longer. Until he could save a little more, she could stay on with her grandfather and take care of him and help him in the business. Brucha's father had had no word about the disaster that had befallen his father, the tannery, and the tavern. He had no way of knowing his advice could not be followed. Brucha remained instead in Rowne, cooking for Tzivia, whose youngest brother had just returned from completing his service for Czar and country. This youngest brother would, in due time, become Brucha's husband, then my father.

When Brucha's grandfather learned that the family would be leaving for America, he refused any plans advanced for his future, deciding it was time for him to die. He took to his bed and died in his sleep a few days before the family was to leave Russia.

Brucha was thus left alone in the world, away from all family for the first time in her life, at the tender age of sixteen or seventeen. Within a very short time, she had married my father, given birth to me, and was on her way to rejoin her family in Boston, to start a new life.

Years later I learned that my grandmother, on receiving the manna from the American heaven, retreated hastily to the outdoor privy where she spent the better part of the day restoring her intestinal equilibrium. The stomach is, perhaps, a more accurate emotional weather vane than even the heart.

Our ship was the *Hibernia*, and we traveled in third class, bound for Boston. The *Hibernia* was carrying my parents and me to join my grandparents and aunt and uncles whom I had never seen. One of our fellow passengers was a boy of twelve named David Mottel, who was being sent by his grandmother to join his parents in Boston. The old lady had prevailed upon my father to look after the child and deliver him safely to his father and mother.

The meals in third class were not haute cuisine, but the food was fairly plentiful. Still, it was not plentiful enough for David Mottel's appetite. My father spent most of his time trying to sneak the boy into the second-class dining room after he had "cleaned up" in the third. Once he even got him into first class. By the time David made his way back to the netherworld of third class, his pockets often held a cold potato or a slice of white bread. On the one memorable raid of the first-class larder he returned with a chicken drumstick wrapped in a piece of discarded newspaper and half an orange in his pockets. David Mottel and my father were never caught in their daring invasions into the territory of their "betters," and when the boy was delivered to his waiting parents, he seemed plumper and rosier than they remembered.

We docked in Boston Harbor, where a small part of our American family was waiting to greet us. Mama's sister, my Tante Sadie, and their younger brother, Nathan, comprised the welcoming committee. They had been chosen to do the honors because they were at the bottom of the family earning scale and the loss of their day's pay would be the least damaging to the collective income.

Grandma, otherwise known as Bubbie, was waiting at home so that we would not come home to an empty flat. I would meet my

Zayde, or grandpa, and Uncle Mike later in the evening, at supper at the end of their twelve-hour day.

I remember thinking how pretty my Tante Sadie was, with her blue eyes and light brown hair and her American clothes. Uncle Nathan, who was only fourteen or fifteen at the time, looked very much like her but seemed shy and blushed a great deal. Everyone was overcome by emotion and found release in hugging me, and my Tante Sadie kept saying in Yiddish, "We'll make a real American lady out of you."

The flat was on Brighton Street in Boston's equivalent of New York's Lower East Side. The trip from the docks was made by streetcar, and Uncle Nathan took charge, getting the little green papers that let us transfer from one streetcar to another. He knew where and when to change; he knew which cord to pull to stop the trolley; he was the leader now, and no longer shy. He pointed out marvels that we passed: a great mortar and pestle jutting out from a drugstore facade, a policeman on a horse, an old man driving a scrawny horse, which pulled a small wagon while his master called a singsong announcement that he was prepared to buy "any rags, any bones, any bottles today..."

The policeman on the horse frightened Mama. "He looks like a Cossack!" she cried. But Uncle Nathan reassured her that there were no Cossacks in America, that this policeman was there to protect the people, even the Jewish people.

Tante Sadie filled Mama in on the family's employment. Zayde sorted mill ends in a textile factory and sometimes brought home nice pieces large enough to make a corset cover or even sometimes a "waist"—or, as we know it now, a blouse.

Tante Sadie worked at the same factory, but she had learned to operate a shuttle. It required much more skill than sorting mill ends but, being a girl, she couldn't, of course, expect to earn as much as Zayde.

Uncle Nathan worked in a cigar factory and went to night school four times a week. But the biggest earner was Uncle Mike, who was a very good men's tailor. He paid his share at home but did not throw his wages into a "common pot," defying tradition and his stern father. He saved every penny he could and planned to have a shop of his own very soon. He would be his own boss then and make his own rules in his own "sweatshop."

By the time we got off at the stop nearest the family flat, I was fast asleep.

When I awoke, the whole family was home: my Zayde, tall and handsome, with a full brown beard and fierce blue eyes; my Bubbie, small, round, with velvety black eyes and a black *sheitel*, the wig that Jewish women brought up in the Orthodox tradition wore after they were married. I have been told that it was designed to spare the young matrons advances from men who were not their husbands. If that impression was correct, the *sheitel* admirably served its purpose. Bubbie would discard it years later when Zayde discarded *her*. There was Uncle Mike, short, dark, lean, looking grim even when he was smiling. And standing possessively close to Tante Sadie was a tall, dark, handsome young man. Later I was told he was going to be my Uncle Max as soon as he and Tante Sadie were married. My father also was soon to become "Max," an Americanization of his Jewish name, but at this point he was still "Mendel."

They were all standing around my bed, beaming, when I opened my eyes and sat up, startled by this admiring gallery. Then Mama picked me up and Bubbie said, "Now we can go to the table!" Tante Sadie didn't have to help because she was entertaining my future Uncle Max. I sat beside Papa while Mama helped serve. First they brought in chopped herring, chopped liver, and fresh white challah, and Uncle Max made the blessing over the bread. Then Bubbie and Mama served the golden chicken soup with fine noodles, and the first plate was served to Tante Sadie and her fiancé. Only one plate of soup, with two spoons! I was puzzled and asked, "Mama, doesn't Bubbie have plates for everyone?"

My question was loud enough to evoke laughter around the table. I saw that Tante Sadie blushed, and I hid my face on Papa's shoulder. "It's all right, kitten," Mama soothed. "Bubbie has plenty of plates, but they are in love, so they eat from one plate, like they were one person. It's a tradition." I was still baffled, but I asked no more questions. Later, however, when Mama was putting me to bed, I asked, "Mama, you and Papa didn't eat from one plate. Don't you love each other anymore?"

She laughed softly and reassured me. "It's only a tradition for when you are not married yet, that's all, kitten. Don't worry about it!"

After supper other relatives came in, followed by friends and neighbors. There was wine on the table now, and Bubbie's famous strudel, and there was a babble of talk, most of it advice for Mama and Papa. Papa had no marketable skill to offer to America, but it was decided he should learn a good trade. All kinds of things were suggested. Papa listened silently. When there was a lull, he astonished everyone by saying quietly, "On the ship I heard from a man who had already been in America. He was coming back to Boston from visiting his parents in Minsk. He said a good trade here is being a shoe cutter. So I shall learn that trade."

He was met with astonished silence. Then someone said, "*Nu!* How do you like that? A greenhorn one day in America and he knows about trades."

"Why not?" Uncle Mike demanded, glaring at the speaker. "He's an educated man. He maybe can't read the small letters in the Talmud, but he's smart. Shoe cutter is a fine trade. You're all right, Mendel. You won't get lost in America!" Everybody clapped and cried, "True! True!" and the wine was poured.

\*    \*    \*

It was summer and the streets were always crowded with people, with laughter, quarrels, hucksters' cries, each sound trying to jostle its way to supremacy. And smells! Smells of cooking from the elbow-to-elbow tenements, smells of fish from the peddlers' wagons, foul gutter smells from decaying rubbish. And children everywhere, romping, shouting, in and out of the crowds, playing tag, chasing the ice wagons to steal pieces of ice. I longed to join them but I was not allowed to go into the street alone.

"Bummers," Bubbie called the wild boys—no fit playmates for a nice little girl who wore long white stockings and ribbons in her hair. The closest I got to that street scene was the fire escape steps, where I was allowed to sit and listen and watch. I was puzzled by the obscene gestures of little boys who would run beneath the fire escape steps, look up, shout strange words and run away, laughing. It all sounded very friendly and I even learned, and proudly repeated, some of their words, to the horror of the family. After that I was forbidden to sit on the fire escape alone.

To make up for my almost total isolation, Tante Sadie got up early one Sunday instead of luxuriating in an extra hour of sleep. She did her usual Sunday chores of washing and ironing and mending her meager wardrobe. Then she packed a lunch and took Mama and me to the lake in Boston's Public Gardens. It was an enchanting afternoon! Music drifted in from somewhere and the rhythmic waves on the lake undulated gently in the breeze like dancers in a slow waltz. And on this lovely water glided the swan boats, so graceful, so beautiful, so proud! Cool water, green grass, blue sky and the wondrous, magical birds, transformed into chariots, within whose sheltering wings sat children, their faces aglow with pleasure.

I looked longingly from my Tante Sadie to Mama; they nodded and smiled, and I felt as though heaven had opened up for me.

My Tante Sadie untied a knot in her handkerchief and let a

stream of pennies fall into Mama's hand. Rides for children were a penny, for grown-ups, three cents. There were enough pennies for four rides for me, two with Tante Sadie and two with Mama. I wanted to stay forever but, to divert me, they decided we would sit on a bench in the shade and eat lunch from the shoe box Sadie had packed: pastrami sandwiches and dill pickles and apples. Then I sat on Mama's lap and she sang a Russian lullaby and I fell asleep. When I woke up, I wanted to have at least one more ride on a swan boat. But the swan money had been spent, and the second knot in Tante Sadie's handkerchief held only carfare home. The enchanted afternoon was over and I wept bitterly for paradise lost. But on the streetcar, snuggled in the circle of Mama's arms, I was comforted and accepted the promise of "other times."

That night, over a dairy supper of lovely pink beet borscht, blintzes with sour cream, a salad of little pink radishes, tender green onions, cucumbers with more sour cream, and fresh rye bread and butter, Papa's future was planned in detail. It was explained that the trade he had chosen was fine; he was clearly smart and would learn fast. But learn you must, and you had to pay the boss while you were learning. Immediately was not a moment too soon to get started.

Nobody had mentioned it, but in the last few weeks I had heard Mama and Papa talking privately about how three extra bodies in that flat presented a real hardship. Uncle Nathan had relinquished his bed to Mama and Papa and moved into Uncle Mike's room, sharing his bed. Neither of them liked this arrangement. As for me, two pairs of chairs facing each other had become my bed. Piled with a small mattress, blankets, and sheets, it was set up in the dining room for the night and dismantled in the morning. It served me well enough, and naps, of course, were on the bed used by Mama and Papa. Nobody had complained, but Mama and Papa wanted to lift the burden from the family as soon as possible.

On Monday morning, accompanied by an unemployed but English-speaking cousin, Papa set off for Lynn, where most of the shoe factories were established. Uncle Mike advanced the necessary learning fee, and Papa was placed on the waiting list in the first factory he visited.

During the three months that Papa was waiting and learning, Mama helped out as a "pants finisher" at home. Uncle Mike would bring the bundles to her and she worked on them using Bubbie's sewing machine, late in the evenings when supper was over and all the day's chores were done.

I was given the priceless gift of an occasional afternoon on the swan boats again, but either Tante Sadie or Uncle Nathan would take me. Mama stayed home and "finished" pants. Once, as she worked late at night, I awakened, terrified by a bad dream. I saw a light in the kitchen and climbed down from my improvised bed and looked in. Mama was bent over her work, making strange little sounds that frightened me. I cried out, "Mama!" She looked up, startled. She was crying; tears were running down her cheeks. I had never seen Mama cry before. It was not to be the last time. I ran to her and I, too, began to cry. She lifted me to her lap and hugged me, wiped my tears and her own.

"Hush, *ketsele*," she whispered. "It's all right. We mustn't wake the Papa. He has to get up early to go to the factory. I'll make you some warm milk, yes? With honey, yes? And you'll go back to sleep."

She did not tell me why she was crying that night. But much later, when I was older and we talked from the heart, I asked her about that night, the first time I had seen my mother cry. "I began to feel the strangeness, even though I was safe with my family," she explained. "They worked so hard, and Papa was going to work in a factory. It was the strangeness, the strangeness...."

Papa learned fast. He was, after all, everyone said, "an educated man, even though an unbeliever." There was a certain pride in having him in the family. Now he was on a payroll. As soon as he could save enough to repay Uncle Mike, he would rent a flat in Lynn, we would move into our own place, and I would have a regular bed. In the meantime, Mama kept on "finishing." But I never caught her crying again. At least not then, not in Boston, not for many years.

She found out about a place called "kindergarten." In it I discovered a world almost as enchanting as the swans on the lake. I found children I could play with, not "bummers." In fact, many of the children who had run wild in the streets in the summer had been scrubbed clean and now became budding scholars. I too was becoming an American.

On the Sunday that Papa was able to pay back the money he had borrowed from Uncle Mike, there was a celebration. Mama cooked and Bubbie baked, and Grandpa brought a piece of "changeable" silk from the shop, from which Mama made herself a new waist. I thought she looked even prettier than Tante Sadie. Her black eyes did not look sad, as they had on the night I had found her crying. They were bright and merry and her black hair lay in soft waves about her round face. Only her hands were worn and older than she was.

All the family came, and boyhood friends of Papa's who, like him, had had secular educations and had become professional men: lawyers, dentists, pharmacists. Like Papa, they were free-thinkers. They read the *Jewish Forward*, English newspapers, and the Russian and American novelists. At the party they sang songs about liberty and enlightenment, accompanied by a young poet on his mandolin.

Mama had outdone herself preparing her special dishes, and Grandma's sponge cake and strudel were acclaimed works of art. Uncle Mike brought a bottle of wine and gave money to Uncle

Nathan to fetch strawberry soda from the candy store. Only Zayde muttered about a houseful of *apichorsim*, unbelievers, and waited for the roof to fall in. It was decided that on the following Sunday Mama and Papa would go to Lynn and look for a flat.

Monday morning, after all the workers had gone to their jobs, a letter came from Rowne, from Tante Tzivia. Letters from home were rare, especially during the Russo-Japanese War, so Mama and Bubbie waited eagerly for Papa's homecoming to hear the latest news. The latest news proved to be a bombshell: Braindele, Papa's beautiful young revolutionary sister, had been discovered operating an illegal printing press in the basement of her father's house. This was serious at any time; it was a capital offense during wartime. The family had arranged to smuggle her out of the country by spreading a lot of Tante Tzivia's rubles in the right places. But Braindele had refused to escape without Moishele Platt, her accomplice and sweetheart. So Tante Tzivia had had to start over. She finally managed to get them both out of Russia.

Much later, it was revealed that Moishele had been dressed in rabbinical garb and Braindele was equipped with a costume that gave an authentic appearance of advanced pregnancy. I suppose they thought the disguises made them look respectable. They were shipped off to Cincinnati, where Moishele's married sister, Freidel Mishkin, lived. They were to be married as soon as they arrived. Unfortunately, between the time of the hasty departure of the young lovers from Russia, and their arrival in Cincinnati, Braindele fell out of love with Moishele and refused to marry him. She hated Cincinnati and wanted only to return to Russia, where she could resume her life's mission: to overthrow Czar Nicholas II and establish paradise on earth. Tante Tzivia's letter ended by saying Papa must do something about his *meshugene* (crazy) little sister!

Shattered was the dream of a new home of our own in Lynn. The money saved for furniture would be needed for Papa's trip to

Cincinnati and other expenses that might arise. Tante Tzivia had said nothing about sending money. So Papa left for Cincinnati and Uncle Mike brought more bundles for Mama, and a present of a sewing machine. My improvised bed was dismantled and I shared Mama's.

A month passed before we learned what was really going on. It was almost like waiting in the old country for word from America, Bubbie said. For Mama, Cincinnati might as well have been across the ocean. But Uncle Nathan, who had advanced to geography in night school, would show her on the map that it was not so very far after all, and Mama would nod and pick up another pair of pants to finish.

One day the long-awaited letter came. Written in Yiddish, it was opened after supper and read aloud by Zayde. Braindele was on her way back to Russia! That is what she had begged for, and somehow it had been arranged. But Moishele had chosen not to return with her and rejoin the revolutionists, even when Braindele said that if he would go back they could be sweethearts again. As her passion for justice had made him a battler for human rights, her rejection of him must have made him a misogynist. He never married.

The letter went on to relate that Tante Tzivia had sent money, and had cleared the way for her headstrong niece to return by spreading more around where it would pave the way. The war with Japan had been ingloriously lost; the short-lived revolution, too, had failed, its leaders leaving the blood of dead comrades to redden the snow in the square before the Czar's palace. "And now," Papa wrote, "here is my important news. I met here, at Freidel's [Moish-ele's sister's], some *landsleit* [countrymen] from Russia. They showed how it would be better for Brucha and the child to join me here, where there is a chance to go into my own business with them. I would be a full partner and they have the money. And I have the brains, the intelligence. The business they have in mind is a junk shop they know is for sale!"

A money order was enclosed between the first and second pages, and now, as Grandpa turned the sheet, it fell to the floor. Everyone praised Papa for sending money to Mama, but the praise abruptly changed to shock as Grandpa read on. The money order was for train fare for Mama and me to join him in Cincinnati "at once." He already had a flat rented, and we were to lose no time in coming to occupy it.

After the first stunned moment, everyone began to talk, shout and scream at once—everyone except Mama. Papa had learned a good trade here! There was a job waiting for him. Instead he was dragging Mama and me away from her family, away from civilization, "out west" to God knows what kind of life, what kind of future! I remember pulling at Tante Sadie's skirt and urgently asking, "Do they have swan boats?"

"Swan boats?" she cried. "You'll be lucky if they have pavements and a tree!"

"Not even kindergartens?"

"What do Indians know from kindergartens?" was her answer. "Indians they got!"

They finally quieted down, moving about in bitter silence. Mama started sorting our clothes to be washed and ironed in the morning. The next day was Saturday, and she began packing our meager belongings while Uncle Nathan went to buy our train tickets. The Sabbath was disrupted; Grandma and Tante were in tears most of the day. In the evening, Uncle Nathan sent a telegram to Papa telling him we were leaving on Sunday, so he could meet our train.

Uncle Mike and Uncle Nathan came with Tante Sadie to see us off. I heard Tante Sadie say to Mama in a low voice, "I'm asking you again, at least leave the child with us until you get settled. Who knows what he'll think of next?"

I think my heart skipped a beat; I tightened my grip on Mama's hand. I heard her say quietly, "I know you mean well, sister, and I thank you. But the child goes where I go." I was still afraid Mama might change her mind, and I was able to breathe freely again only when the train came puffing in.

Uncle Mike pressed a dollar bill into Mama's hand, saying something about a train butcher. Uncle Nathan presented me with a little box, which I found later contained a tiny celluloid swan. In it, sheltered by its wings, sat a little doll. Tante Sadie had been holding a wrapped shoe box and now she handed it to Mama, explaining through tears that Bubbie had packed some food for us. Pullman cars moved slowly past us and then a dining car. I was amazed to see people sitting at pretty tables, eating and looking curiously at the platform crowd as they slowly passed us by. At last the coach section came to a stop. Everyone except Uncle Mike was crying, and he kept rubbing his eyes. I clung to Mama's hand. I heard someone shout, "A-a-all aboard!" And we were on our way. Mama never saw Boston again, but the family eventually, after many years, came to Cincinnati. And the first to come was Uncle Mike.

# 2

# *A New Beginning*

"It will be a new beginning." That's what Papa said when he met us at the railroad station.

"Please God," said Mama, but her voice sounded like she wanted to cry.

The Cincinnati to which we came was not very different from the Boston that we had left. The flat that Papa had prepared for us was on Central Avenue, which was almost like another Brighton Street—a little wider perhaps, somewhat less crowded, but with the same sounds and smells and clutter, and children, just like Bubbie's "bummers," shouting and fighting and playing. The flat itself was over a Kroger grocery store. A narrow passage—dark even at the brightest time of day—led from the street to a courtyard where clotheslines and garbage cans occupied most of the space. A wooden stairway led from the courtyard to the two flats above the stoop. Ours was at the very top.

When we stepped inside the flat for the first time, it seemed so much like Bubbie's and Zayde's in Boston that I almost expected to find them waiting for us in the parlor. But only shadows waited as Papa led us from the parlor to the kitchen to the bedroom, all in a row, and, finally, to a tiny room off the bedroom. It was barely large enough to hold a narrow cot and a chair. On one wall wooden pegs took the place of a closet. This room, Papa said proudly, was *my* room, and the bed was a real bed, not chairs facing each other, like at Bubbie's. All the rooms opened off a narrow hallway, and at the end of the hallway was the toilet. Papa had furnished the flat with the barest necessities, but he pointed to each piece of furniture with pride.

"And I promise you," he said to Mama, "in one year, I give you my word—even, maybe, in six months—you will have a sofa and a carpet and curtains for the windows." He had brought up some groceries, too, and he showed them to Mama: tea and chicory and bread and, in the ice box, milk and butter and eggs. And Moishele's sister, Freidel Mishkin, had sent up a honey cake and cinnamon rolls.

The next day, Sunday, we were going to the Mishkins' for dinner. In the meantime, Papa said, we must go to bed early because we were tired after our long trip, and must be ready for the excitement of the next day when "the new beginning" would really begin. So I was put to bed in my own room, and Mama and Papa went to bed in theirs. They closed the door between our rooms, and I almost asked them not to because it felt strange and lonely in this new place. But I had a feeling it would be better not to ask. I was half asleep when I heard strange, disturbing sounds from their room: murmuring voices, and soft laughter from Mama, who whispered, loud enough for me to hear, "Wait till the child is asleep." I lay very still with my eyes shut tight. They wanted me to sleep, so I tried hard to oblige. The murmuring voices continued and lulled me to that state that Mama wanted Papa to wait for. The new beginning had begun for me. I slept.

When I woke up in the morning and came into the kitchen, Mama was already making breakfast. She looked pretty and happy, and Papa was smiling, and when he saw me, he smiled at me, too. I had a feeling that he was pleased with me because I had gone to sleep almost right away when Mama wanted him to wait.

Papa was telling Mama about the tenants in the flat below ours.

Their name was Corelli and they were a large family of Italians, he explained. Their flat was bigger than ours, he said, and they even had a separate room with a tin tub for taking a bath. We, he said, would have to make do with a portable tub in the kitchen for the time being. Mama looked troubled. "Italians!" she exclaimed. "The Black Hand, I heard!"

Papa stopped smiling.

"You are a fool," he cried. "Even in Russia every goy is not a Cossack. And every Jew is not a money lender!"

"I know, I know. I didn't mean it." Mama hastened to restore the way things were before. "Only why did it have to be Italians? Couldn't you find a flat with Jewish neighbors so I could have someone to talk to? Not just the four walls?"

Papa was really mad now.

"I did it on purpose," he shouted, "so you would have to learn English. And if you learn to say 'Good morning' in Italian, it wouldn't hurt you, either!"

"I'm sorry; I'm very sorry!" Mama pleaded. "I'll try hard to learn. Come, sit down and eat your breakfast." She put her hand gently on his arm and I held my breath. After a moment he turned and looked at her and smiled again, and I stopped holding my breath.

"It's convenient here," he said. "Springer's Grocery is across the street and right under us is Kroger's, but go look for a shmaltz herring in such a place. And next door to Springer's is the kosher butcher." Papa always explained that the only reason he ate kosher meat was because the animals for the kosher trade were slaughtered more humanely than the others.

Now that he was smiling again he called me "pussy-cat" and told Mama and me to hurry and eat breakfast like he was doing and then get dressed quickly. He would take us for a walk and show us the street.

The street was busy, because it was Sunday and all the Jewish stores were open. It had rained in the night, and boys were running barefoot in the puddles. Women were shouting to one another from open windows in the tenements that the rain had cooled things off, thank God. On either side of the entrance to Springer's Grocery stood a large barrel, one with dill pickles, the other with herring. A fat woman had rolled up her sleeves and was putting her arm into the herring barrel, bringing up a herring, examining it, and throwing it back.

"Everything is like Brighton Street," Mama said. "Only the woman in the herring barrel—this I never saw."

"She's a yenta," Papa said. "Wait till Springer catches her." He steered Mama and me away, just as Mr. Springer came out and began shouting at the woman. She shouted back and threw a herring at him.

Mama was shocked, but Papa just laughed. We stopped next at Goldenstern's Confectionery and Cultural Center. Papa went in to buy a *Jewish Forward*, and Mr. Goldenstern came out with him to shake hands with Mama and pat me on the head. He told me he had a little daughter about my age. Her name was Jennie. I did not see Jennie that day, but she was to have an important place in my life before the year was out.

When we started back to our flat, Mama asked why Mr. Goldenstern's candy store was a Cultural Center. Papa told her it was a meeting place for socialists, free-thinkers, actors from the Yiddish Theatre, writers and all kinds of intellectuals. There was always a steaming samovar at the back, and a table for chess, and all kinds of newspapers and magazines. Many years later I heard that Trotsky had been in Cincinnati and Goldenstern's had been his headquarters. I suspect there are as many cultural centers in which Trotsky drank tea and expounded the gospel according to Marx as there are beds in which George Washington slept.

The Mishkins' flat was nicer than ours. They already had curtains on the windows and a carpet on the floor. And there was a dining room, and pictures on the walls. This place really looked like Bubbie's in Boston. It was soon filled with Mishkin relatives who came to welcome us and to say, "It should be in a good hour!"

The three partners were there, of course. There was Moishele, who had borrowed from his brother-in-law, Pinchas Mishkin, the money to be a partner. Then there was Landa. In all the years that followed this day I never heard him called by a first name, just "Landa." He was a "landsman," which meant he came from the province of Wolyn, just as we did, and that made him like family. He was a bachelor, very pale and sad-looking. Everything about him was the color of dust—his hair, his pale eyes, his clothes, all dust-colored. He had business experience: he had once managed a delicatessen. Thinking about it now, I wonder how he applied that expertise to the junk business, but it seems to have qualified him to be a partner.

I remembered Moishele a little from Russia, when he had been my Tante Braindele's sweetheart. He was a kind and loving young man, a peacemaker, short and round like his sister and her husband. As soon as we came, he told me to shut my eyes and hold out my hands for a surprise. When he said I could look, there was a doll looking up at me. Except for the tiny doll in the celluloid swan boat that Uncle Nathan had given me, it was my first doll—the only doll I ever had. Moishele became my special friend.

Papa was made a partner because he was educated. But the most important one of all was Mr. Jake Ostrovsky. He was the "money" man. He was taller than anybody in the room, with an ample belly across which rested a gold chain. He had red hair and a red mustache and eyebrows, and you could see that he felt very, very important. His wife, on the other hand, seemed to say, "I'm nothing, nobody. . . . But look at my husband!" Everybody except Tante Freidel Mishkin and Mama, who was helping her, was in the parlor, all talking at once. Mr. Ostrovsky talked louder than anybody, and everybody stopped to listen to him until Tante Freidel called us to the table.

I took Moishele's hand and went with him into the dining room. Somebody said, "It smells like heaven."

Wine and sponge cake stood on the sideboard, and on the table was a feast "fit for the Messiah," said Mr. Ostrovsky. In the center of the table stood a large platter of roast chicken surrounded by a sweet side-dish—scoops of carrot *tzimmes*. Another platter held fragrant sweet-and-sour stuffed cabbage rolls, and still another dish offered beautiful golden brown, crisp slices of potato *kugel* casserole. When everybody was seated, Uncle Pinchas Mishkin passed the slices of homemade challah, saffron-golden and still warm. Everyone took a slice and joined in the blessing over bread, even Papa, who explained that he had no objection to expressing gratitude for good food and good friends breaking bread together. It made, he said, for good feeling and for fellowship. It seemed like Papa was always explaining why he did some things that a freethinker should not do.

Everybody sat at the table for a long time, talking, mostly about the new business, drinking wine and sarsaparilla soda and eating sponge cake. Everybody made a toast to the partners.

It was almost sunset when we finally walked home. Papa took us through different streets and even to a canal that I would have to cross to go to school when it started, after Labor Day. When we came back to our block, Mama stopped at Springer's and bought a herring, but she didn't put her arm into the barrel. Mr. Springer could see that Mama was not a yenta, and he picked out a very fine herring with his long-handled fork. We bought tomatoes and potatoes and cucumbers, and went up to our flat.

# 3

# *End of Summer*

Summer was drawing to a close, and Mama brought up the subject of school. Papa was too busy now with the business to take me, so Mama consulted Annie Corelli. Annie and her mother had called on us soon after we moved in. First Annie came one morning, carrying a big pot of spaghetti. Although we didn't know what spaghetti was, Mama was too polite to say so.

"You kosher?" asked Annie.

Mama nodded.

"It's all right," said Annie. "This spaghetti kosher. No meat. *Pareveh!*"

Mama was delighted. "You know from kosher and *pareveh!* You Jewish!"

"Not me!" laughed Annie. "Italiano, that's me! My brother married a Jewish girl. I learned from her."

This really puzzled Mama, but she took the spaghetti and invited Annie to have a glass of tea and some cake.

The next time Annie came she brought her mother, whose English was not much better than Mama's. They somehow communicated in a language all their own. Mrs. Corelli spoke mostly Italian; Mama spoke mostly Yiddish; each threw in an occasional English word. But best of all was body language and pantomime, which they used with great skill.

So it was Annie who took Mama and me to get me enrolled in

the Tenth Street District Elementary School. Her little brother, Tony, went to a Catholic school and Annie thought maybe I should go to a Jewish school, but she didn't press the point.

We came to the principal's office, and Annie did most of the talking. I had turned six in April. I could read and write at a first-grade level or better. Annie told the principal I was very smart— smart enough to go into the second grade. The principal said he would test me on arithmetic. I remember exactly what he asked me.

"Suppose three robins and two sparrows sat on the branch of a maple tree, and the sparrows and one robin flew away. How many birds were left?" I was totally bewildered. I ended up in the first grade.

Papa told us the business was doing well, but it was too soon to draw out money except for the rent and food. He had a surprise for us, though. When Tante Tzivia sent money for Tante Braindele to go home, she had included enough to pay the bribes she thought would be necessary to get her little sister out of the United States. Papa wrote her that nobody had to pay to get out of this country— this was America! And he kept the money because, he said, he was entitled. Anyway, Tante Freidel Mishkin took Mama and me to a big store near Fountain Square and bought us winter coats, and there was enough left over for a sweater for Papa.

Sometimes Landa, the landsman, and Uncle Moishele came home from the shop with Papa to talk about plans and problems, and Mama always made them stay for supper. Once Mama asked why Ostrovsky never came with them. Papa and his two partners looked at one another in a funny way. Then Papa said, "I never asked him. I am watching him. Behind my back, I believe he is buying stolen merchandise." Mama gasped; she looked really frightened.

"You have no proof," Landa said mildly.

"I have a suspicion," said Papa. "I am watching him. I will have proof. Then he goes or I go."

Landa shrugged. He was a tired little man, and he still looked dusty, like the first time I saw him.

We were halfway through supper, and Papa was getting angrier and angrier. Moishele tried to change the subject. He turned to me, smiling.

"You know, little one, we better hurry before school starts and do some traveling around the city. I think Sunday we'll go to the zoo, or maybe Chester Park or—"

Papa yelled at him: "Don't change the subject. The subject under discussion is not zoos and Chester Parks. Brucha, bring some hot tea! Your partner was the subject. The crook will land us all in jail!"

Mama tried to placate him. "Mendel," she pleaded, "what do you want from Moishele? He didn't do anything—"

"Brucha, don't mix in," he shouted. "Bring tea."

Years later Mama told me that, after that night, every time she heard a patrol wagon clanging by she knew it was on its way to arrest the four partners.

School started after Labor Day. Mama walked me across the bridge and gave me all kinds of instructions about behaving and coming straight home and being polite to the teacher, "—so you will learn." By this time we had gone up the steps to the entrance. There Mama stopped. She was embarrassed to go in because her English was so poor. In her hand she clutched the certificate of my enrollment. Other small children and their mothers passed us, but Mama just stood. Finally a tall young man, loaded with books, recognized that we needed help, recognized the Star of David that Mama wore on a little chain, smiled, and said in Yiddish, "I am

Jewish. Can I help you?" Mama almost embraced him. She thrust the enrollment certificate into his hand and asked him in Yiddish to do a *mitzvah* (favor) and take her child to the right room. I kissed her good-bye, took our new friend's hand, and set forth on the beginning of my education.

I was assigned a seat in front of a child who was to become my "bosom friend" for a time and who added a dimension to my education that the classroom did not provide. Her name was Norma, and today she would be called a street-wise kid. She would not tell me where she lived, nor anything about her parents. She was seven years old but still in the first grade. Her clothes were always clean but faded and shabby. Her winter coat was badly worn, her shoes scuffed. She wore a red knitted cap in cold weather but never mittens nor overshoes. However, she knew a large part of the city, and I came to know it through her. It was not the city that Moishele showed me, but it was as much a part of Cincinnati as the lovely places he introduced me to. Some parts of Norma's Cincinnati made our Central Avenue look elegant. She would come on Saturday afternoons, stand at the foot of the stairs and issue a shrill whistle, calling me to a new adventure. Mama was a little dubious about my "best friend" who refused to come up to the flat and who would duck out of sight if Mama came out on the porch. But she always brought me safely home, and Mama saw that I enjoyed our outings, so she let me go.

As Thanksgiving Day—a school holiday—approached, Norma confided that we were going to a place that would give away free turkey dinners. She had been very mysterious about this place, and I was eager for us to be on our way. When I heard her penetrating whistle, I raced down the stairs. Our way this time led us to a part of town shabbier than any we had ever visited. The sidewalks were cracked and broken. The cobbled streets were filthy with horse droppings and redolent of stale garbage. At a storefront a double line of people was waiting for the doors to open. A sign on the window read, "God's Mission," and under that, "Jesus loves you."

We took our places in the double line of shivering men and women, some with children in their arms or clinging to their mothers' skirts. It was beginning to snow. Behind us the lines grew longer. The whole scene was making me uneasy. Who was this Jesus who loved me? What was turkey? I tried to tell Norma we should go home. She didn't even listen; she just tightened her grip on my arm. I thought of Mama, who would certainly disapprove of this whole expedition. I was about to break away from Norma and try to find my way home by myself when the doors opened and everyone surged forward.

The room that we entered was large and gloomy but warm. At the far end were rows of benches, but the space between the entrance and the seating area was cluttered with objects that created an obstacle course: large wooden cubes painted black with lettering in white. Each cube had an identifying letter. I could read better than Norma, but she knew them by heart. Each cube represented a deadly sin: Vanity, Greed, Lies, Sloth, and so on. Norma explained that we had to work our way around them and overcome them in order to get to the good part, but that it was worth it.

From another room, we heard organ music. Just as we overcame all the sins that stood in the way of "the good part," a tall man entered from the second room. He wore a black suit, a white shirt, and a black string tie. He had a long, pale face and sad eyes. He took his place on a platform that faced the benches.

He wore gold-rimmed glasses on a black ribbon and held a pointer in his hand. He raised one hand for silence, then spoke in a benign voice. Behind us, he explained, were the obstacles that we all encounter in our journey through life. We can avoid them, he continued, or overcome them. He named each sin, pointing in the direction of the cube that bore its name.

"You must overcome each and every one," he declaimed, "if you hope to live a good and beautiful life—a life acceptable to the Lord Jesus. He loves you and will help you if you put your faith in him. If you do, everlasting life will be your reward and Heaven will be your home."

The sermon continued for what seemed hours; it was probably more like fifteen or twenty minutes. At the end, he told us to make our way around the Devil's traps and enter upon the path to salvation. As he said this, he pointed to a door above which was painted "Salvation." As he opened the door, we heard the organ music again and smelled the Thanksgiving food. We carefully made our way once more around "Greed" and "Sloth" and all the other sins, careful not to stumble over them and land in hell instead of the dining hall. Finally we were at the table, squeezing onto the benches that lined either side. "The good part" followed quickly. A tin plate was placed in front of each of us; on it were thin slices of turkey, a scoop of stuffing covered with gravy, a little cranberry sauce, a few beans or peas or carrots, a slice of bread and a slice of pumpkin pie. At each place was a tract with a picture of Jesus. The door through which we had entered into Salvation was closed. The only sounds were those of the organ playing softly and hunger being appeased. The food was strange to me, and Norma saw that I was just picking at it. Her own was almost cleaned away, and I was still fussing with mine.

"If you're not going to eat, don't waste it!" she said. I moved my plate toward her. She replaced mine with her empty one.

"Hey!" she said. "You must be sick or crazy!" She attacked the food as though it was the first time she'd eaten in days.

Early darkness had fallen when Norma got me back to my home. I was afraid to go in, and Norma refused to go with me.

From the Corelli apartment, Annie appeared. "Oy-oy-oy!" she

intoned—something learned, no doubt, from her Jewish sister-in-law. "Are you gonna get it, kiddo! You better start prayin' before you get upstairs!" I looked pleadingly at Norma; she gave me a quick kiss and hug, something she never had done before. While I was recovering from this demonstration, she disappeared into the dark passageway. Mama's voice brought me back to the dread present. She had heared Annie's voice and came running out on the landing.

"Shame on you," she cried in English. "Bad girl!" Then in the Yiddish that allowed her more scope: "I was out of my mind! I almost called the police! So why are you standing? Come up! Come up! Right now!" Mama had never shouted at me like that. I started up the stairs, dragging my feet, trembling and weeping. Passing Annie, I looked at her appealingly. She winked and laughed.

"Go on, kiddo," she comforted me. "Your mama won't kill you."

Finally I was there, on the top-floor landing, in front of Mama. She grabbed my arm and raised her hand. I turned my head and screwed my eyes shut tight, bracing myself for the blow. Somewhere on its way down, the hand lost its original purpose. Instead it landed a mild pat on my rear end and then propelled me into the house. For a moment Mama glared down at me, then gathered me into her arms.

"It was getting black dark. . . . You scared me. . . . No more you go anywhere with that girl. . . . No more!"

I hugged Mama and begged, "Mama, please don't tell Papa I was bad—please?"

"All right. It's lucky for you they are late tonight again. But *next time!* . . . Only you play no more with that girl, remember? And there won't be a next time." We clung to each other, and then she sent me to wash my face and get ready for supper. I remembered the card I was given at the mission. I had only a hazy notion of what it meant, but I decided it might be better to tear it up and throw it away. As I did so, I thought about Norma and how hungry she had been.

After the Thanksgiving holiday, when I went back to school, I had to tell Norma that I could not play with her anymore. It was the hardest thing I had ever had to do. We were in the hall before the bell rang. She stared for a moment, her face stricken. I tried to take her hand. She slapped it away, tossed her head and said— almost shouted—"Ha, ha! So who cares? Who needs you?" and ran away.

I was bitterly ashamed for having hurt her. But I had had to say it; I had promised Mama. I resolved to talk to Mama again, to try to win a reprieve. I ran after Norma to tell her, but my teacher stopped me and said we were going to the principal's office. She smiled, however, as she said it, so I guessed it couldn't be anything too bad. The principal was smiling, too. I was going to be "skipped" to the second grade!

I was never able to get close enough to Norma to talk to her again. But I have never forgotten the child in the shabby dress, the worn coat that was such a poor defense against the cold. When I think of her, the pain I felt, as I gave pain, returns as fresh and sharp as if it were yesterday. I hope it was not as lasting for her.

I was now in the second grade and had to make new friends. The children were older than the first-graders and looked upon me as a smart-aleck interloper. Except for Jennie Goldenstern, whose father, it was said, had once entertained Leon Trotsky at his "Confectionery and Cultural Center." They lived in the back of the store so Jennie's older sister, Lena, could help her father and look after their invalid mother at the same time. I used to see Jennie on Saturday afternoons, walking down the street to places I imagined to be full of magic and delight. I thought her to be the prettiest girl I had ever seen, and the most elegant, in a confection of a hat with flowers all around the crown and blue streamers down the back. She had never presumed to notice me before because I was "just a baby," but now that we were both in the same room at school, she took me under her wing.

Her patronage did not end when school was out. On the list of places I loved best in all the world, the swan boats in Boston led all the rest. Now Jennie introduced me to the Settlement House, and the swan boats gradually moved down to second place. What treasures the Settlement House offered! There was a lady who told stories about children in faraway places, about animals that talked, about children and grownups who suffered hunger in many parts of the world. I thought of Norma, right here in Cincinnati, and the old guilt and pain surfaced. We must think about them, the lady said, and when we grew older we must help them in any way we could. And there were other treasures in this new, beautiful world. There were plays to watch, and plays to act in, and "pieces" to speak, and all sorts of lovely things to learn and do. And there were books to take home and read—read aloud to Mama while she sewed or cooked or ironed.

My second-grade teacher was a tall, dark-haired, gentle young woman named Miss Abby Crane. She wore lovely clothes, mostly grays and browns, but they were, in my view, fit for a princess. We learned that she had a twin sister, Miss Laura Crane, who painted china. They lived together on Reading Road, where the houses were as elegant as Miss Abby herself.

One day her sister came to visit our class and, together with Miss Abby, invited the girls to tea on Sunday afternoon. The boys, they announced, would be invited to some more suitable event.

We all met, about fifteen of us, in front of the schoolhouse on Sunday afternoon. It was April now, and patches of dirty melting snow made the dreary playground even drearier. But the sky was very blue, and a solitary tree—a great oak near the entrance—was coming to green life with tiny leaf buds forming. Our Miss Crane appeared, more elegant than ever, smiling, greeting us in a voice lighter, gayer, more carefree than on school days. It was a voice that embraced us with affection and the quality of spring, that made the afternoon a promise of joy to come.

We went by trolley to Reading Road and then walked a few blocks to the house where Miss Abby lived. Two of the bolder children ran ahead and seized Miss Abby's hands and walked with her. I had longed to do that, but I was too shy.

Reading Road was really not very far from Central Avenue, but it might as well have been in another city a thousand miles away, so different was it from the street on which most of us lived. The broad avenue was clean and quiet, the houses two or three stories high—red brick with white, marblelike facades, and white stone steps leading up to carved doors with brass knockers.

Inside Miss Laura was waiting for us, dressed in a lacy blouse and a taffeta skirt, welcoming us with outstretched hands and a smiling greeting: "There you are, my dears. Welcome to Crane Castle!" To me it seemed, indeed, a castle. Something that I learned was called a chafing dish was on the mahogany dining-room table. There were soft rugs on the floors, a grand piano in the parlor, pictures on the walls. Everything gleamed—the wood, the silver, the candlesticks on the sideboard.

While Miss Laura took our coats and scarves—and Jennie's hat—Miss Abby left to remove her hat and jacket and, when she returned, revealed a lacy blouse like Miss Laura's. A woman in a black dress and white apron brought in little sandwiches and frosted cakes, and Miss Abby poured hot cocoa from a silver teapot. All of us were silent—except to say "thank you" when we were served. Soon Miss Laura and Miss Abby were making conversation, asking questions, drawing answers. Only I, it seems, remained quiet throughout the chatter, for Miss Abby came to my side, lifted my chin and smiled down at me.

"Why so quiet, little one? What are you dreaming of . . . wishing for?"

"I'm wishing," I said, "that my mama could live here."

"That's a nice wish, but I'm sure that, wherever she lives, she makes the place beautiful with her love for you."

I had no idea what she was talking about, but it sounded lovely; her smile was glowingly warm, and her touch on my face was soft and tender, and I smiled back and accepted a pink-frosted cake from Miss Laura.

School was out in mid-June, and I was promoted to the third grade along with Jennie Goldenstern and most of the rest of the class. Again Miss Abby and Miss Laura issued an invitation, boys included. This time we were going to the zoo! I thought excitedly about the animals I had learned about and then read about in *Aesop's Fables*—the animals that talked! I vowed that I would be perfectly calm if one of them should speak to me, for to be surprised would frighten him into silence, perhaps forever!

Some of us had been to the zoo; all the boys said they had been, "lots of times," but they were probably bragging. Poor Jennie Goldenstern came down with the measles. I was sorry for Jennie, but she had visited the zoo before; so when, in a magnanimous display of friendship, she told me I could wear her hat, I felt that my fairy godmother had willed it so.

The children were told to bring a small lunch if they wished, and Miss Abby and Miss Laura brought a basket of goodies yet to be explored.

Mama had packed my lunch in a shoe box. I had watched her arranging the hard-boiled egg, the sandwich of buttered rye bread, the packet of salt, the shiny red apple and the special treat, a piece of strudel. As Miss Abby had instructed us, each of our lunches had a name on the outside.

Now, with Miss Abby as our guide, we started off to see the animals, while Miss Laura chose a picnic table and benches and stayed behind to guard the lunches. To meet, face to face, the beautiful creatures I had seen only in colored picture books was truly wonderful. I was sure that if I spoke to one of them, softly, like a friend, he would return my greeting. I chose a handsome leopard to engage in conversation. I moved a short distance from the group so that the magnificent animal would not be shy, or annoyed by a crowd of kids. I came as close as I could and said softly: "Hello. You are so pretty. I like you. . . ." At that point Miss Abby noticed that I had strayed and called out, "Come back, dear. We must stay together!"

Mr. Leopard made a sound that I interpreted as disappointment. "I'm sorry," I whispered, "I have to go."

Miss Abby had ruined what might have been the greatest adventure of my life.

It was time to rejoin Miss Laura, who was guarding the lunch and reading a book. We picked up our lunches. Miss Abby carried the basket, and Miss Laura led us to a sheltered table and benches. Miss Abby said, "Let us bow our heads and thank the Lord for His bounty." We did as she instructed, but I peeped, and I saw others peeping as well, and I wondered what "bounty" meant. At my Zayde's house in Boston and at the Mishkins' on Friday, somebody always made a *Motzi*, or blessing, in Hebrew. But this was different.

Miss Laura, her head bowed, offered the thanks: "Dear Lord, we thank thee for the food before us, for this lovely day, the blue sky, the warm sun and the trees and grass and flowers and friendship. We ask your blessing on these dear children. In Jesus' name, amen."

Yes this was a very different kind of *Motzi*, but a loving one, and the "amen" was familiar, if its sound was not quite the same.

Miss Laura had spread a tablecloth and brought out paper napkins. Now the food was put out for all to see, and some trade-offs began. The sisters had brought extras, and they spread the contents of the basket before us. There were sandwiches and cakes and fruit. The most tempting to me were great purple plums in a little basket of their own.

Miss Laura held up a sandwich. "We brought more than we can eat," she said. "Who would like a liverwurst sandwich?" Most of the boys and a few girls waved their hands wildly and cried, "I do!" and "Me! Me!" I sat quietly; I was waiting for the plums.

Miss Abby said, "You are acting greedy. It is not good manners to make such a racket. I'm going to give it to the little girl who is sitting quietly like a little lady and not making such a clatter." She held out the sandwich, which I didn't want, and I took it because I didn't know how to refuse it. A little boy next to me waved frantically.

"If it ain't kosher, she dasn't," he shouted. "She's a yid, but I'm an Irisher, so it's okay."

I handed him the sandwich as Miss Laura apologized. With relief, I tackled my hard-boiled egg and rye bread. When it came to the fruit, the plums were passed in their own basket, and the last one was snatched before it got to me. But I had my apple and my strudel and it had been a glorious day.

Now that school was out, Central Avenue was crowded with children and noise and smells, very much like Brighton Street in Boston. As Norma had been my mentor in the first grade, Jennie was now my guide and model. We could spend more time at the Settlement House, read more books, enter contests.

At home Papa brooded a great deal, was short-tempered, and yelled at Mama without cause, or so it seemed to me. One Sunday morning he went early to the shop, leaving the house without a word to Mama or to me. When Mama asked him if he would be home for dinner, he glared and stormed out, slamming the door. Then he stuck his head in and said, "When you see me, you'll know I'm home!"

He came home well before time for dinner. He carried his jacket, and his shirt sleeve was torn. Without a word, he went to the kitchen sink to wash up. Then he spoke in his normal voice.

"We're going back to Boston," he said.

For a moment Mama was speechless. Then, in the most joyous tone I had heard from her since we came to Cincinnati, she cried, "My prayers are answered! Thank God, thank God!"

"I caught him red-handed—" Papa began. A knock on the door interrupted him. Landa and Moishele came in, both distraught, both talking at once.

"You got into a fight with Ostrovsky—Did you have to fight? Couldn't you just talk to him? How does it look for two Jews to punch each other like a pair of hooligans?"

Papa was calm now. "Sit down. It's over. I went early to the shop. I caught him red-handed. He had let someone in through the back. I followed. He was taking coils of copper wire from a wheelbarrow that the *gonif* [thief] brought in, and he was weighing it. Ostrovsky and the other fellow didn't see me. Ostrovsky told him he'd give him a hundred dollars. It was worth much more, of course. The *gonif* said, 'That's a steal.' *Gonif* Ostrovsky said, 'For what you paid I'm giving you a hundred percent profit! Take it or leave it!' Then I yelled, 'Take your stuff and get out! And you, Ostrovsky, *Gonif* Number Two, you get out, too, before I murder you!'"

That, Papa said, was when they got into the fight. He was going into more details when the door burst open and Ostrovsky almost fell into the room. I had never seen him in our flat before. He was disheveled and holding a bloody handkerchief to his mouth. He pointed a shaking finger at Papa.

"There he is, the *tzaddik!*" cried Ostrovsky. "Brawling like a drunken goy! Look what he did to me!" He displayed the bloody handkerchief.

Papa was amazingly cool now. "I'm no *tzaddik!*" he said. "You are the *tzaddik!* You put on *tefillin* and go to *shul* on Shabbes and deal with thieves the rest of the week."

Moishele and Landa tried to make peace, to quiet them down. Mama tried to take me out of the room, but Papa said, "Stay here! I want you to know what this man is!" To the other two partners, Papa said, "You can keep your business and your pious Jew who deals in stolen merchandise. We're going back to Boston!"

Moishele and Landa were crushed. Papa was considered the brains of the enterprise; he brought class to the business of junk.

"Buy me out and you can change the name to 'Tzaddikkim Company,' " sneered Ostrovsky. "That's how Carnegie got rich, by being a *tzaddik*, you know."

Landa shrugged helplessly. "Who can buy you out? You put in most of the money."

"Ah-ha, you remember that! Good! Good!"

Mama took advantage of a moment's silence.

"At least," she pleaded, "let's have peace now. Sit down, everybody. I'll make tea."

"After he goes!" Papa said. "Not before!" Ostrovsky kicked over a chair, strode out of the room, and slammed the door after him.

Moishele said, "If he promises not to do it anymore—?"

"If a wolf promises not to kill sheep anymore, will you put him in the same pasture?" Papa retorted.

"You have a little money coming, Mendel. . . . "

"I know I do. Don't I keep the books?"

"It's not enough," Moishele said. "You'll need for the train and to live till you get a job. I can—"

"It's enough," Papa interrupted. "Charity we don't need. We'll sell the furniture and start over in Boston."

I thought about Jennie and the Settlement House, about my friends going into third grade and—yes—even about Norma, whom I hoped to find again. I weighed all that against the swan boats and came out pretty evenly balanced.

After supper that night, Papa wrote a letter to Zayde in Boston and asked if we could move in with them just until he got his job back. He knew he had been a good shoe cutter, and he felt sure of finding work. Five days later, a telegram came from Uncle Mike. It said, "Don't come. Stay Cincinnati. Have great plans." A week later, he arrived in person.

# 4

## *A Jew Belongs on the Land*

Almost the first words that Uncle Mike spoke to us when he arrived in Cincinnati were: "A Jew belongs on the land." He continued, "It is honorable; it is healthy; you're your own master; nobody has you in his pocket." He kept talking like this on the streetcar, all the way to our flat, and as we walked up the stairs he said, "There's a song that tells you everything. It goes like this—" He began to sing loudly, if somewhat off-key, a verse of the song that had inspired him to exchange the dream of his own sweatshop for the dream of his own land:

> "In the good earth lies
> Your richest blessing—

"I've got some money saved," he went on. "If we go into this together, I tell you, it's the best thing that could happen. After all, our ancestors were farmers and shepherds. Remember Jacob's father-in-law, what's-his-name? You know, the crooked business about his daughters?"

"So you're asking me to become a crooked sheep farmer like Jacob's father-in-law, 'What's-His-Name'?"

"Of course not! I was just reminding you how far back our people were on the land."

I looked at Mama. She was stony-faced. Her voice was shaking. With unaccustomed boldness she said, "We made our plans already, brother. We're going back to Boston. Please don't mix in!"

Papa and Uncle Mike looked at each other. Then Papa turned and stared at Mama. Mama stared back for a moment. I had never seen her look like that—white, and as if something was hurting her deep down inside, and angry, too. Then she clapped her hand over her mouth and rushed out of the kitchen, all the way to my room. I ran after her, frightened. I found her sitting on my little bed, crying, and not quietly like the first time when I woke up in Zayde's flat in Boston. This time it was like the crying was turning her inside out.

I climbed onto her lap, trying to comfort her, but she couldn't stop. I thought I knew why she was crying: she didn't want any more new beginnings. And I began to cry with her. This was to infuriate Papa through the years; I always shared Mama's tears. I think it was because her weeping frightened me. The tears would come because of something Papa would have said or done—often something cruel. Many times he would first shout, then go into a period of silence. When this happened, the house seemed, not a shelter, but a place where danger lurked in every corner; and my whole world, my very life, seemed threatened. To me, Papa himself became someone to fear, to run from. I would wish, by some magic, to become invisible. To Mama, however, he always seemed someone to placate.

Very suddenly, Mama stopped crying. She wiped her face and mine and rose from the bed.

"So don't cry anymore," she said. "It's all right. It's going to be very good. I'll go make tea." The white flag of surrender always took the form of a glass of tea, freshly brewed—served, in times of great stress, with raspberry preserves.

I picked up my doll and followed Mama into the kitchen. Uncle Mike looked anxiously at Mama, but Papa acted as though nothing had happened. Mama got busy with tea.

"Brucha," Uncle Mike started, in a pleading voice.

"She's got an American name now, Mike, just like you and the others," said Papa. "No more 'Brucha.' Freidel Mishkin told me it should be 'Bertha' or 'Becky.'" This was a surprise. He had never mentioned it before. "And," he added, "I am Max."

"So—let it be Max!"

"And Becky," Papa reminded him.

"I'll have to get used to that," Uncle Mike shrugged. He turned to Mama again.

"You grew up in a *shtetl*—a *dorf*, really—surrounded by land that was owned by the *Graf* and worked by the peasants. Here it will be we who work it *and* own it. Even when you were still a child, you had golden hands. You could stick something in the ground by Zayde's tavern, and it would grow. And when our father bought a cow and brought her home for Shevuoth, it was you who were the first to learn to milk her. Golden hands, like I said. Golden hands. I give you my word, it will be good. You'll thank me!"

"So I thank you now," she replied drily, "in case later I'll be so busy dancing in the streets or the fields for joy, I might forget." She put a glass of tea in front of him and one in front of Papa.

"Don't be such a *chachima*, Becky," said Papa.

Uncle Mike was anxious to change the subject.

"I'll tell you what, Becky," he said. "Take a vacation. Don't cook supper." To Papa he added, "Come, Max, we'll go to a delicatessen and buy ready-made. And we'll talk and maybe make some plans." To me he said, "You come, too, kitten, and pick out what you want."

I looked at Mama questioningly.

"Go, go," she said. "Enjoy yourself."

Annie Corelli was on their landing, helping Tony put up a swing. Papa introduced Annie as our good Italian neighbor. To my amazement, Uncle Mike began to speak to her in Italian. He explained later that in the needle trades in Boston, most of the work was done by Italian and Jewish women, and he had picked up the Italian language in the shop where he had become a foreman.

When we said our good-byes to Annie, Uncle Mike was elated. "Wait till I tell you what I found out!" he cried. "But better I'll save it till Becky can hear. First let's go buy for supper. My treat!"

"Thank you," Papa replied proudly. "Tonight you are my guest. Tonight you do not treat. And we'll buy enough for Moishele and the Mishkins, too. We'll walk by now and invite them."

Much later, we were seated around the kitchen table, eating the traditional Saturday night supper (traditional, that is, for American urban Jews) of smoked whitefish, cream cheese and bagels, the salty, black, pressed Greek olives, the salad of little pink radishes, cucumbers, scallions and sour cream. As we ate Uncle Mike revealed what he had learned from Annie Corelli: "There's a pants factory in Newport, Kentucky! You can walk across the bridge, and there it is! Can you believe it?"

Freidel Mishkin was helping Mama serve the chicory cooked in milk.

"What's your brother so excited about?" she asked. "He's looking for a job in a pants factory?"

"No," replied Mama with a funny smile. "He's looking, I think, for a job in a pants factory for me."

" . . . and what's more," Uncle Mike was explaining to Papa, "they'll deliver the bundles for finishing right here to the house, then pick them up and pay on the spot. And the best part, Becky," he finally addressed himself directly to Mama, "your neighbor, Annie, has an extra sewing machine and she'll lend it to you! How is that for news, sister?"

"Do you have to ask?" Mama's answer could have meant anything, but Uncle Mike seemed satisfied. Tante Freidel was not.

"You were so excited," she said, "I thought you got at least a

telegram that the Messiah would be here the sixteenth of June, 1907, at three o'clock in the afternoon!"

Uncle Mike stared at her in stunned silence. After a moment Papa said quietly, "My brother-in-law and I are going to be looking for land. We'll be spending a lot of time with agents who know who has farms for sale. You don't get paid wages for looking. So he figures it will give my wife something to do, finishing a few pants, while we are away, and it will put bread on the table at the same time. And when the telegram comes that the Messiah is on the way, we'll have a little money put away to pay for our share of the wine and the great fish at the feast in the rabbi's house. In the meantime, we'll eat what's on the table. Agreed?"

Tante Freidel, her husband, and Moishele all stared at Papa. But it was Tante Freidel who jumped up from her chair.

"You're-going-to-buy-a-*farm*?" she almost screamed. A warning nudge from her husband stopped any further outburst.

"The Jew *belongs* on the land!" exclaimed Uncle Mike, and he broke into his song.

"Enough, Mike," Papa cautioned quietly. "A concert we don't need now." There was a moment's silence. Then Papa thundered, "EAT!" And more gently, "Please!" The meal was finished in silence.

Annie not only loaned Mama the sewing machine, but whenever she had a little spare time she would come up and help Mama sew. The heat in the tenements grew stifling, and the stench from the streets permeated everything. Annie would come up with pitchers of cold soda water, an ice-cold watermelon or syrup-flavored shaved ice. Once she brought a platter of little ice cream sandwiches, a delicacy recently introduced, at a penny apiece, at Mr. Goldenstern's confectionery. This time we were joined by Tony, Mrs. Corelli, and a half-dozen neighborhood kids who had followed Annie home.

One day, while Mama and Annie were working on a bundle, Mama asked why they had never seen Annie's papa.

"He travels a lot," said Annie. "With my older brother—you know, the one that is married to a Jewish girl. Hey, you know what?" She changed the subject quickly. "Strawberries are so cheap, they're almost giving them away. You ever make jelly?"

Mama never asked again about Papa Corelli.

Papa and Uncle Mike would be gone every day from early morning until suppertime. After supper they would sit for hours going over figures and notes, discarding some prospects, retaining others. They never invited Mama to join their discussions. She sat "finishing" pants—the parts that she did by hand, such as sewing on buttons. She listened, but never entered into their conversations.

As for me and my best friend, Jennie Goldenstern, we spent hours at the Settlement House looking through picture books and storybooks about country life. We discovered a world of green fields studded with daisies. Here roamed "gentle cows, all red-and-white" that would give us cream "with all their might to eat with apple tart." I had no acquaintance with apple tarts, but was happily looking forward to discovering them—growing on apple trees, perhaps?

All this new knowledge we imparted to the kids on the ill-smelling sidewalk in front of the Kroger Grocery Company as they gathered around to listen. They learned that I would be living in a house sitting in the center of a lush green lawn, surrounded by a white picket fence. There would be every kind of flower climbing over the fence and surrounding the house. Fields nearby would be teeming with ripe watermelons. Trees with all manner of fruits would be there for the picking. There would be a lovely pond on which ducks would teach their young to swim. And I would have a dog named Rover, a cat named Tabby, a cow, all red-and-white, named Bossy, and a Shetland pony named Honey. I invited them all to come and visit. Jennie did come once, but she got so homesick in the night that she had to be taken home the very next day.

One day, Papa and Uncle Mike came home early in the afternoon, both smiling broadly. They had bought a farm and "passed papers." Now Mama had to sign the papers, too, and the agent was going to take her with them when they went again, so she could see what she was signing for. Papa thought it was a lot of nonsense, but the agent said that in Ohio it was the law.

"Why do I have to sign?" Mama's voice was troubled.

"You heard your brother," Papa replied sharply. "It's the law, so you will sign."

Uncle Mike was too excited to notice Mama's distress. "Sixty acres," he told Mama, "with apple trees and pear trees and peach trees and cherry trees. And three cows—"

"All red-and-white?" I asked eagerly.

"No, kitten, sort of brown and tan. Jerseys, the man said."

"Don't interrupt," admonished Papa.

"—and three horses," Uncle Mike continued. "Two wagons. One is called a jolt-wagon because it hasn't got springs, and the other is called a spring wagon because it has. And a buggy, and something called a surrey, and a cart with two wheels, and chickens, and some ducks even. The people who are selling will stay a few days till their house in the village is ready. The head of the house is the grandfather. His name is Mr. Benjamin Lumley. He sells insurance, so he can't take care of the farm. His daughter-in-law is a young widow with three young children. That's why they are selling. It's a big house—plenty of room." He kept talking rapidly, watching Mama anxiously. She kept on sewing buttons. "Room enough for a couple of sons, if it should happen," he added, laughing. Now Mama looked at him sharply, her needle in the air. She looked from him to Papa, who stared. I couldn't understand, but I felt the old fear of danger nearby. Then Uncle Mike began talking very fast again.

"And there's a town called New Richmond with all kinds of stores and even a bank. It's right by a big river, this town, the Ohio River. Wait till you see!"

Mama finally said, "Very nice," but without smiling, as though she did not really care if she never saw it.

They were going to spend the night at the farm while the Lumleys were still there, Uncle Mike explained, so they could learn things from the Lumleys, and the next day they would return on the interurban—the commuter train that ran from Cincinnati to New Richmond with stops along the route. And I would spend the night with the Corellis. I waited for Papa to say, "It will be a new beginning." But I never heard him use that phrase again— not ever.

I was too excited to sleep when Mama and Papa came to bed. I heard Mama ask, "Why can't the child come with us?"

"Not necessary," he replied. "You remember what your brother said? You will have to sign your name. I hope you have been practicing, like I showed you."

"It's not good," she replied, so softly I could hardly hear her. "Can't I sign in Yiddish? I—" There was silence for a moment. Then Papa spoke, not loud, but very, very angry. "You are a peasant, a stupid, ignorant peasant like the peasants you grew up with. You will always be a peasant."

I put my pillow over my head, but I heard no more talk. After a long while I fell asleep.

They left early the next morning, Mama wearing her best blouse and skirt and Annie's straw hat. I thought she looked very pretty with her black hair in soft waves around her face. Papa, too, looked handsome and dignified in his suit and shirt with a high collar. Uncle Mike complimented them both, and he pressed three pennies into my hand to buy candy and treat my friends. I must have looked quite forlorn when they said good-bye, and Annie took me in hand.

"Hey, kiddo," she said, "we're gonna have a party!" And we did. Mama Corelli made cookies, and Annie brought ice cream from Mr. Goldenstern's, and he himself contributed a pitcher of soda water. The kids in the neighborhood came, and, of course, Jennie Goldenstern. After the last cookie was eaten, the last drop of soda drained from the pitcher, and the last spoonful of ice cream relished, the kids turned to me with questions. I had to admit that the cows were not "all red-and-white," but, I assured them, they did give cream. All cows had to do that; it was the law. It was a lovely party, and the bed I slept on that night at the Corellis' was bigger and softer than any I had ever known.

# 5

## *And So, Good-bye!*

Mama, Papa, and Uncle Mike came home the next afternoon. They were all smiling. I was relieved; Mama, I thought, must have done well with the signing.

"It will be good," they all said. "It will be good."

Mama added, "With God's help."

Two weeks later, the furniture van carrying everything we owned and, in addition, boxes of provisions that would not spoil, was on its way to Dunham's Hill. Uncle Mike went along to get everything in place. The Lumleys' house in the village was ready for them, and they would be gone by the time we arrived at our new home.

The last of the pants had been finished, picked up, and paid for. Our flat was bare, and we had two more days in Cincinnati waiting for the van to deliver our belongings to the farm. The Mishkins made room for us somehow; my bed, like the one we had fixed up for Uncle Mike, was arranged on four chairs facing one another. I missed the "good sleep" I had had at the Corellis'.

There was nothing left now except to say good-bye to our good Italian neighbors. Mrs. Corelli gave Mama two loaves of delicious Italian bread that she had baked. They hugged each other, and Mama and Annie hugged each other and cried together.

"You have been like a *shvester* to me," Mama said. Annie looked over Mama's shoulder and mouthed, "*Shvester?*"

"It means 'sister,'" I whispered.

Then the Corellis hugged me, and everybody cried all over again.

At the foot of the stairs we found Jennie Goldenstern waiting. She had brought a present from her father, a book of Yiddish poetry for Papa. To me she gave a little bag of candy which she thrust into my hands. Then she kissed me good-bye and ran. It made me think of Norma, but *she* ran for a different reason. Then we left to join Papa, who was waiting impatiently on the sidewalk. We were on our way to the Mishkins'. It was late August, 1907, and in two days we would be in our new home with "the white picket fence and the daisy-studded meadow."

Two days later, when we arrived via the "black car"—as Mama called the commuter train—at Ten-Mile Stop, Mr. Lumley was waiting for us with the surrey drawn by a tired-looking black horse. The surrey was dusty, and its paint was cracked, but it had fringe all around the top and it had two seats. A shiny new whip stood in a little holder up front. Mr. Lumley shook hands with us, then introduced the horse, which I thought was very polite of him. Her name was "Belle." She was the buggy-and-saddle horse, he explained, and never did any work in the fields. He said it was all right for me to pat her on the nose, but I must never try that with "Ol' Cole," who could be mean. But "Ol' Ned" was friendly, like "Ol' Belle."

We all climbed into the surrey, Papa with Mr. Lumley in front, Mama and I in the back.

Mr. Lumley did not look like the farmers in the picture books. Then I remembered that he was not really a farmer. He was tall— taller than anybody I knew except Zayde. His hair was white, and he wore glasses on a black ribbon, a black alpaca suit, a high collar on his white shirt, and a black string tie. He reminded me of all the important gentlemen in the picture books, even presidents.

The station was about a mile from our farm. Mr. Lumley pointed out all the interesting places on the way. Very near the station, on a beautifully kept lawn, rising away from the road to make a rounded hill, stood a large house with porches and gabled windows, and vines against the walls. Great trees shaded the house— quite the largest and most beautiful house I had ever seen, even more beautiful than the houses on Reading Road. Mr. Lumley told us this house belonged to the Haussermanns, the richest people in all of Clermont County. John Haussermann, he said, had made his money in gold mining in the Philippines. The son of a New Richmond butcher, he was educated as a lawyer. He had enlisted in the army during the Spanish-American War, had been stationed in the Philippines, and had learned about rich gold deposits on the islands, waiting to be developed.

"Fine people," Mr. Lumley said. "We're real proud of them."

I came to know the graciousness of Mrs. Haussermann, whose lovely maiden name was Jessie Moonlight. My first ride in an automobile was with her, on a trip to Cincinnati, in a Dodge with isinglass-windowed side curtains. She was endlessly kind to the skinny little kid from Dunham's Hill, who frequented any house that was open to her where books might be borrowed. Later, when I was a high school student from New Richmond, the literature she loaned me included tracts on Christian Science, of which she was a devout practitioner.

Ol' Belle and the surrey made their leisurely way between the low wooded hills that flanked the mile-long road to Dunham's Hill. Houses were far between, but I was to come to know them all, together with their occupants. Ol' Belle seemed to slow down at every house as though she wanted to stop and visit. At such times, Mr. Lumley would flick her gently with the shiny whip, but he never really whipped her, as I feared he would. I knew then that he was a very fine gentleman.

The road was hard-surfaced, until we reached a dead end where it branched to the right and left at right angles. Here Mr. Lumley stopped and pointed to a row of mailboxes facing us. One of them, he said, would be ours, and he had taken the liberty of printing Papa's name on it: "Max Weisberg." There it was, in bold black letters over the white paint which had blotted out the Lumley name. It made me feel good to see it, as though we already belonged. I thought how nice it would be if this should be our address forever. Having an address meant you had a home—a place in the world where friends could always find you, and where you could stand at the gate and welcome them—just like in the picture books. In Boston we had had an address, but it was really Zayde's, not ours, and I would get it mixed up with our new address on Central Avenue in Cincinnati. By the time I was getting them straightened out, we were ready to become farmers.

Mr. Lumley was explaining that each mailbox had a little red tin flag on the side. When you had letters to go out, you put them in the box and raised the flag, and the mailman would stop his little mail wagon, even if he didn't have any mail to leave, and take out the letters.

A small, drab house stood nearby, occupied, he told us, by a "maiden lady" named Miss Lizzie Lumley, a distant relative of his. She, too, became my friend, one whom I would frequently visit when I came with mail. She treated me to vinegar pickles so sour they turned my lips blue and gave me access to a little shed packed almost to the ceiling with old magazines, including stacks of *Godey's Ladies' Book*—a priceless collection, if she had only known. Certainly I did not!

The road to the right, we learned, led to the one-room schoolhouse where I would be enrolled to pursue my education. At that point, Mr. Lumley told Ol' Belle it was time to move on. She moved, and we turned left. Now the road was no longer hard-

surfaced but dry and deeply rutted; recent rains, Mr. Lumley explained, had turned them to mud. Someday, he assured Papa, the county would have enough money to fix this road, too.

After awhile we approached a two-story red brick house, just where a bend in the road was about to turn us to the right.

"This," said Mr. Lumley, "is Charlie Mott's place. Dr. John Mott is his brother. Everybody calls him Dr. John. He takes care of everybody in these parts. Now, when we go 'round the bend," he turned his head and smiled at me, "you'll be at *your* farm."

I shut my eyes tight; I wanted to see nothing now until our own place, and that alone, filled my vision. I could feel the wheels of the surrey turning to the right, and in a few minutes I heard Mr. Lumley announcing: "Well, here we are!"

Mama seemed to sense why I had my eyes shut. "You can open your eyes now, my child," she said. "We are home."

I was ready to look. The first thing I saw was Uncle Mike swinging open a large wooden gate that squeaked loudly, admitting us to the barnyard. The fence that surrounded this area, as far as I could see, was of faded wooden slats; it sagged here and there. A large barn was to the right, and it proved to be the best-kept building on the place. It had a ramp that led to a wide entrance, so that a horse and buggy, or even a surrey, could be driven right inside before the horse was unhitched. The building itself was on a part of the barnyard that was not level, so that the corners of the barn at one end rested on wooden blocks, leaving a large cool space underneath. Years later Ol' Cole chased a cow under the barn at that end, and it took hours to get her out.

I learned later all the fascinating things that were part of a barn. In the main part there was a place to hang harness and store tools, small machinery, and barrels of oats and other grains for the animals. Then, like the second floor of a tenement house, there was the haymow, where the hay was kept after the fragrant grass was cut and cured in the fields. But the most interesting sections to me were the quarters for the horses and cows. The stalls for the horses were on one side and those for the cows on the other. All this I learned later. Now, as we got out of the surrey, Uncle Mike, almost manic in his excitement, pointed out the corncrib, where the ripe ears of corn were stored—only there were none, at the time, because Mr. Lumley had not planted corn.

"I know, I know," Papa said impatiently. "I was here, too, remember!" Uncle Mike, who was bursting with enthusiasm, directed his tour guide's lecture at me. He pointed out the henhouse and told me there were nests in it where the chickens laid their eggs, but some of them made nests in the barn, so you had to be smarter than the hens to find all the eggs. There was a woodshed, where wood was cut and stored for the winter.

Finally we confronted the house. At this point Mr. Lumley joined us to say good-bye and wish us well. He shook hands with everyone and patted me on the head. He had left his own horse in the stable and his rig in the barnyard. Now, having unhitched and stabled Ol' Belle for us, he was going to hitch up and go home to *his* new place. Papa said he would walk back to the barn with him.

Uncle Mike continued his tour guide's lecture. He turned to Mama. "Can you believe it?" he exclaimed. "Did you see how the field of tomatoes has ripened just since we saw it two weeks ago? We can eat tomatoes till they run out of our ears, then sell all the rest in Cincinnati. I learned lots of things. You ask questions, you learn. The tomatoes you pack in crates; there's a whole pile of crates in the barn. Then you send them by freight to a commission merchant in the city and he sends you the money!"

I wasn't listening. I was looking at the house. Once there *had* been a white picket fence; now it was a dirty gray. Whole sections had been broken and lay on the ground. The "lawn" had long since been trampled to a grassless hardness. The house itself consisted of a one-story section with a porch and large windows and, attached to it by a common wall, a two-and-a-half–story building, its blank wall facing front. The whole structure was badly in need of paint.

I stopped looking at the depressing house. It was too painful. What would I tell the kids from Central Avenue when they came to visit? Well, I could point out the two ancient cedars, which rose so high that I almost fell over backwards trying to see the tops. A lovely yellow rose bloomed profusely against the bleak, blank wall of the house, and flanking the hard-trampled path were two lilac bushes. Their blooming season was almost over, but what was left of the blossoms mingled an exquisite fragrance with that of the roses and made the air lovely, in spite of the ugliness of the rest of the scene.

To one side and in front of the porch was a cistern, Uncle Mike explained. He lifted a large wooden lid to reveal a concrete-lined cylindrical pit. This, he said, was to catch and store rainwater to be used to wash our hair and for any other purpose for which soft water was desirable. The water was drawn in a pail lowered by a rope. There was also a well, which had a manually operated pump. It stood at the foot of a slightly sloping path, about forty or fifty feet from the house. It had been dug deep enough to reach an underground flow, and supplied water for all other purposes. Water for the cattle and horses was pumped into wooden tubs; for the house it was carried in a pail up the path to the kitchen door.

Uncle Mike started to review for Mama the different vegetables in the kitchen garden: lettuce, green onions, beets, carrots, and so on. I continued around the side of the house, the part that had the "blind" wall, and found—to my surprise and delight—steps leading up to a door with windows on each side, windows at the second-floor level, and more windows at what proved to be a half-story with extra bedrooms under pitched ceilings. And, marvel of marvels, a flower bed had been hacked out of the hard earth, edged with old bricks in an attractive pattern and planted with flowers bearing these charming names: bleeding hearts, snowballs, touch-me-nots, and foxgloves. All these unusual names I learned later; the beauty of their presence in this dismal landscape I grasped at once. And that was not all. The fence on this side was in better repair than the front section. The gate was properly hung, and it led into an arbor covered with heavy vines bearing ripe Concord grapes. All this masked the outdoor privy, toward which a path led through the arbor.

I heard Mama calling me, and I joined her and Uncle Mike at the back of the house. Uncle Mike was explaining to Mama the purpose of the small building at the back, connected to the house by a plank walk to the kitchen door.

"This," he said, "is the smokehouse. It's hard to get fresh meat here, except chickens. So every farmer butchers a hog or two for the winter. They smoke hams and bacon in the smokehouse and pack the rest in salt in the cellar."

Next he led us to the cellar, opening up a pair of heavy doors which revealed stone steps leading down into cool darkness. The day had been oppressively hot, and the change felt good. When our eyes became accustomed to the darkness, we saw wooden shelves against the walls, a hand churn in a corner, tin milking pails and two three-legged stools on which to sit when milking. On a shelf there were several glazed brown crocks for "setting" the milk. Uncle Mike said Mrs. Lumley had made us a present of these things when Uncle Mike had come with the furniture. She had left some milk, some salted butter, and the last gathering of eggs for us.

"And that's not all," exulted Uncle Mike, as he held up a mason jar of canned peaches. "The lady said this was fruit she had canned, only she called it 'put up,' for the winter."

We heard Papa's voice as he joined us in the cellar.

"Well, I watched him harness his horse to his buggy. I can do it with my eyes shut!" And I was sure that he could. He looked pleased with himself and pleased with all of us. When he was like that I thought him really handsome. He was tall—taller than Uncle Mike, or Mama, who just came to his shoulder. He had nice blue eyes and a full mouth, but when he was angry his lips would become so thin they would almost disappear. Although still a young man, he was growing bald. I cannot remember ever having seen him with a full head of hair. He could be the most charming of men, the kindest and certainly one of the most intelligent—until something happened to incur his displeasure. Years later, I wondered if some evil genius had given him the potion that transformed Dr. Jekyll into Mr. Hyde. But at this moment, as he came down the cellar steps, he was at his best; he pinched my cheek, kissed Mama's cheek and slapped Uncle Mike on the back.

"It will be good," he said. And I believed him and loved him.

# 6

## *"O Brave New World"*

There were several Lumley families on Dunham's Hill, all in some degree related to one another. The ones who were our nearest neighbors, Mr. and Mrs. George Lumley, came to call on us the Sunday afternoon after we arrived. Mrs. Lumley brought an apple pie and some raisin cookies. Mama served tea in glasses, and *mandel brot*, a hard pastry made with almonds and good for dunking. Tante Freidel Mishkin had baked it for us to take along because "it keeps well," and the Lumleys dunked it in their hot tea and said they liked it. They had never tasted *mandel brot* before, but none of us except Uncle Mike had ever tasted apple pie, so it gave us something to talk about. Uncle Mike made a joke about it. "Nobody," he said, "is really an American until they taste apple pie. So now we are Americans."

Mr. Lumley was a very tall man and very thin, which made him look even taller. He had more straw-colored hair than Uncle Mike and Papa put together, and a droopy, straw-colored mustache with brown stains on it. I found out later that the stains were from chewing tobacco.

The only tobacco I had known of before was the loose tobacco that Papa bought, together with empty cigarettes—half tissue paper and half hard paper, the part that was held in the mouth. He had a brass cylinder that had a hinged back and opened up. Mama would pack the tobacco firmly into the open cylinder, close it up and insert it into the firm end and, with a slender iron rod, push the tobacco into the tissue paper end. Sometimes, when Papa was mad at Mama, he would not let her stuff his cigarettes, as though it were a great privilege. After he tore two or three cigarettes, which Mama pretended not to see, he would stop being mad and let her take over.

Now, as I looked at Mr. Lumley, I saw a man who ate tobacco. I thought it must taste good; at the first opportunity, I tried a little of Papa's tobacco and decided that Mr. Lumley's tastes were not mine.

Mrs. Lumley was short, like Mama, and plumper. She had light brown hair, which she referred to as "dirty blonde," and her brown eyes crinkled when she smiled.

The Lumleys had two daughters; one was fifteen and the other eleven. They also had an eight-year-old boy named Horace, and an eighteen-year-old son, named George for his dad. The girls were Virginia and Katherine, but everybody called them Ginny and Katie. They all, except George, attended the one-room school to which I would go, and Mrs. Lumley said they would come and take me on the day school started, in the middle of September.

We learned many things from the Lumleys that afternoon. There are certain chores on a farm that cannot wait: cows come up from the pasture at day's end when they are ready to be milked; you can hear them lowing to let you know they want to be relieved of the load they carry in their udders. They have to be fed, along with the horses and the chickens and any other livestock you might have. If the weather is fair, you water them and turn them back into the pasture. In bad weather and in winter, the stables must be cleaned and fresh straw brought into the stalls. After that, you can go into the house and eat supper.

Also, crops that are ready must be harvested or be lost. The cherry trees were almost bare of fruit; the pear trees and the peaches were completely gone. There were lots of apples still on the trees, but most important were the tomatoes, ready to be picked and shipped.

The Lumleys were "truck farmers," which, they explained, meant they raised berries and some vegetables for the market. So Mr. Lumley knew all about commission merchants and how to make the connection.

The sun was beginning to set when the Lumleys left to walk home, accepting some of the *mandel brot* which Mama pressed upon them to "take home for the children," an accepted ritual among Jewish friends. In time Mama learned that on Dunham's Hill hospitality required more than she had extended. When guests stayed all afternoon on Sunday—and when else would farmers have time to visit?—it was absolutely expected that they would be invited to stay for supper, even if it were just for leftovers from Sunday dinner. And if you didn't have that, or anything else suitable, you just went out and killed a chicken! Mama almost choked when she heard that. She looked helplessly at Papa. He said, "Don't look at me!" But Mama was not without resources. In time she entertained visitors with suppers of cheese blintzes and noodle puddings and even borscht and became, as a result, a hostess of note.

As to a division of chores in the life on the land, my own role was not yet defined. For the time being, it was limited to gathering the eggs from the chicken coop and seeking out the secret nests. Mama still remembered how to milk a cow, and the time would come when she would teach the art to me. It was one skill that Papa never mastered. I think he didn't want to learn, since he acquired many skills much more complicated with no trouble at all. I'm sure he would have found it demeaning; it was women's work, like weeding the kitchen garden or making butter. I suppose it never occurred to him that when Mama helped bring in the hay she was doing a man's work.

Uncle Mike went about his share of the work with doggedness but a marked lack of enthusiasm, especially when he was cleaning the stables and piling the manure to be used on the fields. Often as he worked he would sing the idyllic song about life on the land, perhaps to remind himself why he was on Dunham's Hill, condemned by his own choice to hard labor.

One by one, new chores emerged for me: churning the butter, gathering the last of the fruit, weeding the kitchen garden. The last was the worst, but the time came when I looked back upon weeding as a lovely way to spend an hour in the sun. The churning was the pleasantest of my jobs. The cellar was cool and smelled of stored fruit and vegetables.

I learned that butter was *made*—it did not come miraculously in chunks, wrapped in waxed paper, from Mr. Springer's grocery in Cincinnati. And cows, red-and-white or brown-and-tan, gave milk and not cream—law or no law. What milk we did not drink Mama placed to "set" on the back of the stove, in the glazed brown crocks, until the rich, pale yellow clotted cream rose to the top. This Mama skimmed and I churned, and I finally witnessed the magical separation of the butter from the buttermilk. This final metamorphosis of milk—buttermilk, cool and refreshing, with flecks of butter floating, like tiny golden beads, in the liquid—was a new gastronomical delight.

That was not all; there was another by-product from what started as just a pail of warm, foamy milk. After Mama skimmed the cream from the earthenware crocks, the watery whey that had settled beneath it became a clabber of custardlike consistency. Mama made cheese out of some of it, and the rest she served with little new boiled potatoes from our garden. Mama of the "golden hands"! When we sat down to a meal of our homegrown vegetables and my churned butter with Mama's bread, we agreed that life on the land was infinitely better than life on Central Avenue or Brighton Street. Uncle Mike kept saying that everything tasted a thousand times better than anything you could buy in the city. He would even feel like singing again—until the next time he had to clean the stables. Papa usually agreed. Mama, who now had to work harder to prepare the meal than when she went to Springer's to buy the food, just put in on the table and said very little.

A week after the Lumleys had come to visit, the tomatoes were fully ready to be picked. All of us worked at harvesting the red, firm, unblemished "fruit." I shared in the excitement with which Mama, Papa, and Uncle Mike attacked the job; we would have cash money now, and really get started. The work in the hot sun was backbreaking. The tomatoes were carried from the field to the barn in bushel baskets and then packed into crates. But no one complained. Papa never got angry, which made it all worthwhile. Mr. George Lumley came to help. That's what neighbors were for, he said. He told us to leave the largest, the reddest, the firmest for the top layer in the crates. "Polish them with a clean rag and arrange them neatly," he advised. "It will make the whole crate look better. And keep the smallest for 'putting up.'"

At supper that night Mama observed that, while the crates did look fine, it seemed a little like cheating. Nothing like buying stolen merchandise, of course, but—. Papa's fork clattered to his plate, and he stood up and glared at Mama. I thought miserably that he was going to shout at her again. But it passed quickly.

"I'm only joking," Mama said hastily. "I'll go make the tea." Papa sat down and winked at me. All was well again.

Now we waited eagerly for the money order from the commission merchant. In the meantime, I stored up new marvels to tell the kids from Central Avenue if I ever saw them again. Marvel No. 1: when the cows came up to the pasture fence in the evening, and the gate was opened, they trotted first to the well where the wooden tubs had already been filled with water for them. When they had drunk their fill, they walked slowly back to the stables and each one went into her own stall! They never made a mistake, never tried to challenge each other for a change of residence.

Marvel No. 2 (this I witnessed first at Mrs. George Lumley's): one of her hens had hatched a set of eggs, and now she was followed by a brood of fluffy, tiny yellow chicks to which she talked almost incessantly, in a wide variety of sounds. When grain was scattered on the ground, she called them in chirps they understood, and they came running to snap up the food. When she saw a hawk fly over the yard, the chirp was very different: she warned them of danger, and they came running again. This time she squatted on the ground and spread her wings. They took shelter under them and became all but invisible. I realized then that I could indeed talk to animals, but I would have to learn *their* language instead of expecting them to learn mine. As a result, in time I became an accomplished chirper, and finally a whistler, and conversed freely with the birds.

A week after the tomato crop had been shipped, a letter arrived from the company. Going for the mail was also one of my chores, and when I saw this letter I knew it was very, very important. I ran most of the way home. I waved it in the air when I saw Papa in the barnyard. He was leading Ol' Ned to the watering tubs, but when he saw me he stopped, smiling broadly. He shouted for Mama and Uncle Mike to come. Uncle Mike had been cutting grapes in the arbor. He came, singing his song, carrying a lovely clump of purple Concords in his stained hands. Mama hurried from the garden, using her apron to wipe the dirt from her hands. By the time they reached Papa's side, he had picked up an enclosure that had fluttered to the ground and glanced at it. He began to read the letter to himself, then he looked up. His face was white, grim, even frightened.

"What's the matter, Mendel? What's wrong?" Mama cried. Any other time he would have chided her for calling him "Mendel," but not now. His voice shook when he answered.

"No money. We owe them . . ." he glanced down at the slip of paper, " . . . twenty-seven cents!"

"How is it possible that *we* owe *them*?" cried Mama. Uncle Mike had dropped the grapes and simply stared.

"It says here in the letter," Papa replied in a dull, flat voice, "that tomatoes are a drug on the market. I don't know what that means. It says further that it was such a fine crop everywhere this year that there are too many. Do you understand that? I understand that like I understand Greek. So our tomatoes, along with a lot of others, spoiled while they waited for buyers. So they had to take them to the dump, and that cost them twenty-seven cents more than they got for the few boxes they sold. So we owe them twenty-seven cents!" The three grown-ups just stood staring at one another. Finally I ventured a question.

"It's very bad, Papa?" I asked.

"Dummy! Yes, it's very bad!" He gave me a shove, and I went slowly to the house, hurt and perplexed. I had not heard yet of the classic fate of messengers who bring bad news. I felt like an extremely injured party—blamed for something for which I was in no way to blame. And the insult on top of the injury: nobody had ever called me "dummy" before.

Supper that evening was a meal eaten in silence. Finally, to everyone's surprise, Mama spoke.

"So we pay the twenty-seven cents!" Papa and Uncle Mike stared at her. "It's not the end of the world. We can eat; there is still grass in the pastures, so the cows still eat. We can manage. What's the matter, brother? Have you forgotten the song?" She began to sing the words softly. She had a sweet, small but clear voice. Uncle Mike tried to join in, but he choked up. When she finished, there was silence for a moment, then Papa said, "Brucha is right. Is there any more buttermilk?" I forgave him everything. He had praised Mama and even called her "Brucha." Everybody began to laugh.

# 7

# *Chicken Blood and Chocolate Fudge*

The way to the George Lumleys' farm was by way of the right fork of a road only about fifty feet from our place. The left fork went to Mount Pisgah, the village about a mile away, where there was a general store, a blacksmith shop, a church, a small flour mill and, of course, a schoolhouse. It was hardly ever called Mount Pisgah, however, but rather Kegtown. This was because once a man had lived there who made kegs—all kinds of kegs: small ones for nails, middle-sized ones for whiskey, and large ones for a variety of uses. The business lasted only about a year because the Methodist church disapproved of the middle-sized kegs. Since those were most in demand in towns throughout the county, Mr. Goodwin, the manufacturer, closed up shop and moved away. Nobody knew where he went, but the nickname he gave to Mount Pisgah remains in use to this day.

All this we learned from Mrs. Lumley when Mama and I went to call on her one Saturday morning. Mama wanted to ask questions, and she took me along to interpret or help her out if she should lack the English to explain or to understand everything. We had started down the right fork of the road when Mama noticed that the triangle formed by the branching of the roads had been planted with shrubs that were loaded with gooseberries, already very ripe and golden-green, and with currants, tiny, rosy-red, firm, gemlike. Mama was amazed that the fruit had not been picked. She gathered a handful, and we ate them as we continued along the descending road to the Lumleys'. A tiny stream bubbled over large pebbles at the foot of the road, which continued upward when we stepped across the water.

We met Mr. Lumley as he drove down the road in a small wagon drawn by a sad-eyed horse. His son, Horace, sat beside his father and blushed and looked down when he saw us. Mr. Lumley said, "Whoa, Marietta." Marietta stopped immediately as Mr. Lumley greeted us. He was on his way to Kegtown and offered to bring us anything we might need. There was nothing, Mama said, and we went our separate ways.

We found Mrs. Lumley plucking a chicken she had just killed by chopping off its head on a tree stump. She was going to fix it for the next day's dinner, she told us, after greeting us warmly. She seemed really glad to see us and called to the girls to take us into the house until she was through with her chore. She was wearing a pink sunbonnet and a polka-dot calico dress. Her sleeves were rolled up, and her hands and her apron were smeared with blood. It was hard to believe that such a nice lady could do what she had just done.

Ginny and Katie came running from the house. They said, "Hi! Come on in!" I followed them, glad to get away from such a gory sight, but Mama said she would wait for Mrs. Lumley, who called to the girls to take me around to the front door, not through her messy kitchen.

I looked at the house for the first time. It was smaller than ours and even dingier. No porch, no second story, just four sides of gray and brown siding topped by a black-shingled roof. But when we turned the corner to the front yard, I saw that the lawn was neat and green. Hollyhocks, with their ruffled pink and white and red blossoms, stood stiffly against the house as though waiting to be invited to dance. Tall maples shaded and cooled the house, and round beds of geraniums surrounded the trees.

"We're making fudge," said Ginny. "Just in case . . ."

"Just in case her beau comes over after church tomorrow," Katie giggled. She put her arm around me and drew me to the front door.

"I was just going to say, 'in case company drops in.' Somebody usually does, after church," Ginny retorted haughtily.

Katie was the younger sister. She was short and chubby, like her mother. I thought her very pretty and I liked her at once. Ginny was tall, like her father, and acted very grown-up. Their blue calico dresses were spotted with chocolate, which was nicer to look at than the smears of chicken blood on their mother's apron.

When we went into the parlor I could smell the fudge, and it made my mouth water. Katie took a blue velvet–bound album from a small round table in the center of the room. She told me to look at the photographs in the album while she and Ginny tended to the fudge. I looked around the room first, to see what I would wish for for our house if I could make my wishes come true. There were stiff lace curtains at the windows, a square carpet with red roses in the middle of the floor. The small table stood in the center of the carpet. On the table stood a decorated lamp. There were four chairs and a sofa, their seats and backs covered with black horsehair, and a little lace doily on the back of each one. Two colored calendars were on one wall, and on another hung a photograph of a bride and groom who, I learned later, were Mr. and Mrs. Lumley. But the most impressive object of all was a small organ against the wall opposite the sofa. I had never seen one before and it made the room very elegant. Not as elegant, of course, as Miss Abby's, but more elegant than Tante Freidel Mishkin's parlor.

I remembered that Papa had once promised Mama lace curtains at the windows and a carpet on the floor. That seemed a long time ago, and the promise had never been kept. In our new home the parlor was in the two-story part of the house, and we had not one thing to put into it except Uncle Mike's bed. So, though I would have liked the organ, I wished for the curtains and the carpet for Mama. Then I began to look at the photos in the album.

Ginny and Katie came in, smelling of fudge. They had spread the delectable candy in a large platter and put it in the cellar to cool. As soon as it was firm enough, they said, they would cut it in squares and we would all have a taste.

We heard Mrs. Lumley come in, followed by Mama. She walked into the parlor, smiling and drying her hands on a kitchen towel, and invited Mama to sit. Mrs. Lumley had cleaned the chicken and taken it down to the cellar. Here in the parlor, without her sunbonnet and her bloody apron, it was hard to believe she had just chopped off a chicken's head with an axe. She said the fudge smelled good. Katie went into the kitchen and brought the spoon that had stirred the fudge.

"Lick it," she said to me, "before I wash it." I licked it very, very clean. It was a harbinger of the delights to come when the fudge cooled. I was sure that Mr. Goldenstern had nothing to compare with it in his Confectionery and Cultural Center on Central Avenue.

Now Mama turned to Mrs. Lumley and, with my help, apologized for bothering her on such a busy day. Mrs. Lumley said it was no bother; it was good to have a reason for sitting to visit awhile. She had finished her Saturday baking, and she was glad to have company. Again with my help, Mama told her why she had come. She wanted Mrs. Lumley to explain how to "put up" the tomatoes that we'd held back from those shipped to Cincinnati. Mrs. Lumley began to give instructions slowly and I wrote them down. "You'll need mason jars," she said. Then she stopped and said, "I have a better idea. I'm going to put up some tomatoes myself next week. You bring yours, and I'll do them at the same time. You can watch, and the next time you'll know how."

Tears came to Mama's eyes.

"You are like a good sister," she said. Mama seemed to find "sisters" wherever she went. She and her own sister, my tante Sadie, were devoted to each other, so to call someone else "sister" was to honor her in the best way that Mama knew—and she knew now the English word for "shvester."

"And I will make for you," she continued, "*povidla* from the apples. Yes?"

"That means apple butter," I explained. Then Mama remembered the little patch of gooseberries and currants and asked whose they were.

"Nobody knows," Mrs. Lumley said. "That little corner of land belongs to the county. Those berry bushes have been there ever since I can remember. Sometimes somebody stops and picks a few, but most of the time the birds get them. You like them? You're welcome to them, I'm sure."

That was not all, we learned, that was in "the public domain." Mrs. Lumley told us that a long time ago someone had set out some old-fashioned roses—"cabbage roses"—beside the road to Kegtown. They were not very pretty, but you could smell their fragrance long before you could see them. Mama said she believed that was just the kind of rose from which you could make beautiful *varenya*. I translated for Mrs. Lumley: "That's preserves."

And then, Mrs. Lumley continued, there was the old Snider Place, a hundred acres or so, half of it fenced with barbed wire, just running wild. There were terrible stories about the place. Long ago, before Mrs. Lumley had come to Dunham's Hill as a bride, there was a man who had had a house there and enticed young girls to work for him. She looked at me and saw fear in my face and changed the subject.

"Oh, that was a very long time ago," she assured us, "and probably all made up anyway. There's no house there now; there's only a great big old empty barn. There's no sign, even, of where a house might have been. A lot of wild berries grow there," she went on, "and sometimes people pick them. Once in a while, people pasture their cows and even horses in the fenced part, but not much. Nobody has ever come to claim the place, but I suppose there's an owner somewhere, maybe named Snider, maybe not."

Mrs. Lumley was going to Kegtown Monday to the general store to trade eggs for sugar and flour. If Mama had more eggs and more butter than we needed, she might wish to come along with her and get whatever supplies she wanted. Mrs. Lumley would pick her up after morning chores. Mama said she would like to come to her house and watch how she harnessed the horse to the buggy. Mrs. Lumley said that would be just fine.

By this time the fudge was cool, and Ginny and Katie came in carrying it between them, and we all said, "M-m-m!"

When we were ready to leave Mrs. Lumley gave Mama two tin pails that had once held lard, in case we wanted to pick gooseberries and currants on the way home. When we said good-bye, they were calling each other "Becky" and "Ollie," which was short for Olive.

"When Papa hears how nice they are he will be glad, won't he, Mama?" I asked.

"Of course," Mama replied. "But we don't have to tell him about me going to learn how to hitch up the horse to the buggy. We'll surprise him. I think he will be glad—maybe. Who knows?"

It had been a beautiful morning, and we had much to relate to Papa and Uncle Mike. In the meantime, we filled our pails with gooseberries and currants.

We picked the last of the apples and the sour red cherries that were in the orchard across the road from our barnyard. Our house and yard were soon redolent of the spicy fragrance of apple butter and cinnamon, cooking to a rich, glossy thickness. The cherries became preserves, hoarded for serving with tea on special occasions. The gooseberries were turned into a tart sauce, stored in the cellar against the day when we might have meat with which to enjoy it. And the currants were transformed into tiny rubies trapped in a sweet sea the color of molten gold. The grapes, too, became jelly, purple as the robes of kings. But the greatest magic of all was the jelly made of the peelings of the apples that had been turned into apple butter. Pale rose in color, they yielded the last of their pectic flesh until only the paper-thin outer skin was left to be strained. The cellar shelves were soon adorned with mason jars and jelly glasses sealed with lids of wax. They became a culinary gallery of my mother's art. Ollie Lumley, given a sample of each of the lovely creations, was impressed.

We began to meet other neighbors. Mr. Joe Hoppe, described by Mrs. Lumley as the laziest man on Dunham's Hill, came by to get acquainted. He was a large man who moved slowly, as if he had all the time in the world. He wore overalls with no undershirt, and he was very sunburned. He also wore a big straw hat. He really didn't care much about farming, he said. His older son, Ben, liked it, so he pretty much left it to him. I was just getting ready to crawl under the barn to find the secret nests when he saw me.

"Is that your little girl?" he asked Papa.

"Yes, sir, that's my little girl."

"You got boys, too?"

"No."

"A farmer should have boys. Girls are all right, but boys are *necessary!*" He laughed very loudly. "You better get to work on that, Max. Keep trying. Maybe you'll get lucky." Then he said Mrs. Hoppe was sickly and asked for Mama to come visit.

I crawled under the barn and wished I didn't ever have to come out. I heard him talking and laughing again.

"I got three girls of my own. One of 'em wants to be a school-marm. That's what girls mostly do, y'know. They get a job teaching till they can catch a man." He kept talking and laughing, and I didn't hear Papa or Uncle Mike say anything. They just kept on getting the stables ready for the cows. I decided I didn't like Mr. Hoppe, and I certainly didn't like what he said about schoolteachers. I intended to be one myself!

I heard the cows approaching. Daisy wore a bell, and all of them were lowing. So I had to crawl out and let them in; that was one of my jobs. When I came out into the open, I saw that Rosie was acting very strange. She was trying to climb onto Daisy's back, and when Daisy got away from her, she tried to climb onto Gladys.

"Hey, Max," said Mr. Hoppe to Papa, "your cow's in heat!"

I was staring at the cows and at Mr. Hoppe. Papa said, "Take the eggs to the house." And to Mike he said, "You take care of the cows." I just stood there, puzzled. Papa told me to go on, to do as he said. I went into the house, told Mama what had happened, and asked her if Rosie was sick. She said not to worry, Rosie was just playing. She started for the barn herself. I didn't tell her about boys being more important on a farm than girls. I didn't want her to feel bad, the way I did.

Rosie kept on acting funny, and in a couple of days Papa and Uncle Mike took her away. Papa drove Ol' Belle in the two-wheeled cart, and Uncle Mike sat beside him holding a long chain attached to Rosie's halter. Rosie trotted along behind the cart. In the afternoon they brought her back. She didn't bother Daisy or Gladys anymore.

The next time I saw Ginny, I told her what had happened with Rosie. She was the oldest girlfriend I had, so I thought she could explain what was going on. Rosie wanted to get married, she said, and laughed. Papa must have taken Rosie to Old Man Ebbets' place. He had a "gentleman cow," registered (whatever that meant), and if she liked him Rosie probably would have a baby. I asked how we would know if she liked him.

"Well," said Ginny, "if she did she won't try to climb on Daisy anymore." Then, as an afterthought: "I guess you don't know where babies come from either, do you?" I pretended to know, but I refused to discuss it, and that ended the subject for the moment. But when I saw roosters acting just as Rosie had done, I was puzzled, because roosters, I knew, were boy chickens. Finally I figured out that boy chickens could want to get married, too. It was the beginning of my education in the facts of life.

# 8

## *The Little Red Schoolhouse*

On the fifteenth of September, 1907, I was seven years, five months and nine days old. I was on my way to the Dunham's Hill Elementary School, walking between Ginny and Katie Lumley; Horace followed us, walking a few steps behind. It was going to be my first day of school, and I was more than a little scared. Almost everything the Lumley girls had told me had prepared me for an experience unlike any I had ever known. All the children would be in one room; there was only one teacher for all the grades. The teacher's name was Miss Annie Puckett, but the children called her "Miss Annie." That was the one familiar note; I remembered Miss Abby and longed to see her.

Mama had dropped the last possible bit of hem on my best dress, a blue-and-white–striped dimity with a white yoke. But there was nothing she could do about the sleeves, which came to just above my bony wrists. She had found a pair of my white stockings that needed only a little darning, and she had tried to polish away the scuffs on my buttoned shoes.

I had watched Mama pack my lunch in one of the tin pails Mrs. Lumley had given us. There was a hard-boiled egg, a sandwich of bread and butter and another of apple butter and, finally, several slices of sponge cake so that I could treat Ginny and Katie and Horace.

Mama had washed my hair and made two braids which became

a "swing" across the back of my neck, each side tied with a somewhat faded blue ribbon. Pinned to my dress were a clean handkerchief and my certificate of promotion to the third grade.

Ginny had made a reluctant Horace carry my books, purchased at the general store, where the older students brought their used and outgrown books to be sold. I had a third grade Baldwin reader, a spelling book, and an arithmetic book that went from addition all the way to "gozintas," as simple division was known to the kids. Finally there was a copybook for penmanship taught by the Palmer method, which, to this day, I have not mastered. I still remember many of the maxims which headed each page: "Waste not, want not," "Early to bed, early to rise, makes a man healthy, wealthy, and wise," etc. A ruled pencil-writing tablet and a pencil box, equipped with two pencils, a pen, an eraser, a pencil sharpener, a pen wiper, and a six-inch ruler, constituted the rest of my equipment. The pencil box lid was decorated with a colored picture of a boy and a girl rolling hoops, the same kind of misleading art that Jennie Goldenstern and I had found in picture books at the Cincinnati Settlement House.

Ginny, who was in the seventh grade, wore a pretty dress of white voile with little black figures all over it. Her hair was elaborately dressed, with a large black taffeta bow at the nape of her neck. Katie said her sister had gotten up at dawn and gone to work on her hair with a curling iron. Katie wore a Ginny "hand-me-down" of pink-and-white–checked gingham.

"Once, just once," she complained bitterly, "I'd like to get a dress of my *own!* When I get married, I'll probably have to wear Ginny's wedding dress, with all the seams taken in and the hem taken up!"

Horace wore new overalls and a clean blue cotton shirt, and he was barefoot. All three carried their lunches in lard buckets. Suddenly a bell rang, a loud and, for me, ominous sound, slowly, slowly, in measured cadence. We had just come in sight of the schoolhouse and I stopped as if the sound had turned me to stone. Katie told me not to worry, that was only the first bell to remind kids not to dawdle on the road. The last bell would be in fifteen minutes.

The schoolhouse stood on a low, grassy rise. It was a one-story brick structure with a white-painted belfry. A short distance to the rear stood a woodshed where cut-up wood was stored for use when winter set in. Not far from the woodshed stood the privy, painted white.

A favorite recess game was "Andy-Over," in which two sets of players would take their places on either side of the woodshed and toss as many balls as there were players over the roof to their opponents. Each team had a monitor strategically placed to watch out for cheating. Since the balls could not be seen until they suddenly appeared over the roof, it took speed, sharp eyes, and skill to catch them. Katie said Ginny was a very good player because she was tall and thus closer to the approaching ball than almost anybody else.

As we approached the school yard, other children were beginning to arrive, staring at me curiously. Ginny told me to pay no attention, she would introduce me later. Horace thrust my books at me and his own at Ginny and ran to join his friends. Miss Annie had finished ringing the bell and was at her desk studying a list of names.

Ginny and Katie put their arms around me and approached the desk. Miss Annie looked up and smiled. She was the prettiest lady I had ever known—prettier, even, than Mama or Tante Sadie. Her hair was a color between brown and gold (Ginny later called it chestnut), her eyes like brown velvet, and her complexion like peaches and cream. She looked up and smiled and greeted Ginny and Katie.

"Miss Annie," Ginny said, "this is Goldie Weisberg. She's new. Her folks bought the Lumley place—you know, my cousins."

"Yes," said Miss Annie. "Welcome to our school, Goldie." Her smile was warm and made her even prettier. "How old are you, dear?" she asked.

"I was seven in April, ma'am." Katie helped me unpin my transfer certificate and I handed it to the teacher.

Miss Annie read it and looked up. "In the third grade?" She sounded surprised. "How old were you when you started school?"

"I'm not sure. Five, I think."

Katie came to my assistance. "She was skipped," she explained with a touch of pride.

"Well, well," said Miss Annie. "You can sit with the third-graders, and we'll see if you can keep up. Ginny, there's a vacant desk next to Horace. Why don't you show Goldie where to put her things? The last bell will ring soon, and then you can go out and show her how we stand in line to march in." She stood up and came around and smiled down at me. "I hope you'll be happy here, Goldie. Run along now."

I placed my books in my assigned desk and my pencil box on top. In the upper right-hand corner was an inkwell with a hinged lid that lifted up. That was just like in Cincinnati, and it made me feel less strange. Ginny showed me the shelf in the cloakroom where we put our lunch pails. They all looked the same, all lard pails. Each one had a name on it, except mine; Ginny had forgotten to tell me.

"Never mind," Ginny said. "We'll know yours is the one without a name. Tonight you can paint your name on it."

Outside the children were shouting at their games. We went out, and some of them stopped and waited to see what I was going to do. Just then the last bell rang, and everyone formed a line to go in. Two black girls, referred to as "colored" in those days, came running up, out of breath, almost late, and ended up last in line. Ginny was first, and I was behind her. We filed in, and I went to my seat and sat down until I saw that everyone else was standing—including Horace, who didn't look too happy at being so close to me. I stood up quickly, like the others.

"Good morning, girls and boys," greeted Miss Annie.

"Good morning, Miss Annie," we responded.

"Welcome back to school, and I am pleased to see that you are all back, all nineteen of you! Isn't that nice!"

"Yes, Miss Annie."

"Now, before we repeat our Pledge of Allegiance, I want to introduce a new pupil, who comes to us from Cincinnati and makes us an even twenty." She motioned to me to come forward. I stood beside her, feeling shy and uncomfortable; I wished she hadn't made a ceremony out of introducing me.

"This new pupil," she went on, her hand lightly on my shoulder, "is Goldie Weisberg."

She turned to the blackboard and picked up a piece of chalk. She repeated my name slowly as she wrote it on the blackboard. "Now let's all say, 'Welcome, Goldie. We're glad you're here.' " The preliminaries were over, and I went back to stand beside my seat.

"And now let us repeat our Pledge of Allegiance," she said. This was something I knew about and I knew what would come next—"The Star-Spangled Banner." Finally Miss Annie said we could be seated. I watched the others, who seemed to know exactly what to do. They folded their hands on their desks and bowed their heads. Miss Annie counted one-two-three, and everybody recited the Lord's Prayer. I couldn't join in, because I didn't know it; I had never heard it. I saw Horace looking at me out of the corner of his eye. I was embarrassed and unhappy.

The rest of the morning we spent talking about schedules and all the things were were going to do: when one class was having their lesson, the others would be studying theirs or doing arithmetic on the blackboard. That's how one teacher could teach all eight grades. There was only one eighth-grader, however—Gertrude, the older "colored" girl.

At noon we all picked up our lunch pails, and I followed Ginny and Katie out to the yard. Three more girls joined us; one was Bessie Hoppe, also in the third grade but eight years old, like Horace. She said her papa had told her about me, and she was glad I was in her class, but how come, when I was only seven? Katie told her it was because I was smart and got skipped.

"I sit right behind you," said Bessie. "How come you didn't say the Lord's Prayer?"

"I don't know it," I said and felt myself blushing.

"Didn't you learn it at Sunday school?"

"I've never been to Sunday school."

"How come?"

"I'm Jewish."

"What's that?"

"A different religion."

"Didn't you have it at your school?"

"No."

"How come?"

"I don't know."

Ginny finally broke in. "Why do you ask so many questions, Bessie? It's none of your business, anyway. Eat your lunch."

Bessie picked up her lunch pail and moved to another group. We never became friends.

When I went to put my lunch pail away, I had a chance really to see what our schoolroom was like. In the very center stood a cast-iron potbellied stove. A portrait of George Washington hung on the wall above the blackboard. The walls on either side of the blackboard were mostly windows, with maps, physiology charts, and a large calendar in between. The desks were pretty old, and most of them had names and dates carved into their tops. Mine had, in addition, a heart and the legend "G + B" carved inside. In one corner of the room near Miss Annie's desk stood a small case with a dozen or so books on its shelves. I longed to see what the titles were, but was not bold enough on this, my first day, to go and look. I found out after lunch without having to look.

School was out early because it was the first day. We really didn't do much of anything. After lunch, Miss Annie read to us from a book by Horatio Alger, her favorite author. Besides the Alger books, she told us, there were *In His Steps* by a Reverend Dr. Sheldon, a couple of the Elsie Dinsmore books, and a volume of Mother Goose rhymes to introduce first-graders, Miss Annie said, to the magic world of literature. Everything in the "library," Miss Annie said, was uplifting, and the Alger books were a great inspiration to the youth of our country.

When school was dismissed at afternoon recess time, Miss Annie held me back. Ginny and Katie waited for me outside. Miss Annie said she had noticed I hadn't joined in reciting the Lord's Prayer, and asked almost the same questions that Bessie had asked. Then she gave me a printed copy of the prayer and said I could take it home and study it. She said they only recited it the first day of every school week, so she was sure I'd have it memorized by the following Monday. Then she smiled and patted my cheek and said, "Bye-bye until tomorrow." I picked up my lunch box and books, which we had not opened at all that day, and went out. Ginny and Katie were waiting for me, but Horace had gone home on the run, Katie said.

"Ol' Horace was afraid he'd have to carry your books, and he'd get teased about being your beau," explained Ginny, laughing.

It had not been a very successful day for me, and I didn't need to be teased about Ol' Horace to make it worse. My one experience with romance and the opposite sex had been a disaster. It was in the second grade in Cincinnati. My admirer's name was Walter, and he brought me a string of colored glass beads as an engagement present. I told Mama, at the time, that it was a present from a classmate. After awhile my conscience nudged me, and I told her the classmate's name was Walter. Papa hadn't even noticed. The next day Walter demanded his present back. He admitted having "snitched" it from his sister, who had made him confess. He told me if he didn't give it back to her he was to be first boiled in oil, then killed. I vowed then and there never to have anything to do with men for the rest of my life. And I certainly wasn't going to change for Ol' Horace.

When I got home from school, everybody was busy and didn't pay much attention to me. I changed into my everyday dress and shoes and took up my regular chores. But at supper that night Mama, Papa, and Uncle Mike all wanted to know about my first day at my new school. Was I polite to the teacher? Did I behave myself? What questions did the teacher ask? Did I know all the answers? I opened my Baldwin reader, took out the copy of the Lord's Prayer, and gave it to Papa and said, "I didn't know this."

Papa, helped by Uncle Mike, read it aloud. "Is this a school you're going to or a church?" he shouted. I said it was a school, of course. I didn't realize he was just being mad. He knew it was a school. He told me to go see if there were any more eggs under the barn. He told Mama to light the lantern for me. I knew there were no more eggs under the barn, but I went. When I came back, Papa was saying, "It doesn't say in here anything about Jesus, just God, and to me that's bad enough." Papa's agnosticism was evidencing itself again. "I guess it won't hurt her, though; it's not good for a child to be different from other children." To me he said, "Learn it like your teacher said."

The following Monday, I folded my hands with the rest of the children. It was the first time I had learned anything of a religious nature of any kind, except for once in Boston, when Zayde arranged for a Hebrew teacher—an old man with a long beard and a long black coat, even in the summer—to come to the house and teach me the Hebrew alphabet. Papa stopped it; he said it interfered with my learning English. And, of course, there was my ill-fated visit to the mission in Cincinnati with Norma.

Miss Annie was not at all like the other teachers I had known. She spent a lot of time writing at her desk. She called on the older children to work with the youngest; sometimes she would look up from her desk, listen to the lesson and nod approvingly. When the first three grades went to the blackboard to do arithmetic, some of the older children would be told to go to the blackboard and grade them. When a child saw a mistake, she or he had to raise a hand, then go to the blackboard and correct it. Then Miss Annie would say, "Now open your arithmetic books, and see who is right." It was as though she herself wasn't sure, but maybe it was her way of teaching. I never found out for sure, because the next year we had a different teacher.

There was one thing Miss Annie did that was really wonderful. In the spring, when the trees began to leaf, the wildflowers to appear, and the birds to return from wherever they had gone in the winter, she took us walking in the woods. We would start right after the Lord's Prayer and come back in time for lunch.

In the woods, Miss Annie *knew*. Sometimes she asked the children to name a flower we discovered struggling to get out of the ground. Sometimes one of us would know, but I was never one of those. Then Miss Annie would talk about the flowers and about the trees. Sometimes a bird would perch close to us on a branch and begin to sing. Miss Annie always knew the bird's name, and could whistle back to it. I decided then and there that I, too, would learn to talk to birds like she did. And in time I succeeded.

The walks in the woods were for me more than a nature lesson. The smell of the thawing earth, the trees so recently bare robing themselves in new green garments, the birds returning so joyously, the clear blue of the sky decorated with the softest white clouds— all this was a new experience for me. It was an emotional experience beyond the delight I had found in the swan boats of Boston's Public Gardens or the animals in the Cincinnati Zoo. It was ineffable, impossible to define to myself, and impossible to communicate to anyone else, even to Mama.

We did not go walking in the woods every morning, but we returned two or three times, when Miss Annie knew that there were changes taking place. The last excursion was in mid-April, two weeks before school was out for the summer. Miss Annie knew that there would be new flowers, new birds, and many more leaves on the trees. There was something else different on this Monday morning. We skipped the Lord's Prayer. Only Bessie challenged this. Miss Annie said, "Don't worry, Bessie. There's a time and a place for everything." The place proved to be a clearing in the woods where yellow and white Johnny jump-ups had appeared, together with Dutchman's-Breeches and spring beauties. A robin looked down on us as we folded our hands and recited, "Our Father, Who art in Heaven." I recited it with a difference. The time and the place seemed just right.

Thinking back to that time, I believe Miss Annie, despite her deplorable taste in literature, was perhaps the best teacher I ever had.

On the last day of school we had a party. Ginny and Katie brought fudge; some of the other children brought cookies. I brought slices of honey cake that Mama had baked after supper the night before. Miss Annie brought lemonade in a brand-new tin pail. She had asked every child to bring a tin cup. All the lunch boxes had something special, and everything was shared.

We sang "Auld Lang Syne," and then Miss Annie told us she

was not coming back next year. We were going to have a new teacher, Miss Velma Mott, who lived close enough to walk if she felt like it. She herself, Miss Annie said, had to board with a family in Kegtown and pay to be driven to and from school. She was sorry to leave us, but it took too much of her salary this way. She would find a school near her home in Amelia, a town some distance away from Dunham's Hill. All the children seemed stunned for a moment. Then the girls began to plead, "No, Miss Annie, please don't go!" Some of us cried, and tears came to Miss Annie's eyes. She wished us a good summer, then crossed the room and rang the bell. The boys ran out yelling, "No more pencils, no more books, no more teacher's sassy looks." But the girls crowded around Miss Annie, and she hugged each of us. When Gertrude and Rosie Mitchell, the "colored" sisters, came by, Rosie, the older girl, shyly held out her hand, but Miss Annie hugged her and Gertrude even longer than anybody else.

Then we said good-bye to one another and went our separate ways, Ginny and Katie and Horace and I together. When we got a little distance away, Horace took my books to carry home. We never heard from Miss Annie again. As far as anybody knew, she did not teach in Amelia.

# 9

## *The Loveliest Summer*

We had survived our first winter on Dunham's Hill. It had not been a severe winter, and we had had good rain in early spring. In March the field that had yielded beautiful tomatoes, but no money, was ready to be plowed. The dead tomato plants were plowed under. Then the ground was flattened with a harrow and smoothed with a broad wooden sled whose runners had been covered with strips of tin. In spite of the tomato disaster, it was decided to try tomatoes once more.

The spring plowing was a shared job on Dunham's Hill as in other parts of Clermont County and, no doubt, everywhere in America's heartland. Not everybody's fields were ready for plowing at the same time. A hillside section might have thawed early, or a piece of bottomland, not sufficiently dried after spring rains, might now be ready. Thus two or three neighbors with their teams and plows (George Lumley used mules) would converge on the first place that was ready. They would all have eaten an early hot breakfast, appearing for work about five o'clock in the morning. At nine o'clock coffee and sweet rolls would be brought to the field, and the plowmen would take their coffee break. When the plowing was at our place, Mama baked her special cinnamon rolls that became famous on Dunham's Hill. Each fragrant hot roll was the size of a small loaf of bread. Mama would slice each one and spread the slices with sweet butter. My job was to carry the basket of rolls, tin cups, and a large graniteware pot of steaming hot coffee already sweetened and rich with golden cream.

Papa had been learning, watching, figuring things out. He knew how to grow the tomato plants in a "hotbed" and how to plant them when they were ready. After the field was prepared, furrows were made, using a smaller plow; that was Papa's job. Uncle Mike came after him, building up little hills inside the furrows at regular intervals. Mama followed right behind him, making a neat hole with the handle of a hoe in the center of each hill. I was next, dropping a tomato plant into each hole, and adding a little water from a watering can filled from a barrel which had been brought to the edge of the field on the sled. Then Uncle Mike started over and secured the earth around each plant.

Today this is known as "stoop labor" and is left to the least skilled and neediest of farm workers. At that time it was simply part of farming. The tomato plants were often the victims of cut-worms, which earned their name by neatly cutting the plant at its base. This necessitated replanting, as well as scattering death-dealing poisons, in the war against the enemy.

Potatoes were planted that year, too, and field corn for cattle and horse feed. In the kitchen garden, of course, Mama planted sweet corn, called "Country Gentleman" and "Zig-Zag," all sweet and tender like no corn we ever bought from Springer's Grocery. It was at mealtime, when the delicious homegrown foods were placed on the table, that Uncle Mike's faith in and commitment to "the land" would be renewed and announced—as though to reassure himself as well as the rest of us. When he was doing his share of stoop labor, however, he was morose and silent except for mumbling to himself.

In spite of the additional chores of helping with the planting and weeding, I had time to explore the upstairs rooms and attic of the big house, the original two-and-a-half–story part of our dwelling. We had no furniture for the parlor, except Uncle Mike's bed, nor for the upstairs bedrooms, in which we spread the black walnuts to dry. But the attic was virgin territory for me. Much to my surprise, I found a treasure of print: a Sears, Roebuck catalogue, back issues of the *Ohio Farmer* and *Farm and Fireside,* and a tattered copy of *Uncle Tom's Cabin.* It was the first book I had ever owned! I recited aloud, "Finders keepers, losers weepers," and carried my rich find downstairs.

Papa was very pleased with my discovery of the *Ohio Farmer.* He and Uncle Mike pored over it together and decided they should order a subscription. To them, especially to Papa, it was like going to a farmers' college. He was so pleased with my discovery that he said I could stay up an extra half hour and read the book I had found.

The attic was not the end of my exploration, discovery, and learning. At one end of the pasture that we used for the cows, separated from it by a barbed wire fence, was a small grove of honey locust trees. Their branches were covered with a growth of sharp thorns as though to protect them from enemies. I was never tempted to explore that little woodland until this, our first spring on the farm. Now the locust trees were almost covered with great clumps of fragrant blossoms that perfumed the air far beyond their habitat. Their individual flowers resembled sweet peas. The blossoms were a soft creamy white, and too high on the tree for me to reach to pick for Mama; besides, the thorns on the branches were very forbidding. I decided the trees grew thorns to protect their flower children from being taken away, and never tried to gather them.

I discovered something else in the locust grove—something perplexing: there were small, flat slabs of weathered marble, half-buried in the earth, scattered sparsely through the woods. Words had been carved into the marble but were worn away beyond recognition. I told Papa about my discovery, and he went with me to look at it. It was nothing really, he said. It must be a very old cemetery. He told Mama about it, laughing.

"Our Goldele is another Columbus. She keeps on discovering— books in the attic, old bones in the forest."

Mama didn't think I should go there anymore.

"Why?" joked Papa. "Do you think the *maisim* will wake up and seize her? Go, child, don't be afraid. Maybe you'll find other things buried there, like buried treasure!"

But it was quite awhile before I ventured into the little locust grove again, and I did indeed find a treasure—not buried, either. Wild strawberries had appeared where the sun filtered through the trees. They had ripened during my absence, and I wasn't sure what they were. Once, in Boston, Tante Sadie had brought home a treat: large, ripe, fragrant strawberries which were very unlike the small, flat, red, buttonlike fruit that grew among the old grave markers. I picked a few and brought them home. Mama knew them at once and was as delighted with the find as Papa had been the *Ohio Farmer.*

"They're wild strawberries, my child," Mama exclaimed. "There is nothing like them or half as good that is grown in the garden. They taste of wine and sunshine!" She kissed me and said I could pick them anytime, but not eat them until they were washed. She said if I could find enough we could have them for supper. I ran back, elated at my success and thinking about how Mama had described the wild strawberries: "They taste like wine and sunshine." I couldn't imagine the taste, but it sounded lovely. Mama often said things like that—like poetry, I thought, recalling the sound of verses by Mr. Longfellow.

At supper, my happiness of the day was crowned with praise. Papa said, "How do you like it? Our little one, like I said before, is a regular Columbus. She discovered the *Ohio Farmer* and wild strawberries!" And I was allowed another extra half hour to read in *Uncle Tom's Cabin,* such a sad and disturbing story. I thought of Gertrude and Rosie Mitchell, who were "colored," and began to cry. It was Papa who heard me first, and he came into the kitchen from the porch, followed by Mama and Uncle Mike.

"What's the matter?" they asked all at once.

"Papa, are all the colored people slaves?"

"Certainly not. There are no slaves in America today! Not the kind you mean, anyway. In the sweatshops, maybe, and the cigar factories and the mills where little children work. But not like in *Uncle Tom's Cabin.*"

I was astonished that he knew about the book. He told me he had read it in Russian and wanted to know why I had asked.

"Because Rosie and Gertrude are colored. They are nice. They go to school, too."

He assured me they were safe from the Simon Legree in the book and suggested I invite them to come home with me sometime.

I cannot remember a happier time in my childhood than that spring and summer. I had made important discoveries. I had a book of my own, and Papa had read it, too! I saw him in a new and wonderful light. And he had said nice things about Rosie and Gertrude.

And the world was beautiful! I had known grass and flowers and blue sky on my visits to the Public Gardens in Boston, and to the Cincinnati Zoo, but they were only backgrounds to the swan boats and the animals. Now I was part of a world that Miss Annie Puckett had opened up for me, more beautiful than any I had ever known. The pear trees were in full blossom, rounded pyramids of fragrant snow rising from their trunks, so light and delicate that they seemed as though they were wearing bridal gowns like I had seen in colored pictures at Bubbie's house. Soon the cherry trees

got dressed up, too, then the apple trees, whose blossoms were delicately pink and as fragrant as the others.

Mama and I had acquired sunbonnets, and Papa and Uncle Mike wore bibbed overalls and big straw hats. That summer, too, I learned to sit on one of the horses when Papa plowed or harrowed in the fields. It was always Ol' Ned, who patiently tolerated the added weight. It was never Ol' Cole, who was mean and unpredictable, though he feared Papa and would not dare—Uncle Mike said—to act up when Papa was around. And after the practice on Ol' Ned, Papa saddled Ol' Belle, who was, of course, the saddle horse by appointment. I was apprehensive at first, but by summer's end I loved riding. When there was no one around to saddle Ol' Belle, I learned to maneuver her to the barnyard gate, from which I could climb to her back. I heard Papa once say to Uncle Mike that I should have been a boy, I took to boyish things so easily. I was not sure whether to be glad or unhappy about it, not at that time, anyway. The time came when I was sure that to have been born a boy would have been the most desirable thing that could have happened to me. But not just yet.

We were now pasturing our cows on the "old Snider Place" that Mrs. Lumley had told us about, and it was my chore to bring them home. They would be waiting there at the barbed-wire gate, as they had waited in our own pasture the year before and at the same time. I had practiced riding Ol' Belle to the gate, leaning down with one foot in the stirrup and lifting the wire that opened the gate. Then I would hoist myself back into the saddle. I became quite proficient at it and learned to bring the cows home, riding behind them as they trotted back to be milked.

One day Mama said, "How would you like to learn to milk one of the cows and learn a lovely game at the same time?" Mama could make up some of the best games I ever knew when we were working on something, and so of course I said, "Yes, Mama!"

She started me on Daisy, who was the gentlest of the herd, a big-boned, sad-eyed creature, pure white. I always thought she was sad because she was different from the other cows. So I told her I was proud that Mama had picked her for me.

After a week, I was able to direct the streams of milk away from my elbows into the pail of foaming liquid, still warm from the udder, Now, I told Mama, I was ready for the game. She agreed and we began what I am certain was the only musical event ever created by the collaboration of a cow, a woman, a tin pail, and a little girl. Mama said, "I am going to play a tune on the milk bucket, and you have to guess what it is. If you are right, you don't dry dishes tonight. Now listen and watch." Mama was milking Rosie for the last time, for Rosie was going to have a baby and would soon "go dry" to save all her milk for her calf. I listened to the beat of the stream of milk against the the side of the pail. Mama had to "play" it three times before I caught on. "I know it! I know it!" I cried. "It's 'Pony Boy'!" And we both began to sing it. Mama had a gift for making games out of many humdrum things.

Helping Mama with the milking became, little by little, one of my regular chores. Another, the most distasteful of any, began when the potato plants developed; with them came an invasion of potato bugs, ugly larvae at first, then beetles. It was my job to plod from plant to plant, carrying a little can half-filled with kerosene, picking off the critters with my fingers and dropping them into the can. I hated and resented this job and considered Papa, who had assigned it to me, as cruel as Simon Legree. I thought he should include this, above all my chores, with "sweatshops and cigar factories and mills where little children worked," as examples of modern slavery. Naturally I kept this judgment to myself. Besides, I did not hear Papa shouting at Mama that summer, and this made up for a lot.

In spite of the potato bugs, it was a good summer. The young people of Dunham's Hill and even Kegtown had parties and picnics, and little kids were not excluded, except from some of the games, like "Post Office" and "spin-the-bottle," where the boys had to "bow to the wittiest, kneel to the prettiest, and kiss the one you love best." In April, during the week of Easter Sunday, there was an egg roast in the woods. In June there was the Sunday school picnic in a grove central to several little villages, and I was invited by the Lumleys to come along. Afterward Ginny and Katie came to our house one Sunday afternoon and asked Mama if I could go to Sunday school with them. Mama was startled. She asked them to wait, and went to look for Papa in the barn. Ginny asked me if Mama was mad at them. I said I didn't think so. Pretty soon Mama came back, bringing Papa with her. He came right to the point.

"You know," he said, "we are Jewish."

"Yes, sir," said Ginny. "Does that make any differences?"

"Maybe. Jews don't believe that Jesus is God's son."

Ginny and Katie looked at each other. Ginny said, "I don't think she has to. I won't try to make her. She can just pray to God. That's all right, isn't it?" Papa and Mama exchanged glances.

"That's all right, then," said Papa. "If she just wants to pray to God, that's all right." Ginny and Katie were delighted, and so was I. It meant not being different, and it meant being included in lots of special things.

The biggest event of the year came late in the summer: the fish fry held every year by the Modern Woodmen of America. Dunham's Hill was five miles from the Ohio River and twenty-five miles from Cincinnati, so fish was a delicacy rarely enjoyed. The men took over the preparation for the fry, which was held in the clearing of another grove where the Sunday school picnic took place. Wood fires were laid in a trench and watched over until they became glowing coals. I don't remember the kinds of fish, but they were brought to the grove cut into large chunks, and then they were fried in long-handled heavy skillets. Among unequaled taste memories that I cherish today are veal kabobs, on skewers made of sturdy, slender green pine sticks, broiled over a great fire in the Wilderness of Rocks in the Catalina Mountains of Arizona; the heel of Mama's still-warm, freshly baked bread spread with sweet butter and crushed, freshly picked blackberries topped with sugar; and the golden-brown crisp chunks of fish piled high on platters by the Modern Woodmen of America.

While the men were frying fish, their feminine counterparts, the Royal Neighbors, were loading the long picnic tables with bowls of potato salad, coleslaw and cucumber pickles, homemade bread, and every conceivable kind of layer cake and pie. Mama and Papa never joined the Woodmen or the Royal Neighbors, but Mama always made strudel and sent it along with me.

That summer, after a gentle rain, Mama discovered mushrooms in a meadow—small-crowned, snowy lovelies, delicately pink where the tight stems were removed. Mama knew mushrooms, she said, like she knew her own child; and she knew these mushrooms were good just as she knew her child was good. When she cooked them with milk, butter, tiny new potatoes, and little green onion tops from her garden, they made a luscious dish; and after they were eaten everybody felt so good that Uncle Mike suddenly—after months of ignoring it—sang his song about the Jew and the land.

The crop of tomatoes was not as bountiful as the year before, and thus perhaps they would not be a drug on the market. But the tomatoes themselves were not as good. Some kind of disease had attacked them. Much of the crop could not be shipped. "You can't win for losing," Mr. Lumley said. Nevertheless they brought in a little money, so it wasn't as bad as the year before.

I had learned to ride Ol' Belle, but Mama had learned to hitch her to the buggy and to drive. She went to Kegtown one afternoon to trade some eggs for sugar and flour, and when she came home she had a surprise for me. She had bought some pretty flowered challis to make a new dress for me to wear on the first day of school. When I hugged her, she said, "You must thank your Papa, too. It was he who told me to get it, so you would look as nice as the Lumley girls." Papa came in at that moment and I thanked him. He said he wanted to see what Mama picked out. He liked it, he told her but, he said, she had enough for three or four dresses.

"I *have* got enough for three," she said, and, seeing his face harden, she added quickly, "Enough for Ginny and Katie."

"What's the matter with you?" he demanded. "You think you are living in Krippa, where you had to give presents to the drunken peasants so they wouldn't burn your house down? This is America!"

"I know," Mama pleaded. "I did it because I haven't got my sewing machine yet, and I haven't got time to do it by hand. So I'll ask Ollie Lumley if I can come over and use hers." Papa flung aside the material he was holding. "Stupid!" he cried. "If a neighbor asks you for a favor, will you expect to be paid?" He stomped out of the house, and my pleasure changed to anxiety. Would he come back shouting? And then go into his silence? Mama looked sad but said nothing, just quietly put the material away. As she walked away, I heard her say softly, "I can't help it."

I believe Papa was right; it was years before she overcame the fear that always shadowed their lives in the "dorf" where she had grown up. Appeasing the peasants was a way of staying alive— and in the end her grandfather's home and business had been burned to the ground anyway, hastening his death.

Papa came back into the house after awhile and seemed to be over his anger. Mama was making supper, and I was helping. He stood in the kitchen doorway for a moment, watching her. Then he said quietly, "You have to get over being afraid in your heart. People have been good neighbors. It's different."

"I know. I'll try." She did try, but once in a while the old fears, the old memories were too much, and she went beyond the normal neighborly exchanges of help and courtesies and, unknown to Papa, went that extra mile of "insurance."

By mid-September of 1908, we had lived a year on Dunham's Hill. The colors of the leaves were changing. There was a different kind of fragrance in the air. The sunsets were even more colorful. I had learned to walk barefoot even on the stubble of cut hay. I had ridden Ol' Ned to the blacksmith shop in Kegtown and had come away with a black-and-white puppy, a gift from Mr. Gillespie, the blacksmith. I named my new pet Prince then and there. I held him close to me on the pommel of the saddle and told him not

to be afraid, I would not let Ol' Ned gallop. I doubt that Ol' Ned
had enough gallop left in him to dash forth if his tail were on fire,
but I thought he would feel proud if he heard me pretend to Prince
that he was still full of vim and vigor.

All the way home I made every magic wish that I could think
of to find Papa in a good mood so that he would let me keep my
puppy. He was, and he did. But of everything that happened that
summer the most exciting was the birth of Rosie's baby, a little,
reddish, wet heifer. Something that Mama remembered from the
"old country" was to sprinkle coarse salt over the brand new calf.
Rosie forthwith cleaned the calf with her tongue, licking up the
salt. We named the newcomer Posie, which was almost like naming
her after her mother, and it seemed like only minutes before Posie
got up on her skinny legs and wobbled to her mama's udder for
her first meal. School started soon after.

# 10

# *Miss Velma*

I walked to school with confidence now, proud of my new dress. I met Ginny and Katie at the place where they took the shortcut. They were wearing their new challis dresses, too, and we decided we were triplets. Ginny had a regular beau now, so she wore her hair in a fancy grown-up way. Katie said it had taken her sister two hours with the curling iron, and if she shook her head it would probably all come down, but Ginny paid no attention and walked haughtily a little ahead of us. As for Horace, he had run on well ahead, determined once again not to be trapped into carrying my books.

Our new teacher was Miss Velma, but she was not really *new*, because almost everybody had known her for a long time. She was Miss Velma Mott, our near neighbor in the red brick house, and she had gone to a normal school and was a *real* teacher, we had been told, not like Miss Annie. Miss Velma was pretty, too, with dimples and reddish-brown hair and cute freckles, but I was glad I had started with Miss Annie, who may not have known how *really* to teach, but who knew about so much else that I have never forgotten.

There was no wasting time, no being read to from the inspirational Horatio Alger books. We had planned lessons and homework and tests on Friday mornings, but Friday afternoons were for "culture." We spoke pieces, sang songs, and could stand in front of the class and talk about how we spent our summer or any other subject that we chose.

We were eighteen children, but some of the older boys were late starting because they had to help with the harvest. However, Miss Velma assured us, they would have extra homework so they could catch up. I was eight years and five months old, and I was in the fourth grade, and Miss Velma lost no time in making me prove that I belonged there. At the end of the year, Miss Velma promoted me to the fifth grade, so I suppose I satisfied her that I had fulfilled all the requirements.

Something else was added to our school experience that we had not known under Miss Annie: monthly spelling bees and weekly arithmetic races. The arithmetic races took place on Monday mornings. Teams of four would be chosen, sent to the back of the room with our backs turned while Miss Velma would write problems in addition, subtraction and, for the seventh and eighth graders, division. Then she would turn, say "Get set—turn—go!," and we would run to the blackboard and go to work. The ones who were the first to finish correctly were rewarded by being chosen to ring the bells, pass out papers, start recess five minutes early, and by any other way that Miss Velma could dream up. Sometimes the reward might even be to skip a lesson and read a book, or to play "tic-tac-toe" two-at-a-desk or, if Ginny won—which was rare— she was allowed to stay at the blackboard and draw. I thought Ginny was a fine artist, but limited to drawing a horse and wagon and flowers. Actually, she could draw only four kinds of flowers: roses, daisies, pansies, and calla lillies, but I knew no one else who could do as much, so I admired her greatly and so did everyone else. When she became engaged at sixteen, the weekly newspaper published in New Richmond printed the announcement of the betrothal of Miss Virginia Lumley, "the beautiful and accomplished daughter of Mr. and Mrs. George Lumley...." I thought she really deserved the description. As time went on, I discovered that every engagement was announced in the same way.

The spelling bees were a much more important event because they were held in the evenings and parents were invited. Mama always came, but Papa and Uncle Mike never felt like getting dressed up. Mama still had the pretty blouse and skirt she wore on the day she signed the papers for the farm. She always wore that costume and was the prettiest mother there, I thought.

The spelling bees were very exciting and were actually social events in a small way.

If the Sunday school and the fish fry were the highlights of the summer, the great social event of the winter was the box social, which was also a benefit for the school or the church. The ladies and girls each packed a box lunch with their special foods and decorated the boxes with colored papers, ribbons, and all manner of trinkets. These works of art and their delectable culinary contents were auctioned with the males bidding—the older men cautiously, the young swains recklessly, especially if their girlfriends had tipped them off with descriptions of their boxes. The high bidder shared the contents of the box of his choice with its creator. Once a swain ran the bid up to five dollars, vying with a rival who had been tipped off, not by the young lady, but by her little brother for a nickel bribe.

The two "social events" of the summer season, the fish fry and the Sunday school picnic—were repeated the next year; only this time I was asked to speak a piece at the picnic. Everybody knew that I loved to recite verses and I eagerly accepted. The poem that was chosen for me disturbed me a little, so I practiced reciting only when I was away from Mama or Papa, bringing home the cows, or going to the mailbox. But one day Papa heard me talking to myself and demanded to know what I was saying. I confessed that I was practicing for the Sunday school picnic. Let me hear it, Papa commanded. Frightened, I mumbled: "I am—"

"Speak up!" Papa ordered. "You are what?"

"I am Jesus' little lamb. / Jesus made me what I am—"

"That's enough!" Papa thundered. "Do you believe Jesus made you what you are?"

"No, Papa."

"Then why are you saying it?"

"They asked me—"

He turned abruptly and walked away. I saw him leave the barnyard and start down the road that led to the Lumleys. I never learned what transpired there. I continued to go to Sunday school with the children, but I was given a different poem to recite: "The Children's Hour," by Mr. Henry Wadsworth Longfellow, as I was asked to announce it from the platform at the picnic. I think Papa never told Mama about the episode, for she said nothing to me about it then, or ever.

That summer, I joined another work force in addition to my chores at home. The Lumleys grew strawberries, black raspberries, and red raspberries for the market. That was their money crop, and it was picked by neighborhood women, teenagers, and a few kids like myself. Picking the strawberries was "stoop labor" because they grew at ground level. The other berries were supported on stakes and required only a little bending. Women saved their worn-out black cotton stockings, cut off the feet, took a stitch at the thumb end, and wore them pulled up to the elbow to protect their hands and arms from sunburn and scratches, and at the same time leave the fingers free for picking.

The raspberries were the easiest to pick, slipping off when ripe at the lightest touch. The black raspberries were my favorites, gleaming black like little jet bonnets lined with pure white satin. But the strawberries were the most challenging. I was probably the slowest of the strawberry pickers, because I had a compulsion about picking them with even stems and not bruising them. At six cents a basket (which held about a quart of berries), I was very low on the earning scale, but my strawberries were chosen for the top layer of little boxes in the crates. I took pride in that, even though I remembered what Mama had said about saving the best tomatoes for the top: "Isn't that cheating?"

# The Last Days of Ol' Cole

Ol' Ned was getting too old for heavy work, and Ol' Cole, forced to do most of the pulling, would nip at Ol' Ned whenever he thought Papa wasn't looking. Papa would use Ol' Ned for lighter work whenever he could, like cutting furrows in the small field in back of the house. Even this seemed to be too much for him. As soon as he heard the dinner bell, he would stop dead in his tracks, whether he was at the end of a furrow or in the middle of it. It was clearly time to put him out to pasture and get a younger, stronger horse to team up with Ol' Cole.

Papa heard of a good horse for sale or trade in Lindale, about two miles away. They would consider an older horse good with kids. He and Uncle Mike harnessed Ol' Belle to the two-wheeled rig and drove off to look into the deal. Ol' Ned, who was being taken as a possible candidate in the trade, jogged along behind the rig with Uncle Mike holding his halter chain.

Ol' Cole was left in his own stall, his long halter chain attached to the manger, secured against any notions of starting some trouble. Mama and I went about our chores without giving him a thought. I filled the tubs with water from the well, to be ready for the livestock's thirst. Mama put rock salt out in the pasture near the gate for the cows, when they should come straggling in for the milking. I gathered eggs. The mother hens were clucking to their young. My little dog followed me about, running around me in a circle to draw attention to himself.

I heard the cows approaching and opened the pasture gate. They would lick as much salt as they wanted and then trot to the well and drink their fill before entering their stalls. Now Mama was pitching hay from the mow. I looked to the road and saw Mr. Lumley approaching on foot.

Just as he came in through the gate into the barnyard, the calm was shattered by an enraged neighing from Ol' Cole. He had had all the confinement he would stand for. He was going crazy, neighing loudly and kicking the sides of his stall. We all froze where we were, although we felt sure he was securely chained—or was he?

Suddenly Ol' Cole appeared, wild-eyed, head shaking, pawing the ground, his bridle chain dragging. Mama appeared at the head of the barn ramp, waving her pitchfork and screaming to me to run. Ol' Cole looked around frenzy-eyed to see which of us he would destroy first. The cows were beginning to return from the well. The chickens ran for cover, frantically calling their young to follow. I grabbed my little dog, not knowing which way to run.

It was Mr. Lumley whom Ol' Cole finally settled on as his first victim. Ol' Cole started toward him. Mr. Lumley tried to get back out onto the road and close the gate after himself, but there wasn't time. He ran across the road to the small cherry orchard and climbed the first tree that promised refuge. Ol' Cole stopped, snorted in disgust. Meantime, I had seen a ladder leaning against the chicken house and climbed to the low roof, with my dog under one arm. Then I kicked the ladder away, ensuring, I suppose, that Ol' Cole wouldn't climb after me.

The cows began to run helter-skelter, and Ol' Cole singled out Rosie and her daughter, Posie, now a plump little heifer, for attention. Rosie was heading for her stall, Posie close behind her. Rosie decided she couldn't make it, got down on her front knees, and climbed under the raised part of the barn as far as she could go. Posie tried to follow her mother, but Ol' Cole stood in front of her, rearing on his hind legs. She turned and ran behind the chicken coop, where a decrepit wooden slab fence slowed her down, but not for long. Posie leaped over it as though she were running the cross-country steeplechase. I screamed; I was sure Ol' Cole would follow and Posie could not escape.

Suddenly Ol' Cole stopped, silent and docile. He had seen Papa and Uncle Mike turning the bend in the road with Ol' Ned jogging along behind as before. Ol' Cole walked meekly to the corncrib and stood with his head down, pretending to nibble at invisible blades of grass.

George Lumley came down from the cherry tree. He had come to borrow something, but he couldn't remember what it was. Mama came down from the barn ramp. She put the ladder back against the chicken coop and I climbed down from the roof. Ol' Ned, turned loose by Uncle Mike, jogged away for water. The trade, obviously, had not been made. Then Uncle Mike unharnessed Ol' Belle, and she followed Ol' Ned to the well. Papa, who was getting a running account of Ol' Cole's rampage, stood looking at him. Ol' Cole whinnied softly and tried to rub his head against Papa. Finally Papa picked up the chain. The cows, now heavy with milk, trotted to their respective stalls. Papa took Ol' Cole's chain and walked him into the other stable and into his stall. In a moment we heard the horse's screams, his hooves pounding against the walls of his stall. I covered my ears and hid my face against my little dog. We all knew what was happening—Ol' Cole was getting the beating of his life. The rest of the animals heard it, too, and bawled or whinnied in fright.

We suddenly realized that Rosie was still under the barn, and Posie was still missing. It took Uncle Mike, Papa, and Mr. Lumley almost an hour to get Rosie unstuck, and another hour to get her turned around and out from under the barn. Then they lighted lanterns and went to look for Posie, following a faint bellowing far in the distance. Mama and I finally began to milk the cows. We played no musical games that evening.

When the men finally got back, with Posie running before them, they told us they had found her about an eighth of a mile away, her head stuck fast in the hollow of a tree that had once held a cache of wild honey in the comb.

Supper, which Mr. Lumley stayed to share with us, was a little late that night. He still didn't remember why he had come in the first place. He said, "That ol' devil's gonna remember the lickin' you gave him for a long time."

Papa said, "He's got to go!"

Mama gave Mr. Lumley some compote to take home. We were exhausted and more shaken by the screams of the horse when Papa was beating him than by anything else that had happened.

"If we get a good price for the potatoes," Papa said, "I'll buy a new team."

We all said good night and went to bed.

# 12

# *The Rains Came*

Mr. Hoppe brought a *Farmers' Almanac* to show Papa. It predicted heavy weather. "Just waitin' there," Mr. Hoppe chuckled, "for your potato crop to be ready. Then she'll come bustin' down, rainin' cats and dogs an' little green tadpoles." I don't know whether Mr. Hoppe enjoyed disaster that befell anyone other than himself, or whether he just needed a little excitement in his life, and disaster filled that need. In any case he was both wrong and right. She *was* "just waitin'"—not, as he thought, until the crop was ready to harvest, but instead until just *after* it was harvested. Some of the neighbors came to help: Mr. Lumley, for one, and Mr. Licht, whose wife was a "layer-on-of-hands" in an offbeat religious sect, which made her something of an outsider in the almost totally Methodist community of Dunham's Hill and Kegtown. I remember her more clearly than perhaps any other of our neighbors. She was a tall, beautiful, Junoesque woman with magnificent flaxen braids wound around her head. Whether she had the hands of a healer I do not know. I do know she had a great store of kindness and forgiveness and love. And when her husband, a lay preacher, came to help harvest the potato crop, she sent along a loaf of freshly baked bread.

It was a fine crop. The potatoes were a good size, well-formed, smooth, firm, top-quality. They were stored in the barn, ready to be hauled to one of the commission produce houses in Cincinnati.

Papa had learned it was better to do this than to ship them. There was less chance of being "hornswoggled."

It began to rain a day or two after the potato harvest was finished. It was Saturday morning, and Papa had planned to load the jolt-wagon on Sunday and drive the team all night, to be on hand Monday morning when the commission houses opened for business. They would start loading as soon as the rain let up. But on Saturday, it showed no signs of letting up. Papa found work in the barn and asked Uncle Mike to help him. But Uncle Mike said he was catching cold, and it would be worse in the damp barn. As soon as Papa left, Uncle Mike started pacing, pausing at every turn to stare out of the window at the downpour. The barnyard was fast becoming a small sea of mud and water.

Chickens, feathers bedraggled, took shelter in the chicken house. I saw Papa letting the horses into the barnyard so they could run to their stalls. I heard Daisy's cowbell and knew the cows, too, were approaching to come in out of the torrent. Mama helped me put on rubbers, a coat, and a thick woolen scarf, so I could help Papa get all the stock safely into their stables. Uncle Mike paced, and paused to look out at the rain. After I got the cows in, I offered to help Papa if he needed me, but he told me to go to the house and get into dry clothes.

When I came back, Uncle Mike was still pacing, and pausing to look out and mutter under his breath.

Mama had made *vishnik*, a delicious liqueur, from some of the sour cherries. As I came in she was pouring some into a glass.

"Besides having a cold, brother," she was saying, "what else is bothering you?"

"What should bother me?" he retorted. "What could bother me here in the Garden of Eden! Look how beautiful it is outside! When the great flood was coming, God told Noah to start building the ark. We don't get any order from God. Maybe that's what we should start anyway, before it's too late."

Mama handed him the glass of *vishnik*.

"What's this, all of a sudden?" he asked.

"There's a saying: 'That which is hidden in a sober man's lung quickly rises to the drunkard's tongue.' So drink, my brother, and maybe you'll tell me what's really on your mind besides Noah's ark."

Uncle Mike pushed aside Mama's offering hand. "I don't have to get drunk," he shouted. "I'll tell you sober. It was a mistake. I'm not made for this kind of life! I want to get out."

Mama nodded. She was not surprised, it seemed. She had seen it coming, she said, for quite awhile. Now Uncle Mike reached for the *vishnik* and drained the glass. I stared at him, open-mouthed. Mama told me to get out of my wet clothes and hang them near the stove to dry before we had to do the milking.

When we went out later, Mama remembered to push aside the cover of the cistern so we would have plenty of soft rainwater. We heard Papa throwing hay into the horses' mangers. I thought Mama would tell Papa what had happened, but she went straight in to the cows. Our milk pails were half-full of water and we emptied them before we started to milk. We tried to play a song, but the pounding of the rain on the roof drowned it out, or played a song of its own. The rain was in charge.

Mama made supper that was just right for a night whose sky was trying to reenact the forty days of the Bible story. There was a thick soup of salt herring, potatoes, and onions, with pumpernickel and sweet butter, late sweet corn, and noodles baked with cottage cheese and raisins and eggs. She opened the first jars of canned peaches and poured glasses of strong, hot tea with lemon. Whatever was on Uncle Mike's mind, it did not affect his appetite. As he ate, Papa revealed his plan for the potatoes.

"The skies have opened," he said. "and we can't wait till they decide to close up again. With this dampness, we can't keep the

potatoes too long. They'll start to sprout, and then it's 'Good-bye Charlie.' If we had enough canvas, we could maybe cover them enough to keep the rain off, but we don't have and I don't know who has. So we'll bring the spring wagon in the barn and load the potatoes into that instead of the jolt-wagon. We'll still cover them, and with the heavy cover of the wagon itself, I think they'll stay dry. And the covered wagon will give us some protection too."

Mama waited until he finished, then she said, "Mendel . . ." Papa looked up startled. She never used his Jewish name unless something serious was on her mind. "I think, Mendel, my brother has something to tell you." She took my arm and propelled me into the kitchen. She closed the door and created a clatter as she washed the dishes and gave them to me, one by one, to dry.

We heard the stumbling murmur of Uncle Mike's voice, then a shout from Papa, clashing with a reverberating roll of thunder. He flung open the kitchen door.

"What do you think of your brother, the idealist who said a Jew belongs on the land!"

"He may be right."

"He wants out!"

"I know."

"He wants his half of the potato money."

"First find out if we don't end up like with the tomatoes last year."

Mike pushed his way into the kitchen. "Sister, I beg you not to turn your back on me. I can't help it. Try to forgive me."

"I forgive you. We are what we are."

"And you too, Mendel! Try to find in your heart—"

"Don't you try to find out what's in my heart. Go! I can't wait to see the last of you. Go back to Boston. Write a new song: 'A Jew belongs in the sweatshop'!" Mike walked out, his head low.

To Mama, Papa said, "I should have listened to you!" I couldn't believe my ears. He had never, in my presence, made any remark remotely like this one. "We'll sell out and go back to Boston. This time there'll be no turning back. . . . Yes, I should have listened to you."

Mama dried her hands on her apron. She spoke quietly but firmly.

"Then listen to me now. I don't want to go back to Boston. I don't want to go back to anything. I don't want to hear about new beginnings anymore. Go to bed. Tomorrow load the potatoes, and take Mike with you. Give him his half of the potato money. We'll still owe him plenty. When you come back from the city, we'll sit down and we'll see what we should do. Go to bed now—and sleep!"

Papa was too amazed to say a word. He looked at Mama as

though he were seeing her for the first time. Without a word, he turned and went to the bedroom.

"Mama," I asked fearfully, "is it going to be all right?"

"We'll try to make it all right, my child. Now, I want you to help me." She took a ruled tablet and a pencil from the kitchen table drawer. I looked at it in amazement. She had been practicing writing her name!

"Now, sit down and write for me what I tell you. Begin like this: My dear, true friend Annie, we are all well and hope you and your dear Mama and all the family are the same. I want from you a favor, please. I am asking you to go in to Mr. Springer at the grocery and tell him I want to start a business to bring every week to the city, fresh eggs and fine, sweet butter and cheese, if he wants to buy from me. And I ask you, too, if you will be a customer and if you have friends. I promise everything will be first class and a fair price. I send you my thanks from the heart. I wait for your answer. I embrace you and your dear Mama. Your friend, Bertha Weisberg. Address: Route 3, New Richmond, Ohio."

She had dictated so slowly, we finished together.

"Sounds good. Write it nice, and I will sign it myself!"

"Yes, Mama."

"And don't tell the Papa yet. We'll surprise him. I myself will write to Tante Freidel in Yiddish. And to Tante Sadie too. I will write and tell her she can buy my sewing machine for . . . twenty-seven dollars."

She leaned down and kissed my bewildered face. I kissed back and went slowly to bed.

# 13

# *My Parents, the Entrepreneurs*

Mama decided not to say anything about her projected "business," until she should hear from Annie Corelli and from Tante Freidel. Since going to the mailbox was my chore (the most pleasant of a long list), I was the first to see the two letters from Cincinnati. It was Saturday, but I skipped my usual visit with Miss Lizzie Lumley and her dynamite vinegar pickles and hurried straight home. The letters were addressed to Mama, so I thought it right that I should give them to her and only to her. But Papa saw me first! He was coming out of the barn and saw the mail in my hands.

"Just a minute, Goldichka," he called out. "You have letters?"

"Yes, Papa, and the *Ohio Farmer.*"

"So why are you standing there? Bring me the letters!"

I went to him reluctantly. "I was going to give them to Mama," I dared to say. "They're addressed to her and—"

He snatched them angrily from my hand. "Your mama has secrets from me?" he cried.

Papa was such a puzzle! In time, as I grew older, the pieces came together. He was a man whose ideas were advanced in many areas: his political philosophy, his views on racial discrimination, his concern for the rights of labor. But I never heard him expound on the rights of women and children. Where family was concerned, he was the patriarch and totally authoritarian. Now he opened the letters as his right. He ignored the *Ohio Farmer.*

"Go in the house," he commanded.

Mama looked worried when I told her what had happened—not only worried, but a little scared. Then she shrugged.

"So, he has the surprise already. If I failed and the letters say 'no,' he'll be mad that I didn't ask him first. If they say 'yes,' he'll be mad that I didn't *tell* him first. but maybe only a little mad." She shrugged again and set about getting dinner on the table. I laid the *Ohio Farmer* next to his place, hoping it would draw a share of his attention.

Papa came in in a few minutes, threw the letters on the kitchen table, and washed up in the basin by the door. His face was grim. We waited for his anger to explode. Mama, with her back to him, was busy at the stove.

"So," he said, "my wife is going to be a business lady. She is so smart already in America she doesn't need a husband's advice at all anymore."

Mama set a bowl of *milchik* barley soup before him.

"Of course I need your advice. But first I wanted to hear if they said 'yes.' Then I was going to talk to you. If 'no,' I wouldn't bother you at all."

He pushed the letters toward her.

"So you can do me the honor to talk to me. There are customers waiting for you already, standing in line. Annie Corelli and Mr. Springer and Freidel and her friend Fruma Green. And who knows where it will end! So you have saved us from starvation."

"It will just help a little, that's all. And it will bring in more than trading at the store."

"And how, may I ask, do you plan to deliver? You will take the jolt-wagon maybe, the way I deliver potatoes?"

"I sort of figured it out—so you wouldn't have to bother your head. You have more important things on your mind. . . ."

"Well, go on, go on!"

"I figured out that once a week I'd take Ol' Belle and the buggy and go to Nine-Mile Stop. Ollie Lumley has a cousin there. They live near the tracks. Ollie said she would fix it so I could unhitch and leave the horse and buggy until I come back. I can take along some feed for the horse—" Her voice trailed off. Papa was staring at her as though he couldn't believe his ears.

"So you talked it over with your neighbor, but me, you forgot I was alive."

"I had to know would it work before I bothered you. . . . Your soup is getting cold."

"Thank you for your consideration!" He ignored the soup. "Now I have some news for you. There is a farmer near Lindale who has a large dairy. He raises the heifers, but he sells the bull calves. I'm going to buy them and fatten them and sell them to a slaughter house. I learned about this from George Lumley. So we're even. And between us, especially with *your* help, we'll maybe save the farm. . . . Sit down and eat, my smart wife, and you, too, my daughter, who knows how to keep secrets from her papa." He started to eat his soup.

He was sarcastic and sort of mad, but he didn't shout, and maybe he was even glad. They were in business. I remembered that Mama had offered her sister the sewing machine she had left behind for twenty-seven dollars. But Mama didn't mention that.

"All in good time," she told me later. "All in good time."

Papa had one more thing to say and he said it bitterly.

"You never thought that I might have some plans, too, about getting through the bad time. You never—"

Mama interrupted. "And you never told me about *your* plans either! Maybe—if you'd excuse me. . . . " She broke off, amazed at her daring. Papa stared at her but said nothing.

"I'm babbling," she shrugged. "I'll go make tea."

The next Saturday a letter came addressed to Mama. I saw that it was from Boston and knew it must be from Tante Sadie. I muttered a magic spell that would make Papa be absent from the barnyard when I got home. The magic worked. I could see him in the far distance, riding on his disk-harrow, trying to hasten the thawing of the earth. I hurried into the house.

Mama was in the cellar preparing the molded pounds of butter she would be bringing to her customers for the first time on Tuesday. She was packing a one-pound wooden mold with the pale gold, freshly churned butter. When it was firmly packed and smoothed across the top, she pushed the handle that was attached to the movable carved insert, and out came the beautiful, delectable unsalted delicacy yielded up by our small herd of Jersey cows "with all their might and main." It looked like a little sculpture with a design of roses carved into it on top. Mama gazed at it with pride before she turned to me.

"I have another mold, too. Square, with tulips." She looked again at her handiwork. "Good *and* beautiful, yes?"

"Oh, yes, Mama!" I handed her the letter.

"From Tante Sadie," she said, and opened it carefully. A money order fell to the earthen floor. Mama picked it up.

"*Thirty* dollars!" she exclaimed. When she looked up there were tears in her eyes. "*Thirty* dollars, and I asked for only twenty-seven. I don't know why; it was like making fun. I thought it would be a dollar for every cent we lost on the tomatoes." She stood quietly for a moment, as though far away, then turned to the brief letter.

"She thanks *me* for selling her the machine," she smiled. "My dear, kind sister." She was quiet again, and a tear rolled down her cheek. Then she straightened, shook her head as if clearing it of memories and loneliness, and spoke cheerfully.

"I shall take some cold buttermilk to your papa in the field and show him the letter. He shouldn't be mad. I didn't ask for charity. I sold something that was mine. He knows the chicken feed is low and the cattle feed, too. The cows' milk is falling off." She lifted my chin and looked down at me.

"But of this we will say nothing. You understand, *ketsele*?"

"Yes, Mama." I was proud of her trust. We were in a conspiracy together, but a benevolent conspiracy (another new word I had recently learned), not an evil one.

Mama filled a mason jar with buttermilk, rich and creamy with little golden flecks of butter floating in it. She told me to finish molding the butter, using both the round mold and the square one, so people could choose. Then she left, carrying the letter and the money order in her apron pocket, and the buttermilk in her hands like a peace offering.

When she came back I had finished molding the butter. I looked anxiously at her face.

"Papa was nice?" I asked.

"Papa was nice. He made fun. He said we should spend the money on a rope of pearls for me, a fur coat and a little Cossack hat for you, and for himself a gold watch and chain like Ostrovsky the *Gonif* used to wear. And with what's left we'd buy some chicken feed."

"Will he *really*?" I marveled. Her eyes twinkled.

"Well, I told him the other ladies would be envious and have bad thoughts about me and the same about you and your friends. And if he was seen wearing a gold watch and chain, people would think he was a millionaire and want to borrow money."

"And what did he say then?"

"He said he had a wise wife, as wise as Deborah in the Bible who was a judge. And then he said maybe, *maybe* it would be better to buy some chicken feed and even some hay for the cows and horses."

"But, Mama," I cried, "that's what you wanted in the first place!" She put her fingers to her lips and then I knew. It was another conspiracy, and I was in it with her. We were a benevolent secret society, and I would never tell even if someone tortured me unto death. And now that Papa was pleased and making fun, perhaps he would never shout again, and everything would be beautiful and loving. I would think of all my best magic words and say them over and over. Maybe it would help.

That night after supper Papa read the *Ohio Farmer*. He learned something new all the time, he said. Something about rotating crops, and not letting the soil get tired, and maybe planting soybeans to put back nitrogen. He said he'd have to find out more about that, and exactly what "rotating" meant. I could have told him, but he didn't ask me, so I kept quiet. And he learned something else, he said. Red clover made fine pasture for cows. It raised the butterfat in the milk. Then he stopped reading early and said everybody should go to bed right away because he had to go to Kegtown early to buy feed, and then to Lindale, where a man had timothy hay for sale. Mama, he reminded me, was going to start her new business very soon, and I must help her all I could and maybe she would make me a partner. He was making fun again and I thought, "I made good magic."

Before I fell asleep I heard them speaking in whispers and Mama laughing softly, just like on that first night in Cincinnati. I did not hear Mama say, "Wait until the child is asleep," but I fell asleep quickly anyway, because I knew I would have happy dreams.

# 14

# "A Baron, Yet!"

Mama's business was doing well. Fortunately so was Papa's enterprise with the little calves. When he brought one home, I was taught how to wean him. I would pour milk into a pail and then put my hand down into the milk, with only one or two fingers showing. The "baby" would think my fingers were his mother's teats and suck on them and take in the milk at the same time. After a few days of this, as Mama instructed me, I would pull the fingers gently away and the little calf would start drinking on his own.

I hated this chore; I knew I was cheating him, getting him ready to go to market and be killed. At first I gave the calves names, but that made it harder; it was like cheating friends. In time I performed the job without feeling quite so conscience-stricken. That frightened me, because I feared I was becoming a cruel person. I worried about it for awhile; then, finally, almost without realizing it, acceptance was complete. Many years later I read Pope's pronouncement on "Vice," whose face which " . . . seen too oft we first endure, then pity, then embrace!" It recalled to me all the little creatures I had sent on their way to become veal chops.

As for Mama, she had to start turning down would-be customers. She could buy eggs from some of the neighbors but there was a limit to the butter she could provide, especially as so much of the milk was going to the calves. Every week she carried two heavy baskets into the city and brought back the two baskets heavy with provisions that we could not get in the general store in Kegtown, nor even in New Richmond. We had the good Jewish rye bread now, kosher meat, herring, and once in a great while, for a special treat, halvah, a confection made of ground sesame seeds and nuts mixed with honey.

There was at least one less successful side venture of Mama's enterprise. One of her customers had a used clothing store, and sometimes Mama would trade apple butter or her beautiful rose preserves for a dress or a coat for me. The garment was often pretty but usually too large, often too old, sometimes too young or too short or too long. These garments were always described by the store's owner as "like new, outgrown by the children of the rich." When they needed alteration, Mama would sit up late, hemming or adjusting, always, of course, by hand, since she had no sewing machine of her own. Mine was a very eclectic wardrobe.

When Mama traded for clothes, she never traded butter or eggs or the little heart-shaped packages of "farmer's cheese" that she made from clabber. That would have taken money that had to be accounted for to Papa. That, he said, was the businesslike way. She never told him about the apple butter or the preserves.

One night when Papa woke up at ten o'clock and did not find Mama on the pillow beside him, he discovered her in the kitchen, sewing up a hem by hand. He put an end to that activity then and there.

"No more second-hand *shmattes*," he ordered. "No more making over other people's castoffs."

My wardrobe was greatly diminished by this edict, but when I did get a new dress, it was really mine. And Papa said that one of these days he would get Mama a sewing machine. I couldn't help wondering if it would come before or after the lace curtains and the carpet for the parlor.

But there were other benefits that derived from Mama's business, and the greatest of all was the friendship that ripened with Fruma Green, or "Frumcha," as she was familiarly known, and with her husband, Charlie. His given name, in Hebrew, was Chaim, and he figured that "Charlie" was a legitimate equivalent, since both began with "Ch." We became really close friends, so that they became my Tante Fruma and Uncle Charlie. Charlie was a designer in a ladies' dress factory, and he made dresses for me that were the prettiest I had ever owned. The Greens had no children, and they lavished affection and kindness on me. They came to visit us frequently, arriving on a Saturday and staying over until the late "black car" on Sunday. Papa or Mama would meet them at Ten-Mile Stop, and sometimes they would allow me to do the honors.

Once in a while, when I could be spared from my chores, and there was a school holiday, the Greens would take me back to the city with them. They lived in a nice flat not far from Tante Freidel, and on each visit I discovered new things at which to marvel: the warm rolls and coffee cake, and the milk and cream left outside their door in the morning; a separate room with a *curtain* at the window, for the bath and toilet; and a full-length mirror on the door, which even Tante Freidel didn't have. And I went at last to Chester Park, where there were merry-go-rounds and pony rides and countless other delights.

Once they took me to visit Jennie Goldenstern at her papa's Confectionery and Cultural Center, and Mr. Goldenstern treated us all to strawberry soda water. But Jennie had a new best friend, so it wasn't quite as I had expected it would be. I wondered about Norma, and the old pain came back, and I hoped that she, too, had found a new best friend.

For Papa, too, there was a special treat as a result of Mama's weekly trips to the city. Mr. Goldenstern saved the *Jewish Forward* for a whole week every time and even sent along the latest *Cincinnati Post*.

Papa had to admit that Mama was doing very well. Of course, the real money lay in the fattened calves, he said one evening, adding, "By the way, I forgot to mention. I found out about a farmer near Amelia who raises hogs for the market and is willing to sell some of the shoats, the little ones. So I'm going to do business with him—fatten them like we fatten the calves."

"Pigs!" exclaimed Mama.

"You don't have to eat them!" shouted Papa. "Just feed them! Fatten them!"

"With my fingers? Like the calves?" I asked, dreading the prospect.

"No, don't worry. They'll be weaned already. They wean faster than calves. Suckling pigs bring the best money. And both of you can stop looking like I'm some kind of criminal!" He gave us the silent treatment for awhile until Mama said just the right thing.

"I think that's a fine idea, Max. The pigpen that the Lumleys used is just sitting there. Now it will be useful. I'll go make tea."

"I found out something else," Papa said, relaxed again. "A new family moved in on Pond Run Road, not far from the tracks. The man's name is Josiah Crane. He's looking for day work. Sometimes I might need some help, and I could try him out."

"That's good to know," Mama approved, and all was well again. She added, "You could use some help right now."

The greatest need, however, had for some time been for a new team of horses. Ol' Ned was really getting old and was ready to be retired, or, to my horror, when I heard it mentioned, "sold to a glue factory." But Mama secretly assured me that that would never happen.

Aside from the need for horses, things were going well. A payment on the farm mortgage was coming due, and every dollar possible was put aside to meet it on time. After that, new horses would be next.

Only one thing kept recurring that puzzled and troubled me.

Sometimes, after supper, even when I was reading, I would hear Papa and Mama speaking in low tones, something that rarely occurred. At one point I heard Papa say: "If he wants you should stay overnight for the examination, it's all right. I'll understand. If you don't come back like always, and it's very late, I won't worry. Just tell them at the place where you leave Ol' Belle to put her up for the night if you don't get back."

"What about the child? She'll be frightened if I don't come home all night."

"Don't worry. I'll take care of that, too. Just do as I say. It will be all right."

There was more, which I couldn't hear. But I had heard enough to worry about. An examination! What kind of examination? Maybe reading and writing English? In a night school, like Uncle Nathan went to? I remembered that Mama had been practicing writing her name.

It turned out after all that Mama did not stay in the city overnight. She came home at the usual hour, bringing her usual basket of provisions. Papa met her as she drove in. I ran out to help carry the baskets.

"So early!" was Papa's greeting, his voice beginning to sound cross.

"I had to make an appointment," Mama explained. "I couldn't see him without an appointment. He's a very busy man."

"How long will you have to wait?"

"A month at least. Maybe more. He's been invited to teach in a college in London. He said this is not an emergency."

"How does he know what's an emergency? What could be a picnic for him could be an emergency for me." Papa jerked poor Ol' Belle's head as he unharnessed her, though it wasn't her fault at all. "He goes off to some fancy business in London and tells me it's not an emergency."

Mama's voice was shaking when she answered.

"I'm sorry. What could I do? We have to have patience and wait a little longer." With a burst of courage she added. "Sarah waited longer and God heard her prayer."

Papa looked at her, shaking his head, but he calmed down.

"My wife is full of surprises. She is not only a business lady, but she's even a *rebbitzen*. All right, so I will try to be patient—as long as I can, anyway." He led Ol' Belle to the stable and Mama and I took the baskets into the house, though I wasn't really much help, they were so heavy.

I was completely baffled by what I had heard. Who was Sarah? I was afraid to ask Mama, but she wasn't looking worried anymore, so I decided to stop thinking about it. Whatever it might be was a whole month away, maybe more, and I hoped she would explain when she wanted me to know.

After supper Papa took the bundle of *Jewish Forwards* and began to read. All of a sudden he looked up, very excited.

"This I never knew!" he exclaimed. "Listen to this!" Mama put tea in front of him. "It's about an organization called the Baron de Hirsch Society." This society, he said, was a foundation to help establish Jews on the land. That was a funny thing for a foundation to do, I thought, but it didn't seem to bother Papa. Mostly, he read, the Jews that it helped were in New York, and they started chicken farms in New Jersey and still worked part-time in the city. But anybody could write, and the society would send a man who would give advice and even lend money.

That very night Papa dictated a letter to me to send to his remarkable foundation. Two weeks later there was a reply. It said an expert named Baruch Mandelbaum would come on such and such a day and Papa should meet him.

Mr. Mandelbaum turned out to be a short, stout young man with a round, jolly face and a neat, small mustache. He wore gold-rimmed glasses, a high, stiff collar on his white shirt and a light-colored suit with a folded handkerchief sticking out of his pocket.

Papa told us later, when Mr. Mandelbaum had gone back to the city, "When I saw him get off the black car, with his gold glasses and his shiny leather suitcase, I thought he looked like a lawyer, or a bookkeeper, or just a plain sport. What could he teach me about farming? But I've changed my mind, no mistake about that!"

When he came, he followed Papa into the house only long enough to leave his suitcase, from which he took a notebook, and said he would like to walk all over the farm before they even sat down. Papa was not used to somebody else taking charge like that, but he went along.

When they finally came back, Papa looked very impressed. Mama had put on a clean dress and apron, and this time Mr. Mandelbaum shook hands with her and with me, and he and Papa sat down at the dining room table and Mama excused herself. She started to take me out, too, but Papa said I should stay and listen. I could learn something.

Mr. Mandelbaum had taken a lot of notes and now he read them aloud and talked and talked, and Papa listened. I had never known Papa to listen to anybody so much. Mr. Mandelbaum explained all about rotation of crops and how to build up the washed-out, worn-out fields and to fill in the ditches. Many of the things he talked about Papa had read in the *Ohio Farmer*, but Mr. Mandelbaum spoke more in Yiddish than in English and made everything clear. And while they talked, Mama served glasses of tea with her rose preserves, brought out only for very special guests.

Papa told him with pride about fattening calves and shoats, but he didn't say anything to Mr. Mandelbaum about Mama's business. I wanted to tell so badly that I thought I would burst, but I didn't dare.

Mr. Mandelbaum thought fattening the calves and shoats was a good way to make extra money, but feeding them whole milk was too expensive and not necessary. Papa should get a cream separator and use the skim milk instead of the whole milk, except maybe for a day or two, and then, as soon as the calves and shoats were weaned, make a mash of the skim milk and bran, and the animals would do just fine, and there would be more cream for butter. And the Baron de Hirsch Society would lend the money for the cream separator and Papa could pay it back a little at a time. Papa had seen DeLaval cream separators advertised in the *Ohio Farmer*, he remembered, but he knew he couldn't afford one. Now, Mr. Mandelbaum said, he could.

I had never seen Papa so happy when someone was giving him advice. He made fun, too. He said maybe he could keep out enough whole milk to set so we could have clabber to eat with new potatoes, and Mr. Mandelbaum laughed and said he didn't blame Papa, and maybe he'd come back and eat some, too. And everybody laughed, and Mama said he would always be welcome.

Before Mr. Mandelbaum left, he told Mama her rose preserves were fit for the President of the United States, and if she ever went into business, he would be her first customer. I thought, now Papa will tell him, but he didn't, and I thought that was really mean of him. But Mama was pleased at Mr. Mandelbaum's praise. She blushed and gave him a little jar to take home.

Papa said, "I don't want to hurry you, Mr. Mandelbaum, but if you have to catch the next train to Cincinnati . . ." Mr. Mandelbaum shook hands with Mama and me and followed Papa to the barnyard where Ol' Belle had already been harnessed to the buggy. Mama and I stood on the porch until they drove away, and Mr. Mandelbaum waved.

"A fine gentleman," Mama said. "And a baron yet, like the *graf* in the old country." Mama had taken Baron de Hirsch's title and bestowed it neatly on Mr. Mandelbaum. "Who would have thought it?" She shook her head happily. "Maybe America *is* the *goldeneh medina*!" Then she turned to me and said, "Now, my child, we get to business. I need for tomorrow an extra dozen eggs for the Mishkins. So take the little basket and go for Mama to Mrs. Mott.

She always has some to spare. I will give you money to pay and also, for Mrs. Mott, some jelly from the apples."

When I came to the Motts' I saw a horse and buggy standing in front with the horse's reins hanging loose. A smart horse always knew that that meant his owner wasn't staying and he was supposed to stand still, even though he wasn't tied up.

I went around to the back of the house and Earl, the oldest son, was outside. He said his ma was feeling poorly, and his Uncle John was with her. He took my basket and went into the barn, then came back with a dozen eggs. I noticed he had put an old magazine in the bottom to keep the eggs from rolling around. I gave him the money and the jelly and said he should tell his mother I hoped she would feel better. Then I started for home.

As I walked along, I wondered what the magazine was. So I sat down by the side of the road and took out a few of the eggs, enough to expose the title, which turned out to be *Comfort*. I thought that was a very strange name for a magazine, so I had to take out the rest of the eggs and look at the inside of *Comfort*.

It turned out to be all stories, except for advertisements for things like Castoria and Mrs. Lydia Pinkham's medicine of some kind. I started to read a story about a poor but beautiful orphan girl who was employed by a rich but mean old lady, so I didn't hear a horse and buggy approaching and stopping. Then I heard a voice and I looked up. It was Dr. John Mott. I knew because I recognized his horse.

"Climb in, young lady. I'll give you a lift." I started to go to the buggy.

"Maybe you'd better take the eggs," he said and smiled. I turned back, embarrassed, glad that he couldn't see me blush. Then I climbed into his buggy.

"I live at the Weisberg place," I told him. "Right around the bend."

"I know," he said. "I see you like to read."

"Yes, sir. This magazine has a funny name. It's called *Comfort*."

"Maybe it tries to print stories that will comfort people who are sad. I'll bet I can get you better things to read—good books."

"Whole books?" I marveled.

"Whole books," he nodded.

"*I've* got a whole book," I said proudly. "*Uncle Tom's Cabin*."

"Good, good." We had arrived at our place and he stopped to let me out.

I thanked him and said good-bye. And I knew at once that he was going to be one of my grown-up "best friends," along with Moishele and Charlie Green.

# 1910—1918

# 15

## *Snowbound*

The summer of 1909 had been a busy one for all of us. The farm looked better and better, and Mama and Papa both worked harder and harder. Papa had Josiah Crane's help more often. He was learning more about farming from the literature in Yiddish which came regularly from the Baron de Hirsch Society, as well as from the *Ohio Farmer* and from another publication to which he had subscribed. This was *Farm and Fireside*, a family magazine with features for the farmers' wives and children as well as for the "head man" himself. There were patterns for patchwork quilts, hints for using leftovers, and cooking and canning advice. For the children there were puzzles, games, and contests.

Ol' Cole had long ago been sent into exile. A farmer near Amelia had said there wasn't a horse living that he couldn't break and "gentle" at the same time. He knew Ol' Cole's reputation, as did almost everyone in Clermont County and beyond. He offered Papa and even-steven trade: a Guernsey heifer ready to be bred for the big, beautiful, notorious bay. The deal was closed.

Less than three months later Ol' Cole tried to get over a barbed-wire fence to join a horse on the other side, whether for companionship (he may have missed Ol' Ned and Ol' Belle), or to do battle, no one ever knew. He got tangled in the barbed wire, we were told, and went completely berserk. In his struggle he broke a leg. He had to be shot. We could now say, "Poor Ol' Cole, what a sad end."

Papa had sold the heifer that he got in the trade and, with the potato money, which was even better than he had hoped for, it had been enough for a sizable down payment on a fine team of young mares. They were Maudie, a beautiful buckskin with black mane and tail, and Queenie, a bay like Ol' Cole, but without his temperament. And they were going to foal! As for Ol' Ned, he had finally become a "pensioner," doing only the lightest of work, just to keep him exercising, so privileged that he was allowed to follow visitors and children around, nuzzling them for treats of sugar lumps or apples.

Papa had decided to use most of the skim milk and mash for shoats and fatten only the bull calves that our own cows "dropped." He had already bargained for a litter of the little pigs as soon as they were born and weaned. Now that we had a cream separator, skim milk would be a perfect food to start them on.

December was almost half over, and still a remnant of Indian summer prevailed. The ground was very lightly frozen, the sky often gray. When the sun attempted to brighten the landscape, clouds quickly closed ranks across its face, as if to insist that some semblance of what is expected must be maintained, or anarchy would reign in the skies.

The older men, sitting in one another's barns mending harness, or cleaning tools, could not remember such a mild winter since the year John Harkins' mule, Ol' Rusty, tried to walk across Ten-Mile Creek and fell through the wafer-thin ice.

Early on a Saturday morning, when the sun outwitted the clouds for a whole hour, Papa harnessed Queenie and Maudie to the jolt-wagon, that springless conveyance so accurately named, and set out to bring home the first litter of shoats he had bought. They had been weaned and would be fed skim milk and mash until they were old enough for a heavier diet.

Mama had packed a lunch for Papa, because it would be well

after midday dinner before he would return. About three o'clock we saw him turn the bend in the road, and I ran to open the big wooden gate that swung into the barnyard. The sun was feebly shining again and the rutted, lightly frozen road had been softened so that the heavy wheels of the jolt-wagon were coated with mud. I knew it would be my job to wash them down, and I did not look forward to the chore.

From the wagon bed I could hear the squeals of the little pigs, and I ran after the wagon to help unload them into the pigpen. A proper shelter had not been completed for the piglets, for Papa had not expected them to be ready so soon. But with the mild weather he was sure they would be fine until morning, or even Monday, when Josiah Crane was scheduled to come.

I climbed into the wagon and saw eight little frightened squealers. They were pink, plump, and curly-tailed, and I found them quite delightful. I made ready to pass them to Mama, who would in turn deposit them in their new home. Papa maneuvered the horses to bring the wagon alongside the pen, and we began the transfer. The first six allowed themselves to be passed from hand to hand without too much fuss. The seventh wriggled and squealed, but we managed to make the transfer without incident. However the last one, larger and stronger than the others, gave me trouble. I finally grabbed him and held on. Mama reached for him and took him from me, but he intensified his battle for freedom. Mama slipped and fell to her knees but managed to clutch the rebel with both arms. Impatiently Papa climbed down from the wagon, muttering about "butterfingers" and other shortcomings common to females. He grabbed the pig and I jumped down to help Mama to her feet. The struggling little animal now let out a tremendous squeal right next to Maudie, and it seemed to terrify her. She topped the squeal with an angry whinny and kicked out at the offending creature, but the kick landed against Papa's knee. Papa managed to hang onto the squealer long enough to drop him over the low fence into the pigpen. We could see that Papa was in pain, and he let us help him to the house, but not before he shouted an angry command to poor Maudie, always the gentlest of mares: "Stand still, you murderer!" Maudie stood still.

On the way to the house Mama and I received *our* orders: she would feed the shoats with the skim milk saved from the morning milking before doing anything for Papa. I was to drive the team to the stable, unhitch them, water them, stable them, and give them grain and hay. While they were eating I would feed the chickens and gather the eggs. By this time the horses, including Ol' Belle, already in her stall, should be through eating. Then I would turn Queenie, Maudie, and Ol' Ned into the bare meadow to get their exercise and their roll on the ground. With the weather so mild, they might as well stay out all night.

Mama was to do the milking without my help, but I would bring the cows in for her. Then, and only then, was I to saddle Ol' Belle and ride to Kegtown to the general store and call Dr. John. And then, while I was there, I was to find out where Arthur Parsons was staying and see if I could get him to come out and help with chores, even though the next day was Sunday.

Arthur, now eighteen, had appeared a year or so after we had come to Dunham's Hill. No one seemed to know where he came from, who his family was, or even if he had any family. He had just turned up one Sunday at the church in Kegtown and sat on the ground outside until the worshipers emerged after the morning service. He waited until the minister had finished shaking hands with the people and then walked up to him and asked if there might be someone who could use a handyman for room and board and whatever pay they thought he was worth. The minister and his wife took the boy home for Sunday dinner and told him he could stay with them for a few days. At Wednesday evening prayer meeting the pastor would introduce him, and maybe somebody would hire him that very evening. Somebody did, and Arthur became everybody's handyman. By a sort of grapevine of communication people were kept informed of Arthur's whereabouts, usually by way of the general store, and he went from place to place as he was needed. He was "a little slow," people said, "not real bright," but he could usually be depended upon to do a fair job if it was not too demanding.

From the general store telephone I called Dr. John and told him what had happened. He said he would come out later in the evening; he had to call first at the Messermans', about a quarter mile from our place. In the meantime Papa was to stay off his feet, and Mama was to put cold packs on the knee.

I learned that Arthur had been staying at the Goetzels' in Lindale, about a mile or so from Kegtown. They had a telephone, and I called Mrs. Goetzel and explained what had happened and why we needed Arthur. She said yes, Arthur was still there, and of course we could have him. I said I would come for him in the morning after milking time, and she said that would be just fine. He liked to go to church with them on Sunday, but she would explain that this was an emergency and the Lord would forgive him.

By the time I got home it was dark. The air had become crisply chilly. I was tired and hungry, and light shining through the windows was a welcome sight. I unsaddled Ol' Belle and turned her out with the other horses for the night.

I found Papa sitting in the kitchen with his leg propped on a chair. His mouth was tight from pain. He had taken off his overalls and had a quilt draped over his knee. I told Mama about the cold packs and she got busy with that right away. The kitchen was warm, supper was on the stove, Dr. John was on his way, and I would bring Arthur in the morning. And Josiah Crane would come on

Monday as he always did. He would finish the shelter in the pigpen, and all would be well.

I was allowed to stay up until Dr. John came; he usually had a book for me or a copy of *The Youth's Companion*. Besides, I helped keep cold packs on Papa's knee. Dr. John came about nine o'clock and, sure enough, he brought me a copy of *Little Women*. He had borrowed it from one of the Lumley families who lived in Kegtown and kept it until he should be coming our way. He brought something else with him—a crutch for Papa so that he could move around a little, but not much, just from bed to the table. Not even to the privy. It looked, he said, like a torn ligament, and Papa would just have to be patient and let it heal. He bandaged the knee, gave some pain pills to Mama, and told her how many Papa could have at a time. He visited a little while, partaking of hot tea and one of Mama's famous cinnamon rolls. When he opened the door to leave, we could feel a gust of cold air.

"You folks got enough firewood laid in?" asked Dr. John.

"Yes," said Papa. "It needs cutting up, but we'll have Arthur in the morning." It was very late when we all got to bed—nearly ten o'clock.

I was awakened toward dawn by a sense of newness, difference, strangeness in the atmosphere, and I was cold. I crept out of bed, wrapped myself tightly in my quilt, and tiptoed to the window. When I looked out, I almost cried, "Mama!" The world that spread before me was not the world which I had left to go to sleep. The barnyard was a thing of beauty; snow, which must have begun to fall hours ago, had covered the ground with a whiteness made jeweled by a high-riding moon and stars more brilliant, it seemed, than any I had ever seen. Wind had banked drifts against all the buildings within my sight and against the barnyard fence. But the wind had ceased, and snow was falling still, or again—falling gently,

dreamily, each lovely flake like a blessing, like a promise of for-giveness for all our sins, a promise of peace forever.

"We're snowbound!" I exulted, like the people in Whittier's poem. We had been reading it that week at school, and I had memorized some parts. I began to whisper to myself:

> Shut in from all the world without,
> We sat the clean-winged hearth about,
> Content to let the north wind roar
> In baffled rage at pane and door,
> While the red logs before us beat
> The front line back with tropic heat....

We had no "clean-winged hearth," but we could sit our kitchen stove about—or even the fancy stove in the dining room, with its isinglass-windowed door. Papa would read the accumulated copies of the *Jewish Forward*.

Suddenly the portrait of "Snow-Bound" exploded in my mind. I remembered the horses and the little pigs. I tiptoed into the other bedroom and gently touched Mama's shoulder. She woke with a start and leaped out of bed. Papa heard none of this; the pills Dr. John had left for him had drugged him into a deep and painless sleep.

"What is it? What's the matter?" Mama cried. I whispered, "S-s-sh!" and led her to the window. The sight did not enchant her as it had enchanted me.

"Woe is me! The horses, the *little* creatures! Hurry, get dressed! Warm! Your arctics, too!" The arctics were the ankle-high over-shoes, warmly lined, that everybody had in their winter wardrobes. We dressed as quickly and quietly as possible. Mama said she would look at the poor little pigs while I went to let the horses into their stalls. With each step I broke through the crusted snow, shattering the jeweled beauty. I felt bitterly guilty that it was I, rather than someone else, who had committed this desecration. I heard the horses whinnying and returned to reality.

The field in which they had spent the night was across the road from the barnyard. I opened the stable door and swung the big gate wide; then I made my heavy-footed way to the pasture. Dawn was breaking, and the moon paled. The snow was still falling, gently, tenderly, touching my face with wet kisses. When the horses saw me, they came racing to the pasture gate whinnying loudly and, it seemed to me, accusingly. They had run in circles all through the night, it appeared, and the field looked as though it had been plowed by runaway horses and a drunken plowboy. So it was not I, after all, who violated the landscape. I unfastened the wire on the pasture gate, and Maudie, Queenie, and Ol' Belle raced out and past me across the road while Ol' Ned followed, a poor fourth, as fast as he could go, into the barnyard and into the stabled stalls.

Mama was already in the pigpen when I came back. Tears were running down her cheeks.

"Look at this! It breaks the heart!"

The little pigs had tried to huddle for warmth, to crowd under one another, each fighting to get near the bottom of the pile. The smallest, the weakest, ended up on top, exposed to the snow and wind. We picked up the two weakest ones. They could scarcely whimper. In the house, Papa was still asleep. I sat on the floor holding the two shivering little shoats inside my coat. Mama emptied the firewood box, lined it with old papers, and put the piglets inside. She built a fire quickly and warmed some milk and tried to feed them. One responded, but the smallest one could not eat. Mama covered them with some old toweling, murmuring to them the whole time: "Poor little creatures. May God forgive us for what we did to you!"

There was still skim milk and mash left from the day before. Mama took it to the pigpen and filled the trough after she had scooped out the snow and ice. She sent me to feed the horses and cows, and the chickens inside the henhouse, and told me to come back for something hot, too. The snow had stopped falling and the sun had risen by the time all the chores were done. I had some hot "mush" and milk and braced myself for the hardest chore of all—going to Lindale to fetch Arthur.

The mile and a half to the Goetzels' seemed endless. The snow was too deep for anything but walking, on the part of Ol' Belle. The snow had stopped, but the wind had risen and stung my face as with needles. If it had not been Sunday, I would have dismounted and gone into the general store to thaw out, but there was nothing to do but get on to the Goetzels' and pick up Arthur. Some people had already arrived at the church, so some of the snow on the road had been packed down. I saw one or two sleighs, with blanketed horses, hitched to the railing at one side of the churchyard—the first sleighs of the season. Ol' Belle picked up a little speed, and the Goetzel place was finally in sight. I hitched my horse to a post in the sun and went in.

Arthur was in the kitchen, all ready for his journey, even to his mittens. He was eating a great slice of hot corn bread, the crumbs flying in all directions.

Mrs. Goetzel pulled off my mittens, sat me down by the kitchen stove, and brought me a cup of hot cocoa.

"I told Arthur he didn't have to get dressed so soon, the kitchen being so warm and all, but he would do it. You know Arthur," she said.

"I say if you're gonna get dressed to go some place, you might as well go ahead and do it and not be dilly-dallyin' around," Arthur replied, his mouth full and sputtering corn bread crumbs more than ever.

"Arthur," I said, "going home you can sit in the saddle, and I'll sit behind you and protect your back."

"Now ain't that real nice of Goldie—ready to take the wind at her back so's you'll be warm?" said Mrs. Goetzel.

"S'pose," said Arthur, "the wind's in my face. I'll take a chance on my back. You sit in the saddle!"

"I guess you never read *When Knighthood Was In Flower*," I said bitterly.

"Never heard of it. Heard of a flower called nightshade. You wanna go now?"

Mama had a hot meal waiting for us when we finally got home. Papa was in the kitchen, his crutch by his side, his leg on a chair in front of him. I heard a squeal behind the stove and went to look at the two little pigs. I saw only one. I looked at Mama. She shook her head; the littlest one had died. The other had survived, but had lost all his hair. I didn't feel much like eating, but Mama said, "Come now, eat your dinner. We're all sorry, but nobody knew what was going to happen." We always spoke Yiddish among ourselves; now Arthur looked up from his hot soup and said, "Talk so I can understand you—if you ain't talkin' about me."

Papa returned to English. "Nobody's talking about you, Arthur. Now you eat up and go out to the woodshed. There's plenty of firewood out there. All it needs is cutting up to fit the stove. You're lucky you'll be out of the cold. You take a piece from behind the stove to measure by and make sure you don't cut it too long."

When we were all finished with dinner, Arthur went to the woodshed, and Mama and I went to put up a temporary shelter in the pigpen. I didn't ask what she had done with the littlest pig; I didn't want to know.

We were in the barn gathering pieces of discarded lumber, old sacking, anything that would protect the "poor creatures" until Josiah came the next day to build a more permanent shelter. Suddenly, Mama stopped and listened.

"What do you hear, Mama?" I asked.

"Nothing. That's what worries me."

"Why?"

"Because I should be hearing a saw cutting wood. And I don't hear it."

I joined her in listening. There was no sound. We looked at each other, worried.

"Maybe he's just picking up the wood he cut," I suggested.

"Let's go see," said Mama.

When we got to the woodshed, there was no sign of Arthur. One length of firewood had been cut up. The rest was untouched. The saw lay on the ground. We went outside, calling his name. I glanced down at the snow-covered ground and told Mama to look. Footprints led from the woodshed toward a field next to the well. We followed them that far. On the other side of the fence we saw the footprints moving in the direction of the honey locust grove.

Soon there was the sound of sawing wood—but it was Mama and I, not Arthur, making the noise. When we had enough wood for the evening, we went back to work on our improvised shelter in the pigpen.

In the meantime, at church, Mrs. Perkins of the general store got the word around about our plight. While Mama and I were struggling with the shelter, the six little pigs getting in the way, George Lumley and Charlie Mott, Dr. John's brother, our nearest neighbor just before the bend in the road, came over. Mr. Lumley was carrying a cream pie his wife had sent along. They took over our job in the pigpen.

"Tell Ol' Max not to fret," Charlie Mott said. "We'll be lookin' to see can we help some." And George Lumley said to me, "Don't you try to walk to school tomorrow. Snow'll be up to your skinny little knees. I'll be takin' our young'uns, maybe in the sleigh, and we'll come by for you."

The prospect of riding to school in the sleigh, with sleigh bells jingling, was so attractive that I forgave his insult to my knees. It was dusk when Mr. George and Mr. Charlie finished their job. They came in to see Papa and stayed long enough to accept a small glass of cherry *vishnik*, Sunday or no Sunday.

We were sitting down to supper, Papa coming to the table with the aid of his crutch, when the kitchen door opened and Arthur walked in. We stared at him wordlessly. He was carrying a length of the firewood he had cut. He threw it behind the stove and pulled off his mittens, his cap, and his jacket. Then he finally spoke:

"Never got 'ary a one; never even *seen* 'ary a one."

"One what?" asked Mama.

"Rabbits, of course! This deep a snow you could find 'em stuck in a drift an' just hit 'em over the head. This time—" He was now moving toward the table and pulling out a chair.

"You got wood to cut out in the shed," said Papa, without raising his voice. "Take that lantern in the corner and git!"

"I'm hungry!" wailed Arthur.

"You'll have even a better appetite after you do your work!"

Mama glanced pleadingly at Papa, but he looked down at his plate and resumed eating. We could hear Arthur muttering as he lighted the lantern and put his jacket and mittens on again. Pretty soon we heard the sound we had missed earlier in the day. Suddenly it seemed funny, and we all began to laugh. Nearly two hours later, when Papa was back in bed, he called out, "Better call Arthur in. He must have a real good appetite by now!"

By the time we had gotten the spare room ready for Arthur, and washed up after his supper, even I was too tired to reenact "Snow-Bound" in our kitchen—sans fireplace, sans hot chestnuts, sans apple cider. But Mama did make hot cocoa for everyone. She had heated bricks for the beds, including Arthur's. Se we hurried out of the cold of our bedrooms into the warm beds, under quilts (a feather bed for me) and blankets warm as toast. But I stopped for a shivering moment to look at the snow again. The moon made it look pristine once more and almost as though it had not been trampled all day.

Mama came to bed last, as always, making sure the glowing coals in the stove were safely banked and enough water had been brought into the house for cooking breakfast. I heard her finally coming toward my room, and I ducked quickly under the soft, warm feather bed and closed my eyes. I heard her open the door carefully and knew she was looking at me to be sure all was well. Then she retreated. Soon I heard her get into bed, careful not to awaken Papa. Sleep crept in beside me, ready to take possession. But I was not ready to yield. I "saw" again the scene of the snowbound family in Whittier's poem, and I began to recite it to myself: "Shut in from all the world . . . " That was as far as I got.

# 16

## *"Please, God, a Miracle"*

It was April, 1910. My tenth birthday had passed, and it was near the end of the school year. The countryside was beautiful and fragrant; the dogwood trees, pink ones and white ones, were in full bloom, the small trees completely covered with a snowfall of blossoms. The redbud added a brilliant touch of its own, while here and there clumps of blue spruce provided a timeless background for the spring burst of color. The birds were returning from wherever they had wintered, adding joyous sound to the blossoming hills and roadsides. It was the loveliest time of the year.

For me it had been a year of magic, of dreams fulfilled, of a future rolling out before me like a silken carpet leading to whatever enchanted country I chose to make my own. It came about because Papa had added a subscription to the *Cincinnati Post* that year, so that we could have an English as well as a Yiddish daily to inform and educate us. On reading it one day I had discovered a "Poets' Corner" to which readers were invited to submit poems. Well, I thought, I was a reader, so surely the invitation included me! Whereupon I submitted two poems. One was entitled "Spring." The other, the longer of the two, was invested with a high moral tone and called "A Little Sermon." Today I remember nothing more about them except that I had the good sense to include my age when I mailed them in.

They were accepted, and a few days after my tenth birthday they appeared in the "Poets' Corner" of the *Post*, with my age in bold type beneath my byline. And I received two dollars—the first money ever paid me for my modest contribution to American literature! I was torn now between a choice of two careers: writing or teaching. Meantime, at school I was a celebrity, and my fame spread as far as Kegtown on the one hand and Mr. Goldenstern's Confectionery and Cultural Center on the other.

Mama had hugged me and cried, and Papa had said, "My daughter will be a professor some day and wear glasses with gold frames and a black ribbon." I wasn't sure whether I should be pleased or not at that prospect, but he had kissed me, too, so I decided it was praise of some sort.

Now, on this lovely April day, a Tuesday, in what seemed the best of all possible worlds, Mama was late coming home from the city. Papa was working in the cornfield, hoeing weeds between the tender green shoots that were just appearing above the ground. I had already brought the cows in and watered and stabled them. Now I carried cool water to Papa and waited at the end of the row until he reached me. I thought how marvelous it was the way things grew. The little green shoots would be tall and straight some day, strong enough to carry the weight of the ears of corn that would provide food for the horses. I wondered if they knew, from the time each grain was planted, that this was what they were meant to grow up for.

I had learned a new word in a book that month, and when I happened to see Dr. John I asked him what it meant. The word was "destiny." He explained it very carefully. So I wondered now if the young corn plants knew their destiny. As I thought about it, though, I was still puzzled. A chicken might know it was her destiny to lay eggs and hatch them so more chickens would grow. But was it her destiny to have her head chopped off to make Sunday dinner? I made a mental note to ask Dr. John the next time I saw him. I might even ask Papa, but Dr. John was easier to talk to; he never made me feel foolish.

Papa reached the end of the row and took the cool water from me, and drank long without stopping. Then he told me I'd better get started on the milking and not wait for Mama. She might be very late, he said. I asked him why and he said, "Never mind why. Just do it!" Suddenly the whole frightening conversation about appointments and emergencies came back to me, and it revived the old fear. But I did not dare ask any more questions.

"What are you waiting for?" Papa demanded.

"Nothing, Papa." I turned and ran. We had eight cows now but three were going to have calf-babies, and so they were holding back their milk. By the time Mama came home, I had finished milking all the other five. She praised me and gave me an extra kiss. She got busy with supper right away. It was like a special holiday feast. She had brought Papa's favorite meal—short ribs, already cooked at Tante Freidel's and packed in ice in a tin pot borrowed from the kosher butcher. And there was barley soup with dried mushrooms, onion, carrots, and split peas, besides the barley. There was fresh rye bread from the bakery on Central Avenue, horseradish from Springer's Grocery, and, from the cellar, canned tomatoes. And, finally, there was a compote of canned pears and apples and raisins.

Papa didn't mind that supper was late; he was in one of his best moods. And when we finally sat down to eat, he praised every dish extravagantly. Mama should have been happy like in the song we learned at school: "Oh, do you remember sweet Alice, Ben Bolt— / Sweet Alice with hair so brown, / Who laughed with delight when you gave her a smile / And trembled in fear at your frown?" Mama tried to smile "with delight," but I could feel that something was bothering her.

After supper, when the table was cleared and the dishes washed,

Mama brought the week's issues of the *Jewish Forward*, and Papa read the latest news aloud to us. Then, instead of going on to other features as always, he said we'd leave the fiction and the humor until the next night. Even the "Bintel Briev"—literally "a bundle of letters"—could wait. These were letters from readers who used the feature to unburden their heavy hearts of all the ills they suffered from "unfaithful husbands," "ungrateful children," and their struggles to cope with life in America. Mama was disappointed; this was her favorite department. But I welcomed not having to listen to all this when I preferred to read my own books to myself. And I happened to have such a shower of riches that I didn't know what to read first. There was a book by Mrs. Meade which I had won for "headmarks" in spelling. There was *The Castaway*, a novel about George Gordon, Lord Byron, which Dr. John had borrowed for me from the Clausens and dropped off when he passed our house. And, finally, Mama had picked up a magazine left behind on his seat by a passenger on the "black car," when he got off at a stop ahead of hers.

Papa and Mama went out to sit on the porch and enjoy the cool of the evening, the fragrance of the lilac buds, and the starry sky that Mama said "hung over the world like a million billion candles, a blessing on the earth." Papa said, "My wife is suddenly a poet," but he said it nicely, not as though he were making fun of her. They were quiet for awhile; then they began to speak softly. The door was open, and the screen let the evening fragrances and their voices drift in.

I heard Papa say, "You went? You saw him?"

"You mean the doctor?" I sensed again the troubled note in Mama's voice.

"Who else would I mean?"

Now I was really frightened. I stopped reading. Mama had to see a doctor? A special doctor in Cincinnati? Mama was sick? Too sick for Dr. John to help her? Mama was going to die! I began to shake. I couldn't go back to my book.

"Yes, I saw him," Mama replied.

"So why don't you tell me? What did he say? Speak!"

"He told me I was all right." If she was "all right," why didn't she sound glad instead of frightened?

"He told you you were all right? Then why—?"

"He said sometimes it has to do with the husband. It could maybe be fixed. He said sometimes a couple could have one child and something could go wrong—they couldn't have any more. But it could be fixed lots of times. He wants *you* should come to see him."

"Are you lying, or is the doctor crazy?"

"I am not lying! Freidel Mishkin said he was the best doctor for this kind of trouble. He's a specialist. Frumcha Green said so, too. That's why they wanted him to come and teach in London. And he did say maybe it could be fixed."

Papa spoke with suppressed rage. "My sister Tzivia went to all kinds of doctors in Kiev and Moscow and St. Petersburg and Odessa to find out why she couldn't have a child. She went to all kinds of rabbis, too, they should pray for her and all that nonsense. They couldn't help her but nobody told her to send Isaiah, her husband, to see them! So if you're not lying...." I heard him knock over his chair. "My mares, Queenie and Maudie, are with foal, but my wife wants *me* to go to a doctor because she can't give me a son!" He was shouting now.

"Did your brother-in-law, Isaiah, compare your sister to a mare?" Mama, rising from her chair, shouted back—something I had never heard her do before.

"Leave my sister out of this!"

"Of course, I forgot! Your sister was the lady of the house, and I was the cook! Maybe I should go away and you could find a fine lady worthy of you, and she would give you a son, maybe two sons, maybe three!"

I saw Papa clench his hand. I screamed, "Papa, don't be mad! It's not Mama's fault I'm a girl!" He stared at me as though he were seeing me for the first time. Then he came into the house, slammed the screen door, and said, "Go to bed! Now!" He went into the bedroom, and slammed that door, too.

I didn't go to bed. I went out to Mama. She was sitting on the porch step now, her face in her hands. I touched her, spoke to her, but she didn't look up.

"Do as he said. Go to bed." I obeyed, but I lay awake for a long time. When I finally fell asleep, I did not wake in time to help Mama with the milking. Papa was already in the field. I had some bread and butter and a glass of milk for my breakfast. My lunch was already packed. I gathered up my books and left the house. My little dog, Prince, was waiting to walk with me to the bend in the road. There wasn't time to find Mama and say good-bye. As it was, I had to run to keep from being late.

I wasn't very good in school that day. I didn't hear the questions, and when I heard them I didn't know the answers. Miss Velma asked me if I were not feeling well. I said I was all right, but she could see that something was wrong. She said I could go home, it would be all right. She was so nice that I wanted to cry. She came to my seat and put her hand on my head and felt my forehead and smoothed my hair. Her hand was soft and gentle and loving. She said I'd better go home, and she would let Katie walk home with me if I'd like that. I was afraid to speak because I would start crying. I shook my head and managed to whisper, "Thank you, Miss Velma." She said, "Don't worry about homework tonight." I knew she was going to marry Dr. John's assistant, Dr. Leeds, and wouldn't be our teacher next year. I had never cared before, but now I loved her, and I wished she would come back. All the children stared at me, and Miss Velma told them to get back to their lessons. I slipped out of my seat and took my lunch pail from the cloakroom and ran out. Now that I was alone, I could let tears come. I was grateful that I didn't have to answer questions from the kids. I ran and sobbed, stumbled, fell, rose, ran and sobbed.

Suddenly I was approaching the bend in the road. My little dog, Prince, always waited for me, but he was not there this time, and that frightened me, too. Then I remembered that I was early, and he seemed to know always when to come. I sat down on the ground and tried to wipe the tears from my face before I turned the bend for home. But I couldn't move. I was afraid to go home.

I sat for what seemed a long time, and the longer I sat the harder it became to go home. I remembered how Mama had shouted back at Papa. It was different from any fight I could remember. Mama always used to say, "I'll make tea." Now she had stood up to him and *shouted!* But the most frightening thing was *what* she shouted: "Maybe I should go away!" I couldn't go home—not yet anyway. But where else could I go? To the Lumleys'? What would I tell them? I finally decided I would cut across the fields to the old Snider Place. I wouldn't have to take the bend in the road. I wouldn't have to pass our place. Then I would sit in the deserted barn until I heard Daisy's bell, and I would know that the cows were ready to come home and be milked. I wouldn't have to go home alone; the cows would be with me.

The field I crossed was still wet from recent rains, and I had to roll under a barbed-wire fence. Now I cried for the mess I was in. Then I remembered that I had left my lunch pail behind. What would Prince think when he found the pail, and I was not there to open it for him and give him the treat that I always saved for him? Once Mama had found out about that; afterwards she had always put a little extra into my lunch pail. But there was no going back now.

The old Snider Place had never seemed scary before. It was full of wild plants, lush growth, and friendly trees, and in the summer many kinds of berries and wild grapes. When I reached the barbed-wire gate and opened it, I hesitated to enter. What had been a lovely place to explore now seemed strange and threatening. Finally I went in, but left the gate open so that if something terrible confronted me I could turn and run quickly. I made my way to the old barn. This, too, seemed to say, "Go away, you're a bad girl!"

Once, when Ol' Belle had been pasturing there, I was sent to bring her home on a Sunday afternoon. I got the chain attached to her halter, but I couldn't get her to stand near any place from which I could mount her. I heard voices from the barn and led her there to find someone who would lift me onto her back. I saw

a group of young men, all known to me, who were playing cards—
a pastime frowned upon in this community, especially on Sunday.
They were startled when they saw me, and one of them—his name
was Clyde—walked over to me and asked, "What you doin' here,
kiddo?" I told him I just wanted someone to put me on Ol' Belle's
back. He said I'd come to the right place.

"We fellows are holdin' a little prayer meetin' here, but don't
you tell anyone. It's just between us an' the good Lord!"

He lifted me up onto Ol' Belle and I promised, and I kept my
word.

I longed now, as I stood in the great emptiness of the barn, for
a human voice to relieve the silence. There were discarded newspapers lying around the place. I picked up a few, some on which
to sit, and one or two to read until I should hear Daisy's cowbell.
Then I remembered what Clyde had said about a prayer meeting.
Katie had once told me that Jesus could make miracles. She said
she prayed for a miracle sometimes, like passing her arithmetic test,
and he helped her, and she passed. But I couldn't pray to Jesus. I
was a Jewish child. Yet if Jesus could make miracles, God could
surely do it.

"Please, God," I whispered. "I need a miracle very, very much.
Please make a miracle so Papa can have a son. He wants it so very
much. And it will make Mama happy, too. If you think it would
help, I would go away and you could make the miracle. God, I
don't really want to go away but I will, if you tell me where to go.
Or if you want me to, I'll die."

I fell asleep on the spread newspapers. Suddenly I woke up. It
seemed to be much later. It was the sound of Daisy's cowbell that
awakened me, though it seemed faint and far away. I ran out to
listen and started off in the direction from which the sound seemed
to come. Here in the woods dusk was already gathering, but I
knew the paths and the whole fenced section of the abandoned

pasture. The sound of the bell was elusive—sometimes closer, sometimes farther away. I was becoming tired and frightened; what had always been a familiar and wildly beautiful place was becoming more and more menacing. As I pursued it, the sound of the bell seemed, as before, now closer, now farther. The whole time and place seemed in league to bewilder and drive me out.

Suddenly I found myself at the section of the fence that divided the familiar part of the old Snider Place from the totally unused and wilder section. Now the sound of the bell seemed to come from that part of the place. I walked along the dividing fence in the direction of the sound and came upon a broken-down section of the barbed wire. I was sure now that the cows had broken out into the wilderness and were trying to find their way back. I longed for Prince to be with me, not only for the comfort of his presence, but for his help in locating the cows.

Again, the sound of the bell seemed to come from a different direction. Finally there was no sound of the bell at all. I knew that I was lost! I walked aimlessly, my panic mounting. Brambles tore at my clothes, my arms, my legs, even my face. A wind rose, adding to the anger I felt all around me. Small trees swayed, and large trees furiously waved their branches. Creatures I could not see scurried through the undergrowth, becoming monsters who were gathering to destroy me.

Suddenly I fell over what felt like a barrier place across the path to imprison me. At the same time something clutched at my dress. I screamed. Then I lay still.

After what seemed a long time, stars began to appear and a half-moon dispelled some of what had been total darkness. Bruised and shaking, I got to my feet. Now that there was some light, I recognized that the evil creature which had tripped me was a thick, ropelike vine which would bear wild grapes in the summer. It had crept along the ground and attached itself to a small tree. Blackberry vines had twined around the thick grapevine, and it was into all this that I had fallen. I became calmer now, and I remembered that some boys who had ventured into this part of the abandoned place said there was a creek nearby, a real humdinger of a creek, with fish in it, and a swimming hole. I listened intently and was sure that I heard water somewhere below me. The ground where I stood sloped sharply downward and, as I made my way, I had to go sometimes on hands and knees. The sound of the water became clearer, and when I reached it I felt, for the first time, some hope for finding a way out of this wilderness. The creek turned out to be a small, swift stream—but nothing like the creek the boys had described.

I had read in a story that if you follow a stream carefully, you would come sooner or later to habitation. The important thing was to know in which direction to follow it. I had nothing but eeny-meeny-miney-mo to help me choose. I closed my eyes and decided to go to the left. Behind me was the hill I had descended, before me a steeper hill. The stream wound its way between the two, with no hint of where it was going. Then, as it turned from its straight course and I turned with it, I looked up and saw a light high on the hill, coming from a house. At the same time, I heard again the sound of Daisy's bell, coming now from beyond the hill I had left. I even thought I heard a dog barking, but I did not turn back. The lighted window was a promise of rescue. The sound could be playing tricks again. The house remained steady. I waded the stream in my shoes, and began the long and difficult climb to the beckoning light.

It seemed hours later when I reached the house. I had never seen it before. I had no idea where I was in relation to my own home. I was bedraggled, tear-stained, bruised, scratched, miserable, but I knocked on the door. A man opened it and looked down at me. I burst into tears. When he brought me into the house, I was able to answer some questions: my name, where I lived. No, we had no telephone. The only one I knew of was at Perkins' General Store in Kegtown. The lady of the house took me in hand, comforted me, cleaned me up as much as possible, took off my wet shoes and stockings, and dried my feet. Then she fed me. Her name, she said, was Mrs. Sickler, but I could call her Aunt Susan. By that time Mr. Sickler came into the kitchen. He told Aunt Susan that he had found out from someone at the general store that my father and a number of other men had been out looking for me for hours. The man at the store said he would ring a bell, and they'd know that I'd been found.

"Do you know how far you are from home, child?" asked Mr. Sickler.

"No, sir."

"About six miles. So we'd better get started."

Aunt Susan gave me my wet shoes and stockings to carry home. Mr. Sickler, whom Aunt Susan said I could call Uncle Amos, lifted me into the buggy, to which he had already hitched his horse, Lady.

Six miles is a long way to go with a horse and buggy, but I didn't mind because it put off my homecoming and what punishment must be waiting for me.

Uncle Amos said, "You must be clean tuckered out. I'll get you home as quick as I can without drivin' Lady too hard. Meantime, maybe you can snooze a little. I'll sing you a lullaby." He began to sing "Frog Went Courtin'," and pretty soon I was asleep. I slept until I felt Uncle Amos's hand on my shoulder.

"Better wake up, child. You're home." Mama and Papa must have heard us drive in. Mama was running to the buggy, Papa following more slowly, still using his cane. Prince was barking wildly and jumping at me. Mama reached up for me and held me. We cried together. Papa came up to Uncle Amos and asked him to come in. Uncle Amos thought he'd better get back. Papa thanked him. Uncle Amos said, "Don't be too hard on your little girl. Young'uns get strange notions." He turned Lady around and drove away, leaving me to face I knew not what. Mama and I followed Papa into the house.

"Sit down," Papa said.

"Are you hungry?" asked Mama.

"No, Mama."

"What do you have to say for yourself?" asked Papa.

"I did a bad thing."

"Why did you do it?"

"I don't know, Papa."

"Why—did—you—do—it?" he persisted.

"I didn't want to come home."

"Is your home such a bad place?"

"No, Papa."

"Half of Dunham's Hill was out looking for you. Your mama was half-crazy. She rang the dinner bell, and the neighbors came running. Katie Lumley said you left school early because you were sick. Somebody found your lunch pail and your dog sitting beside it. The cows came home without you." His voice rose. "Where did you go?"

"I went for the cows and sat in the barn till they would come."

"You sat and waited in the barn! You are making a lot of foolish talk!"

"I—I—made a prayer in the barn."

"What kind of prayer did you make in the barn? What are you talking about?" He was shouting now. Mama touched me, but a glance from Papa made her take her hand away.

"Answer me!"

"First, I thought if I went away forever, maybe you could get a boy. Then I didn't know where to go forever, so I asked God—" I could only whisper now "—to make me a miracle. Katie told me once that Jesus made miracles, but I couldn't ask him, because I am a Jewish child—" I couldn't go on.

There was silence for a moment. Then Papa spoke again, but his voice was low and different.

"What was the miracle you prayed for?"

"I prayed that He'd make it so you could have a boy, and if I had to, I'd go away, if He'd tell me where to go. And if He needed to make me die, that would be all right, too."

A strange thing happened. Papa turned white. Then he said something I never had heard him say before. He said, "God help me!" He sat down and covered his face with his hands, and cried in a terrible way, as though it hurt him very, very deeply. It frightened me. I had never seen him like that. I stood and looked at Mama, but she was looking at Papa. She walked over to him slowly and held his head against her. After awhile he stopped crying and looked up. His face was wet with tears. Mama wiped them away with her apron. He held out his hand to me. I hesitated, and then I went up, and he drew me close.

"I have to tell you something, my child," he said. "It would be nice to have a little son. But not in place of you. Never in place of you. Do you understand that? Do you believe me?"

"Yes, Papa."

"The next time you talk to God will you tell Him never mind the miracle? We don't want it. Will you tell him that?"

"Yes, Papa."

He kissed me on the forehead.

"Papa," I whispered, "I'm sorry I did a bad thing."

"Maybe—" he began to cry again. He held me close. "Maybe it was, after all, a good thing."

Mama said, "I'll go make tea."

I never again heard them speak of an appointment with the doctor for Papa. I never heard any more talk about a brother for me or a son for Papa, except once in passing. It was as if they had closed a door on the subject—closed it, and locked it tight. But I know now that the door was between them, too. They were not behind it together. There were times again of laughter, when friends came for the weekend: the Greens and Uncle Moishele Platt and sometimes Landa. But when they left, the door was closed; again everything was peaceful, except, perhaps, the hearts of my mother and father.

# 17

# *Alexander Graham Bell Comes to Dunham's Hill*

If winter was late in coming, spring retaliated by being also late. Papa's knee was slow in healing; but because the fields were ready for plowing later than usual, everything worked out satisfactorily. Neighbors took turns plowing our fields, and Papa, who could do just about anything except follow a plow, sat in the seat of his disk or harrow and finished the neighbors' fields.

I came home from school one day, and Mama told me Papa had driven to New Richmond. He didn't tell her why. He only said that "if it works," he would tell us, and if it didn't, there wouldn't be anything to tell.

We were finishing the milking when Papa arrived, driving Ol' Belle and the two-wheeled rig. I went out to help him unharness and stable the horse. He had discarded his crutch, but he still used a cane.

"Papa, are you going to tell us?" I asked.

"Wait and see," he replied, but he smiled. "First finish the chores."

Not until we sat down to supper did we get the news: Dunham's Hill was going to get a telephone line! But first we had to get ten subscribers to the service. Second, the men had to cut and dress the timber for the poles—just the right height, the right girth, and as nearly identical as possible. They would have to be distributed at intervals designated by the company. Then the holes had to be dug, and the poles placed in the ground and cemented firmly in place and in perfect alignment with one another. All this would have to be accomplished by the subscribers. After that, the company would put up the lines and install all the necessary equipment, as well as the wall telephones, and assign each subscriber's signal ring, such as one-long–two-short or whatever. To call a number not on our own party line it would be necessary to ring the operator in New Richmond.

As Papa was counting off on his fingers the order and nature of the tasks involved in getting telephone service, we had stopped eating and were listening open-mouthed and wide-eyed.

"Eat!" Papa commanded, but again he was smiling. "We've got work to do."

"You never said anything about it," Mama exclaimed.

"I've been thinking about it ever since I got this knee business. I made up my mind it was time for Dunham's Hill to move into the twentieth century. If anything happens—an emergency, if you need a doctor and have to ride a mile on a horse or with a buggy to a telephone—we might as well be living in a Russian *shtetl*. So we're going to move into the twentieth century."

"Suppose," posed Mama, "you won't find nine others who want to move with you?"

"If we were looking for a *minyan*, I agree it would be impossible on Dunham's Hill. But this we have to try." Papa turned to me. "You, Goldele, have to help me. First, after supper, write down the things the company says we have to do. Here is the list they gave me. Write down: first, second, third, and so forth. Very carefully write it down. Then, tomorrow, you'll saddle Ol' Belle and go to ten neighbors. I'll tell you who: Charlie Mott, Ol' Fred Hoppe, George Lumley, Mr. Licht—I'll tell you the rest when I think more about it. If they want to come in, let them sign a paper they gave me in New Richmond. I'll give it to you and the paper that tells on it everything we have to do. And after that, we'll have a meeting, and the ladies and even the young'uns can come, too."

Mama said, "Maybe everybody else will come, but not Hoppe. He's too lazy to share in the work and too stingy to share in the cost."

"He'll come," assured Papa.

I felt like Paul Revere that Saturday morning, riding from farm to farm. I wanted to shout, "The telephones are coming!" I restrained myself, but as I approached each farmhouse I did urge Ol' Belle into a gallop to add a touch of derring-do to my mission. Most of the men—and it was the men, of course, I had to see—were in the fields or barns. Most of the ladies were doing their Saturday baking, and the fragrance of the kitchens was mouthwatering. In each place I devoured a cookie, or the heel of a fresh-baked loaf spread with butter, jam, or honey. And in each kitchen, I had to repeat what Papa had told me to say if the lady of the house asked what I wanted to see the head of the house about.

"Just say," he told me, "it's a surprise." But since he hadn't told me not to say anything more, I added, poised to run, "It's about moving into the twentieth century!"—and ran.

When I came home, arriving at a triumphant gallop, I had ten signatures but little appetite for dinner. Papa was very pleased and began making plans for a meeting.

"How were you so sure Hoppe would sign?" wondered Mama.

"Because he loves gossip, and everybody who knows anything about telephones knows you can listen in on other parties on your line."

Sometime after we had gotten used to the miracle of communication, Ginny told this story: she was talking to her beau, Forrest Perkins, when they became aware of someone listening in. Ginny shouted, "Get off the line, Mr. Hoppe, you sneak!" And, she said, he shot right back, "You can't no way prove it was me, Miss Smarty-Tarty!" and hung up.

Meantime, a notice was put up in the general store inviting everybody involved in the enterprise to a meeting at our house— a meeting that became known as the ten-party gabfest—on the following Sunday afternoon. By way of the remarkable grapevine by which the Dunham's Hill women maintained their own line of communication, a potluck supper was planned for the meeting.

When Mama came home from her weekly trip to Cincinnati, I was milking the last cow to the tune of "Tenting Tonight." I was practicing the tune, with which I would confound Mama. I carried the milk to the woodshed where the cream separator had been installed, while Mama carried in the things she had brought from the city. Papa was nowhere to be seen. I told Mama he had gone to New Richmond soon after she left, but had returned before I came home from school. He had told me he had a surprise but wouldn't tell me what it was. We were putting away things in the kitchen when he came in.

"Becky," he said, "you're back."

"Yes, and you were away, too."

"And I'm back, too."

"What is this I hear about a surprise?"

"A long time ago," said Papa, "I promised you something, but things happened and I couldn't do it. Then I would say to myself, 'When such-and-such happens, I'll do it.' One time I said to myself, 'When we have a son, nothing will stop me—I will do it!'"

There was a moment's silence. I began to shake. Was that starting all over again? But he went on: "None of those things matter so much anymore. So now I am keeping my promise in time for Sunday's meeting. Come!"

He walked out and we followed. He led the way to the big parlor, as bare all these years as it had been when we first came to Dunham's Hill. Only the walls had ever been "furnished," mostly with an enlarged, color-tinted, gilt-framed photograph of Tante Braindele, the beautiful young rebel who had brought us to Cincinnati and then opted for a return to Russia. All around her portrait were hanging wire photo holders filled with small pictures of family members and friends who were left behind when we left, first Russia, then Boston, then finally Cincinnati. On the opposite wall were colored calendars featuring babies, flowers, puppies, and farm implements.

We followed Papa into the room. He pointed toward the windows. They were hung with stiff lace curtains! Papa waited. Mama finally came out of shock.

"*Gottenyu!*" she whispered, and I followed as she walked slowly toward the windows. We suddenly felt a difference under our feet. We had left the wooden floor and were standing on a carpet of very red roses on a very green background. "Axminster," said Papa proudly. It was at that moment that I remembered the promise Papa had made to Mama when he had decided to remain in Cincinnati and had showed us the flat on Central Avenue. "I promise you, in six months, maybe even less. . . . " Now, after years had passed, he had kept the promise. I looked up at Mama. She was crying.

"Here, sit down," said Papa. He led her to a black horsehair sofa which I had not noticed before.

Mama smoothed it lovingly. "But how?" she asked through her tears. "It must have cost a fortune."

"You can buy on time," Papa explained. "Mr. Perkins, from the general store, stood good for me."

"But how could you carry it in? So heavy, and you with a bad knee!"

"On the way to New Richmond I picked up Josiah. He did it all and then went home. You are pleased?"

"Who would not be pleased?" She wiped away her tears. "I thought I'd never live to see the day!"

"Well, you lived! And we won't be shamed before our neighbors. With so many, I figured we'd have to hold the meeting here in this room. There was nothing here. Now there is something."

They had paid no attention to me. It was like something very important was being settled between them. I slipped away unnoticed, and went to separate the milk. But I was disappointed that Papa had really done it for the neighbors and not just for Mama. Thinking back to that day, I believe that the door which had been locked between them may have been opened a little way.

The ladies had decided, and word had been gotten to Mama, that the potluck would be at noon, after church, instead of in the evening, after the meeting. So Sunday dinner was going to be, for the first time, at our house! A long table, made by placing boards on "sawhorses," was set up in the yard, and sheets were used for tablecloths. Mama contributed her famous noodle pudding, made with raisins and with apples that were stored in the cellar. And she baked sponge cake and twist loaves of "challah." The ladies brought fried chicken, coleslaw, sweet potatoes, canned vegetables, and piccalilli, and cakes and pies.

It was, as described later in the New Richmond *Independent News*, "a highlight of Dunham's Hill's social season." No such event had ever taken place at our house before. We were on good terms with all our neighbors, but had never exchanged dinners or entertained so many at one time. I felt that we really belonged now, and that being Jewish in a totally Christian community made no difference. Going to Sunday school with the Lumley children had left me confused about myself and about being Jewish. I was to learn, some years later, that being Jewish did make a difference. Still, it was not on Dunham's Hill but in another farming community that I experienced my first demonstration—a silly, childish demonstration though it was—of overt anti-Semitism.

The dinner was a great success, and when it was over it was decided that we should make a toast to the success of the project. Papa boldly suggested that Mama bring up some of her cherry *vishnik* for the purpose. After all, it was not like they'd be drinking whiskey; just a little sip to celebrate. The men immediately agreed; the ladies, with the exception of Mrs. Licht, followed suit, bridling a little but agreeing it could do no real harm. Suddenly Mrs. Licht added her approval and, seeing the astonished look on all the faces, including her husband's, pointed out that the New Testament actually advocated "a little wine for the stomach's sake." And with a mischievous smile in response to her husband's surprised look she added, "Timothy 5:23." So the *vishnik* was brought up and served sparingly, "for the stomach's sake," and the toasts ended with "three cheers for Ol' Max," who really knew how to get things done.

After dinner the men went inside to sit around the dining room table and got down to the business of planning the work, while the ladies did the washing up. The children played outside, but I was ordered to stay by Papa's side and write down what transpired, especially what each subscriber agreed to do. I felt this was unfair when all the other young'uns were having fun, and Mr. Licht, apparently sharing my feelings, offered to be secretary. But Papa said it would be good experience for me. I think he want to show off my "advanced" writing skills—or perhaps my unquestioning obedience. Soon the women tiptoed through the dining room on their way to the parlor, where they would sit and visit—and undoubtedly exclaim over its new look. And I had to miss that, too! Later Mama told me, "Oh, yes, they liked it very much; they liked it." Then she paused and, lowering her voice, added, "Myself, I think I would like not so many roses, and maybe not so red, maybe pink. But don't tell Papa!"

In the meantime, I prepared to write. Papa, of course, could not yet share the hard labor, but he had taken care of that, too. He had arranged with Josiah to take his place and, of course, he would pay him. The others protested that Ol' Max didn't have to do that; he had done his part already. But Papa insisted. And he had an announcement to make: from now on, he was going to pay Josiah or any other hired man he might need, provided he was as good as Josiah, one dollar a day and found (his dinner), plus all the produce in season he could carry home on his back! There was a stunned silence, then surprise, even shock. Henry Ford's announcement years later that he was instituting a five-dollar-a-day wage base could hardly have created a greater stir. The men began talking, arguing, one or two even agreeing that it was only right. But the most vociferous was Fred Hoppe, who said it would eat up all the profits from farming if you had to pay out that kind of money to a hired man. Besides, it would spoil the labor market for everybody. Since his reputation for laziness was well known, he had little support.

"I'm not saying everybody should do it," Papa interposed. "I just know it's right for me. The Bible says...." He stopped dramatically. He had everyone's attention. I guess they were startled that a non-churchgoer should quote the Bible. "The Bible says," he repeated, "that the laborer is worthy of his hire." There was a moment's silence. This time it was *Mr.* Licht who smiled mischievously and said, "New Testament, I Timothy 5:18." Everybody laughed, and Papa said to me, "Run along now, child. Go and play with the others." The men began a din of talking again; the cause of labor had been served. I myself was awed. My "free-thinker" agnostic father had never, at least in my presence, quoted the Bible before—and the New Testament at that! I had not gone to Sunday school for nothing! Papa, I thought, was full of surprises. At the first opportunity I told Mama about this amazing remark of his.

"And not even our Bible," I said. "It was from the Jesus Bible. Mr. Licht said so!"

"Don't worry," Mama replied with a funny smile. "Papa didn't get it from any Bible. He hasn't even got a Bible, you know that."

"Then how did he know? It *was* from the Bible. Mr. Licht said so, and he really knows!"

"I'll tell you how he knows: he read it in the *Jewish Forward* a few weeks ago. It was an article about a strike. He read it aloud to me. And he never forgets anything he wants to remember!"

The trees to be cut were selected from the patches of woodland that almost every farm on Dunham's Hill had. The cutting and dressing and preparing of the poles began very soon after the meeting at our house. It was late in the spring before the ground had thawed a sufficient depth for the holes to be dug. But school was out now, and the sons were free to work. Besides, other farmers on the Hill offered help. Even though they were not subscribers, since the line was limited to ten parties, it was automatically accepted that no Dunham's Hill neighbor would ever again have to go all the way to Kegtown to make a telephone call.

Thus, when the great day arrived, and a new dimension had been added to the life of the entire community, the celebration was held in the schoolhouse so that everyone could participate. Then, when everyone had gone home, Mama rang the Lumleys and everybody got on the line and sang, "Happy Birthday To Our Telephones" and then "Good-night, Ladies, Good-night, Gentlemen!" and hung up. We had, as Papa had said we should do, "moved into the twentieth century." And New Richmond's *Independent News* gave us a front-page story with a headline that announced: Alexander Graham Bell Comes to Dunham's Hill!

# 18

# *One-Upmanship?*

They seemed never quite at ease with each other; I could sense it. When the excitement of the telephone lines was over, Mama and Papa settled back into hard work, each doing more than his share, more than was needed, perhaps. The best times were when company came from Cincinnati.

Papa returned home one day and told us at supper that there was a notice at the general store that the county was going to do some road improvement in our area. It needed men with good teams to work on the road, hauling rock to hard-surface the worst of the mud roads. Papa said he had signed up. It would be, of course, between harvest time and planting time.

Mama looked startled. "You don't have enough to do now? And your leg isn't all healed yet."

"I'll have Josiah every day while I work on the road." He was showing irritation. "It shouldn't make any difference to you."

"It makes a difference if you try to kill yourself!"

"Thank you, but you don't have to worry. The horses will pull the wagon. Laborers will break up the rocks and load the wagon. And I drive the team."

The rest of the meal was finished in silence.

The next time Mama came home from the city, she, too, had news. And she kept it to herself until after the evening chores were done and we were almost through with supper.

"I heard something very interesting today in the city," she addressed herself to Papa. "You have maybe heard of Dr. Boris Bogen?"

"Doctor?" Papa gripped the table's edge. "What kind of a doctor?" I think the old dream of a son suddenly burst into his mind. Mama must have realized what an effect her question had created.

"No, no! Excuse me," she hastened to explain. "A different kind of doctor; I think a doctor from philosophy."

Papa slumped back in his chair. "I do not know your doctor from philosophy."

"He is the main manager of the Jewish Charities in Cincinnati. They help poor Jewish people. And if someone in a family is not so well, and needs fresh country air and fresh food, Dr. Bogen sends them to a farm. He likes best, for them, Jewish farmers, but there are not so many. We have a big house—"

Papa's knife and fork clattered to his plate. "You want to fill the house with sick people? You want to start a hospital?"

"Not sick like that. They just need fresh air and good food. I told him we could take maybe six people." Papa stared at her, stony-faced.

"We have two bedrooms upstairs," Mama continued. "Sometimes they send couples. We could have four people up there, and in the extra bedroom downstairs, two ladies, or two gentlemen, or another couple. We would have to buy some beds and other things, but it would pay."

Mama waited for his anger, looking like she was ready for it; but the fight seemed to have gone out of Papa. He rose from the table and walked out of the house.

"Mama," I whispered, "why do you want to do it?"

"To buy myself a rope of pearls," she said, but not making fun. "And a little Cossack hat for you and a gold watch and chain for Papa."

For the first time I felt that Mama had shut me out.

"We'll get everything ready, and next spring they will begin to come. I'll bring them in the surrey, and we'll get started. It will be like having company all the time." Mama had changed!

The next day when I went to get the mail, the *Farm and Fireside* was in the mailbox. I read it as I walked slowly home. A full-page announcement in the children's section drew my attention. Young readers were invited to win hundreds of prizes by obtaining subscriptions to the *Farm and Fireside*. The grand prize was a Shetland pony, pictured, complete with a basketlike pony cart and harness. I had not thought of a pony since Jenny Goldenstern and I had seen one in the picture book about country life we had found at the Settlement House. We had been sure that it was standard equipment on any farm, and I had promised all the kids on our block on Central Avenue rides in the elegant equipage. There was, of course, no pony on the farm. The kids never came. And I had never thought about it from that time on. Now the old dream returned. Maybe if I really had the pony, Jennie would come to visit and bring lots of the kids with her. Maybe she could even find Norma for me. I ran the rest of the way home.

I said nothing until we sat down to supper that evening. For the first time I had not first consulted Mama. Papa was glancing through *Farm and Fireside* as he ate.

"Papa," I almost whispered. He looked up. I was afraid to go on.

"Well? 'Papa' what? You have something to tell me, so tell me."

"It's in the *Farm and Fireside* contest to get subscriptions." I gained courage. "I could win a pony."

"And you want to do this?"

"Yes, Papa, please." He seemed to be studying my face.

"Why not?" he said finally. "Your mama is going to take in boarders, and she didn't even ask me. Did you ask your mama? You'd better ask her, too." I looked at Mama.

"Why not?" she said, just like Papa. "Your papa is going to build roads, and he didn't even ask me! So you have my blessing!"

Later, when I was helping Mama clean up in the kitchen, Papa came up to her.

"Becky," he said awkwardly, "It's all right, what you want to do, if it won't be too hard for you. We can use the money, and it will be like company in the house."

"Yes. It will be like company in the house."

I never doubted that I would win a pony. I neglected my chores, and I wasn't punished. I went into areas I had never seen before. I rolled under barbed-wire fences and climbed over stiles. I got burned by the sun and sometimes soaked by rain. When the contest was over I had won—a dozen silver-plated teaspoons.

"You did your best," Mama comforted me. "We can't always win. All we can do is try our best. I'll put the spoons away for you. It will be part of your '*nadan*.'"

Papa comforted me, too. "Your mama is right," he said. "You did your best. And now, no more excuses for not doing your chores."

But Mama and Papa were not yet through with a game I learned about many years later: one-upmanship.

# 19

# *Summer Boarders*

Mama started bringing them home on Tuesdays that summer, two at a time, as soon as space could be provided for them. She drove the surrey now instead of the buggy, which could hold only three passengers comfortably, with no room for luggage.

The first to come were Mr. and Mrs. Martin Dobkin, a young couple with a small baby, a little girl. Mr. Dobkin was the one who needed the fresh country air, but the baby was sickly, too, so Dr. Bogen arranged for the mother and child to come with him. Mama said we would have to buy a crib in New Richmond for the baby, and Dr. Bogen said the charities would pay for it if necessary. But Mrs. Lumley had one for which she had no further use and loaned it to us.

We all felt a little strange having people living with us who were neither family nor friends. And almost at the same time, Mama and Papa realized that if we took as many boarders as had been agreed on with Dr. Bogen, we could no longer have visits from Tante Frumcha and Uncle Charlie or Moishele Platt or the Mishkins. I had been agonizing over this but was afraid to say anything. To my great relief, Mama and Papa agreed they would take no more than four at a time.

As it turned out, the Dobkins themselves became like family. Mr. Dobkin was a tall man with a sensitive face, lightly freckled and hollow-cheeked. He had kind blue eyes and curly, light brown hair.

He had brought his mandolin, which he played, in my opinion, like a musical genius. His wife, Tania, was small, dark. Her hair, straight and black, was cut short, a style not yet the fashion nor even acceptable. She wore rimless glasses and was a very earnest lady, and totally devoted to the baby, Sophie. She and her husband were socialists and free-thinkers like Papa, but Mr. Dobkin wore his irreligious and political convictions lightly, while his wife never let anyone forget her views.

Mr. Dobkin knew songs, Yiddish and Russian, that Mama and Papa knew, too, and they and the Greens and any other visitors, when they came, sang along with him. We would sit on the porch in the cool evenings after supper, and the city folks would take deep breaths of clean air laden with the fragrance of lilacs and roses, and Mama would bring out lemonade, and it would be like a party. When little Sophie had a birthday, I was sent to Lindale to Mr. Kramer, who had a pond which would freeze heavily in the winter. He would then cut the ice and store it with sawdust in a special building. I brought back ice, and we made ice cream and sang "Happy birthday, dear Sophie," and it was a lovely time.

Mama had to give up all her customers in the city except the Greens, the Mishkins, and the Corellis, because she needed the butter and eggs and cheese for the boarders.

The next couple who came were people the Dobkins knew and they, too, became like family. They were Anna and Sam Shuster, and our friendship with them endured, through the distances of time and space, until death left one vacant chair after another and the circle came to an end.

Over the two summers that boarders came and went, not all were sources of pleasure. There was Mrs. Rose Bloom, who demanded ham with her breakfast eggs, and when she did not get it said that she would find a Christian family to board with who were not so "fanatisht."

There was Mrs. Zuckerman who seemed to be thriving on the benefits of country living, except on Sundays when her husband was expected to visit. Then she would take to her bed with wet cloths on her forehead and moan piteously.

There was Mr. Litvinsky, who followed Mama around while she was doing her work, chattering incessantly, interrupting his monologues only to say, "You are working too hard, Missus. Stop awhile and come have tea." She would tell him each time that if *he* wanted tea she would make it for him but *she* didn't have time to stop for tea every time *he* wanted it.

Mr. Litvinsky was a very tall, very thin man with very long legs. When everyone else sat on the porch in the evening, he would place his rocking chair behind one of the lilac bushes, facing the barnyard, out of sight of everyone else. But the sound of his chair striking the lilac bush with mounting speed could be heard. He said that by doing that he became one with the blossoms and the fragrance and even the stars, which, he said, seemed closer and closer the harder he rocked. One evening everyone was startled by cries for help coming from the lilac bush. Waving in the air above the lilacs were Mr. Litvinsky's long legs. He was rescued from his overturned chair amid hysterical laughter. He never followed Mama around anymore, and he left a few days before his time was up.

And there was Eli Gordon, a tall, handsome, broad-shouldered man who looked the picture of health, except for the excessively high color of his cheeks. Once I heard one of the other boarders whisper that he was spitting blood. His fiancée, Molly Schecter, came to see him every Sunday. She, too, was tall—Junoesque, beautiful. Once I heard them talking.

"Molly, I don't want you to come anymore."

"You're going to throw me over? You found somebody else? Tell me who. I'll kill her!"

"Don't joke, Molly. It's just no use. I'm not getting any better. We have to end it. It's over."

"You won't get rid of me so easy," she replied.

"Do you know what I've got, Molly? I've got galloping consumption!" he shouted.

"Shut up!" she shouted back. "Just shut up." And then, joking again, "I'm not going to waste a perfectly good marriage license, so put it out of your mind."

I didn't hear any more, except he laughed. But it wasn't a funny laugh.

When Molly came back the following Sunday, she brought a rabbi with her. Mama and Papa were in on her plans, and Mama had prepared chopped herring and cucumber salad and a twist loaf of challah for the blessing. And there was *vishnik*, of course, and honey cake and sponge cake and strudel, and even a little schnapps. Mama and Papa stood up with the bride and groom, and Eli Gordon cried like a child. So did everyone else, except Molly. She stood tall and straight and smiling, holding tight to Eli's hand. They went back to the city together to a flat that she had prepared. Eli died in less than a year. Mama said Molly knew it would happen, but she wanted to share what life was left to him because she truly loved him. "*Ein emesse liebe*," Mama whispered through tears. A true love. She made a special trip to the city to attend the funeral and wore a black velvet hat trimmed with a black and white ribbon, borrowed from Ollie Lumley, who had gotten it through the Sears, Roebuck catalogue. It was not the best choice for midsummer, but it was either that or go bareheaded, and Mama said that would show a lack of respect.

All the boarders believed, and even some of our city friends, too, that milk, taken warm and foamy just as it was drawn from the cows, had great healing powers. They would stand outside the stables at milking time, glasses in their hands, to drink the elixir straight from the cows' udders. Raw eggs, too, were thought to be beneficial, and some of the boarders would follow me when I gathered the eggs, which were sometimes so freshly laid that they were still warm. The boarders would carefully break open the narrow end, add salt, which they carried with them, and suck the raw eggs from the shells.

There was another lineup at the stable at milking time: the kittens and cats who were the offspring of Maggie, left behind for us by the Lumleys when we bought the farm, as a gift of the "better mousetrap" that Nature herself built. Maggie was very pretty, soft gray-and-white, and she disappeared from time to time on journeys that ended in a litter of kittens, some with her looks, others obviously resembling a father never known to us and apparently never known to them. A feminist before feminists changed the mores of America, Maggie did not wait for a tomcat to come a-wooing, but took matters into her own paws whenever she felt "by love possessed." Thus she spared us the caterwauling of feline love-making, for which I hope we were grateful, even though giving kittens away became increasingly difficult.

Like the boarders, Maggie's progeny lined up at milking time, morning and evening, at the wooden trough that Papa had built for them, and waited for their milk to be poured. Maggie never joined them; she sat a short distance away, viewing the scene, washing herself in preparation for breakfast or supper, never deigning to join either the humans or her own descendants. She would eat when she was ready, from her own dish, in what, I am sure, she thought of as her own kitchen.

At the end of the second summer, when the last of the boarders had left until they could be reevaluated by Dr. Bogen, Mama told Papa she would like to terminate the project. She wanted to pick up her old customers in Cincinnati again. Besides, there had been some correspondence about Bubbie coming to stay with us for awhile, and we'd need the downstairs spare bedroom—of course, if Papa approved.

"Why do you think I wouldn't approve?" Papa demanded. "Am I such a terrible person? Such a *gazlin*?"

"Of course not!" Mama's voice was soft and gentle as it used to be always, before things changed somehow. "I just wanted you to have your say. It's only right." Papa nodded and Mama went on. "I'll have to get a few things, a few new dishes and one or two pots, so everything will be kosher for her."

"So get them." He was reading the *Cincinnati Post* and turned a page, indicating that the discussion was at an end.

"I have something else to tell you, Max." Papa put his paper down and looked interested. I suspect that every time Mama had something special to tell him, a secret, unquenchable hope would light up his face. I think he never stopped hoping that the "something" would turn out to be that she was "with child."

"So tell me," he said, allowing a touch of eagerness to creep into his voice.

"Yes—well—I found out there is a Jewish farmer, he lives not too far from here if you go over our red clover field, down the hill behind it and down to the road. He isn't a regular farmer. He has a business. He hires men to push the carts on the streets in Cincinnati to sell hot chick-peas, and sweet corn on the cob, and different things. And now he is going to be a *hatamalchik*, too." The word turned out to be a blend of Yiddish and Russian, and meant that the man was about to become a maker and purveyor of hot tamales, something new for the streets of Cincinnati.

Mama didn't know exactly what hot tamales were, but when they were ready to be cooked they had to be wrapped in clean corn husks and twisted shut at either end. He had tried a few, Mama said, and they were snapped up. The trouble was, she said, he couldn't get enough good corn husks to turn the tamales out fast enough.

"So why are you telling me about it?" Papa demanded, ready to pick up his paper again.

"Wait, I'm coming to that," Mama went on. "Like I said, he needs plenty of corn husks. So I thought, when you harvest the corn we could save the husks, clean out the silks and throw away bad husks, and pack the good ones in sacks. We could do it right here in the house on winter evenings, and sell them to the *hatamalchik*. It would make up for not keeping boarders, and wouldn't be so much work." She waited for a reaction. It was slow in coming. She went on hesitantly. "Now the husks just go to waste." Finally Papa spoke.

"Who told you about this?"

"On the black car, I got to talking with a Jewish man who is a farmer, too, on Nine-Mile Stop. Only he works in the city, and somebody works the farm on shares. There are more Jewish farmers like him, I found out, and they all work in the city or have businesses. Mr. Kullman, the man that told me this, says some day he hopes to be a real farmer. I told him about you, how you are a real farmer and a good one—"

"Forget the compliments; get to the *hatamalchik*."

"Well, Mr. Kullman is the one who told me. He said they don't raise corn on his farm, so he can't do anything. But you do—"

"Does this *hatamalchik* have a name?" Mama took a slip of paper from her apron pocket and handed it to Papa.

"Mr. Kullman, on the black car, wrote it down for me," Mama explained.

Papa read aloud: "Mr. Herman Goldschmidt. No telephone number. A business man and no telephone number!" Papa sounded scornful. He had a right, I thought. Didn't he bring Alexander Graham Bell to Dunham's Hill?

"Well," he went on, "he wrote how to find his house, at least. By the way, I meant to tell you, but you put it out of my mind with your *hatamalchik*. I made a down payment on a second-hand binder today."

"A binder? What's a binder?"

"It's a machine that cuts grain. Oats, rye, wheat—only wheat is not so good here. This binder cuts the grain and binds it in bundles, ready for the threshers. It's another step into the twentieth century, like we made with the telephone."

"You are going to plant oats and rye?"

"Maybe some rye. We can grind our own flour at the mill in Kegtown. But that wouldn't be enough for a binder. There are three farms right around here that have idle land. I have arranged to plant and harvest them on shares. Then the thresher will come with his threshing machine, and we'll have our share of the grain to sell."

Mama and I stared at each other. She sighed, "At least you won't break your back hauling rocks for the roads." There was a pause. "So I guess we forget about the *hatamalchik.*"

"Why? One has nothing to do with the other. If you want, on Sunday we could hitch up Ol' Belle, and go and see this Mr. Goldschmidt who manufactures food that you wrap in corn husks but has no telephone!"

"Why not?" Mama replied happily. "Won't hurt to find out!"

There they were, neck and neck again: grain binders and hot tamales. Not adversaries, perhaps, but rivals, whether they knew it or not.

The Sunday excursion was a great success. The Goldschmidts greeted us warmly. Their house was the finest I had seen in our part of Clermont County. But I didn't see any books. They didn't have much land, Mr. Goldschmidt explained, because he wasn't cut out to be a farmer. He bought the place so they could live in the country and some day retire from business altogether. He had learned about tamales on a trip to California, and decided something new like that might catch on here. It was worth a try, and it looked good already.

Before we left, a handshake sealed the business arrangement. Mr.

Goldschmidt would buy all the clean corn husks we could supply, and he would provide the sacks. Papa would deliver the stuffed sacks to Mr. Goldschmidt's plant in Cincinnati, where they would be weighed. A price per pound was agreed upon. A *l'chaim* toast was drunk in wine to seal the bargain, and we started home. On the way Mama suggested we could store the filled sacks in one of the vacant bedrooms upstairs, since we would be cleaning the husks in the kitchen in the winter. And we wouldn't be needing the rooms for boarders anymore.

Papa's mind was on something else. "Mr. Goldschmidt said he wasn't cut out to be a farmer," he remarked wryly. "I guess one look at me showed him that's *all* I was cut out for."

"You shouldn't say that, Max," Mama exclaimed. "Whatever you tried to do you did fine! You could be anything you wanted to be!"

All I could think of was the winter evenings devoted to cleaning corn husks in the kitchen. No need for Dr. John to bring me books anymore; there'd be no time for reading. How could Mama have done this to me?

But done it was, and it became, after all, a pleasant activity. It was one of those tasks that allowed you to work and talk at the same time, and Mama would tell stories about her childhood with the peasants in the *shtetl*. She told about her grandfather, who believed that the peasants were his friends, and then they burned down the inn and the tavern, and it broke his heart. And Papa would tell about how things were when he studied at the "gymnasium," and when he was in the army, and that was almost like reading a book, too.

# 20

# *A Promise Broken, a Promise Kept*

When school reopened in September, 1910, the older girls were aglow with anticipation. The smaller children, myself included, were a little scared. The big boys plotted mischief. The occasion for all this emotional and mysterious behavior was the arrival on the Hill of our new teacher. Miss Velma had married young Dr. Leeds, her uncle John's assistant, and her replacement as the Dunham's Hill teacher was a man, the first male teacher any of us had ever known. He was unmarried, which was the reason for the older girls' excitement. The uneasiness of the younger ones was simply the fear of the unknown. As for the big boys, they were making plans to revive a tradition they had never practiced but about which they had heard, in great and embellished detail, from their fathers and grandfathers. The name of the game was "Lock the new teacher in the woodshed until he cries 'uncle' " and agrees to any reasonable demands, such as two recess periods every day, no tests for the first six months of school, and homework only one night a week.

The new teacher's name was Mr. Frank Franz, and we faced the dilemma of what to call him: Mr. Frank? Mr. Franz? Or just Teacher? We found out even before he came that he was not going to stay in any of our homes but instead would live with the Boettchers, an elderly couple with no children, whose home was within easy walking distance of the schoolhouse. Later, when we came to know him better, he told us that the reason he had chosen the

Boettchers' over one of our homes was that he didn't want to subject any of us to being teased as "teacher's pet."

Among the teacher's duties was to keep the wood box filled and in the winter to get the fire started in the potbellied stove in the center of the schoolroom.

On the first day of school that year, when we were to meet Mr. Franz, everyone had come early, well before he arrived to ring the schoolbell. Not only were we eager to see the new teacher but, even more, nobody wanted to miss the fun of seeing him locked in the woodshed and hearing him cry "uncle." Everyone hovered in the vicinity of the shed where this drama would soon take place. Ol' Earl Hoppe, one of the older boys, had gone into the woodshed to find the whittled wooden stick that served as a lock to keep stray animals out during the summer. He was still looking when we heard a deep, pleasant voice greeting us with "Good morning, boys and girls. My, you're all here bright and early!"

We all said, "Good morning, sir."

He wasn't very tall and he wasn't very handsome, but he had nice brown eyes and a deep dimple in his chin, and when he smiled I knew I was going to love him, and I felt terrible that any minute he was going to be locked up in the woodshed. Jed Brauer was beginning to look nervous. He had to get Ol' Earl out of the woodshed before he tricked Mr. Franz into it. He edged close to the door and spoke in a loud voice, "I was just goin' in to see if there's enough wood for the winter, Mr. Franz." I guess Ol' Earl heard him. We heard some wood falling; Ol' Earl must have tripped. I looked at Mr. Franz, but he looked as though he hadn't heard a thing.

"I don't think we have to worry about the winter wood just yet," he said. "But I think the woodshed should be kept locked. I just happen to have a padlock in my pocket and. . . . " He really did have a padlock, and he walked over to the door to lock it. From inside, Ol' Earl shouted, "Hey, don't lock me in!" Mr. Franz opened the door and said, "Sorry, young man. Do you have some unfinished business in there?"

"No, sir," stammered Ol' Earl. "I was just checkin' things out."

"Good. Then let's go. We'll raise the flag and start the day's business of getting an education."

And that is how we began our school life with Mr. Frank Franz. Nobody ever again thought about locking him in the woodshed. He was the best teacher any of us had ever had up to that time. We called him Mr. Franz, and all the girls had a crush on him, and the boys thought he was "swell." When we entertained a school from another district on Lincoln's birthday that year, he told me ahead of time to memorize the Gettysburg Address for the occasion. There was no question as to whether I could do it; he just seemed to take it for granted. The teacher of the visiting school was Miss Behymer. Mr. Franz was to break my heart the following year when he married her, but I made a miraculous recovery.

School was out at the end of April. It was 1911, and I was going to be in the seventh grade. On the Sunday after the last day of school, we had a surprise visit from Mr. Franz. He came to talk to Mama and Papa. Mama was embarrassed that he had caught her scrubbing the dining room floor. I was in the kitchen cleaning the smoked-up lamp chimneys. I heard Papa ask, "You have some complaint about our daughter?"

"Certainly not!" Mr. Franz answered. "But I would like her to be present to hear what I have to say."

Mama called me from the kitchen. I was barefoot, and I knew my face was smeared with lampblack. I tried to wipe it with my petticoat before I went into the dining room. Papa was leading Mr. Franz into the parlor. I wondered fearfully why he had come. I asked Mama to come with me. She told me to run along—she would come in a minute.

In the parlor, Papa was introducing Mr. Franz to Tante Braindele in the large colored photograph. When Mama joined us, Mr. Franz was ready to tell us the reason for his call. He had come, he said, to tell us about something called the "Boxwell examination." It was held every year at Batavia, the county seat, and it was open to children who had completed either the seventh or eighth grade. This was required for entrance into high school in New Richmond, the nearest secondary school.

"Your daughter," Mr. Franz concluded, "is perfectly capable of passing the examination at the end of the next school year. I know she is young, but she can do it, and I want her to do it. I wanted you to know what I had in mind, and I hope you will encourage her. She can enter New Richmond High School when she is twelve and be ready to enter college at sixteen." He rose to go. I was speechless. I was fighting tears. He came up to me, lifted my chin, and smiled down at me.

"I'll see you in September," he said. "Everything's going to be just fine."

He shook hands with Papa and Mama. They thanked him and followed him to show him out. Mama had placed *vishnik* and sponge cake on the dining room table. I heard her call me, and I joined them.

"Did you thank your good teacher, my child?" She had tears in her eyes and in her voice.

Mr. Franz said, "She herself is my thanks." He raised his glass of *vishnik* and, to the astonishment of us all, said, "*L'chaim.*" When he left, Papa said, "You can go finish your job now. And after that, you can read your books until suppertime." And then he added, "And if you do what your teacher said you could do, I'll buy you that Shetland pony you've always wanted."

"Oh, Papa!" I cried, running to him. He patted my head and said, "First things first. Go finish your job."

"Thank you, Papa! And if you get a little cart, I can drive myself to high school."

"High school is more than a year away and five miles from here. We'll talk about that later. The first thing you have to do is pass that examination."

I glanced fearfully at Mama. She smiled reassuringly and said. "Go on, child. Like Papa said, first things first."

I turned to go, dragging my feet. I was suddenly frightened. Papa sounded so strange about high school. I heard Mama, speaking softly, say: "Why do you worry the child? You know she must go to high school." I heard them moving toward the kitchen, and I got busy with the lamp chimneys. Later, when we were milking the cows, I asked Mama fearfully if she thought Papa might not let me go to high school.

"You will go to high school. I *promise* you. Papa is worried about how to get you there every day, and who will do the milking on Tuesdays when I go to the city. That doesn't mean he doesn't want you to go. And I *will* find a way. I give you my word!"

The Boxwell examination was given on a Saturday in March. The day before, as we were dismissed for the weekend, Mr. Franz handed me a note to give to Mama and Papa. It was in a sealed envelope, and all the kids were curious about it. I was the most curious of all, but I did not dare open it. I walked with Ginny and Katie as far as their shortcut road and then I ran.

The note told Papa and Mama that Mr. Franz and his friend and future wife, Miss Behymer, would like to drive me to Batavia the following morning. He thought it would give me confidence, and we could review some subjects on the way. They would come quite early, about seven o'clock in the morning, so we would reach Batavia in good time. And he added that we were not to bother to pack a lunch.

Papa's first comment was: "He's getting married?" Mama's comment was: "It's nice that the lady is coming, too. Yes, very nice." She drew me to her. "It's going to be good for you, my child. It will be a good year." She looked at Papa. "Won't it be a good year, Papa?"

"I hope so," he said. "I am not a prophet. First pass the examination. Right now that's all you have to worry about."

The day in Batavia was memorable, especially the lunch in a restaurant with Mr. Franz and Miss Behymer. I don't remember what I ate; I doubt if I even knew what I was eating at the time. But I remember their kindness and the laughter, and their refusal to talk about the morning's examination beyond letting me say that I thought I had done well. What did I want to do, they asked, when I grew up and got through high school and then college? College! I hadn't thought beyond high school, and that only in fear that I might not even get to go. I didn't tell them that, though, and besides, Mama had promised. But I had to answer the question. Of course, I told them, I had always wanted to be a teacher and still did, I hastened to add, not wishing to diminish my admiration for the profession. But now, since I had read so many books, I wanted to be—I wondered if I dared say it!—a writer, maybe a poet.

"Then be it!" Mr. Franz exclaimed.

"Frank thinks you can be anything you want to be," Miss Behymer added, smiling. I told them shyly about the two poems that the *Cincinnati Post* had published the summer before Mr. Franz had come to Dunham's Hill, and I promised to bring them to school.

As we drove home that evening, I was full of hope and happiness. The results of the examination would arrive within a month. Mr. Franz was so sure I had "made it" that I, too, became completely confident. When they brought me home, the sun was going down, and the evening chores were in full swing: the lowing of the cows waiting to be milked, the whinnying of the horses anxious to be fed, the contented clucking of the chickens eating their evening meal, the ducks and geese vying for their share, and the setting sun touching all with its grace and promise of a bright day tomorrow. The day had been so beautiful, and it was all so lovely now, that I could not bear to see it end. Then I saw the buggy drive away and felt a great sadness that these two people would soon go out of my life as other fine things had done: the swan boats in the Public Gardens in Boston. The two dear teachers in Cincinnati who had opened their home to us, and had shown us such affection and kindness. Jennie Goldenstern, who had brought me to the Settlement House and let me wear her dearest possession, her hat with the flowers and ribbons. And Norma—Norma, on whom I had inflicted pain; Norma, whose pain was mine thrice over, touched as it was with guilt; Norma, whom I have never forgotten, as I have never forgotten the pain itself.

Each day, walking home from school, I looked with mingled hope and fear as the mailboxes came into view. Often the red flag on our box was raised, and I would slacken my pace to pretend I was unconcerned about what might be waiting in the box. Finally, on a Saturday, when I went as usual to pick up the mail, I stopped the pretense and, seeing the red flag from a distance, ran the rest of the way—and then all the way home. I had passed the Boxwell examination!

Mama hugged me and cried. Papa said, "What are you so excited about? Did you ever doubt that she would pass?" And then he smiled at me, his very best smile. We were still talking when Dr. John drove into the barnyard. He had picked up a copy of Hawthorne's *Tales From Grandfather's Chair* for me, and now he heard my news. He beamed and, like Papa, he said he wasn't surprised, of course—any more than he was surprised when the *Cincinnati*

*Post* published my poems. And he promised to stop by the Boettchers' and leave word for Mr. Franz.

After Dr. John left, there was a question I wanted desperately
to ask, but I waited until after supper, hoping that Papa would
bring it up himself. Instead he opened the new *Jewish Forward*,
which had also come that day.

"Now, what shall we read first?" he asked.

"Papa, please, I have a question," I ventured.

"Good," said Papa. "Questions are good. What is your question?"

"It's about your promise."

"What promise?"

"About the Shetland pony."

He burst out laughing. "You are a big girl ready for high school!
What would you do with a Shetland pony? That's for little kids,
not for a girl like you who rides Ol' Belle at a gallop, and can drive
a team of horses, too! People would laugh at you."

"But why did you promise?"

"To make you try harder to pass the examination, of course."

"You didn't have to do that! I would have passed it anyway.
Because Mr. Franz wanted me to!"

"So what Mr. Franz wants is more important than what I want."

"No, Papa, no! It's just that he said I *could*, and he made me
*believe* I could. He didn't promise me anything!"

"*Ketsele*, Papa is right—and you are right. He shouldn't have
promised, but he meant well," said Mama.

"You made a promise, too, Mama." I said.

"And I will keep it. Mendel, read first, please, the 'Bintel Briev.'
And I'll go make tea."

I lay awake that night for a long time. The lovely day was tar-
nished. I could hear Mama and Papa speaking in low voices. I
listened; I knew it was about me, and I had to know what it was.

Mama was saying, "I will find a way. I will keep the promise. She will go to high school."

"You will drive every morning five miles, and five miles in the evening to bring her back?"

No answer from Mama. He went on: "There's no other child going from here. A year in the eighth grade wouldn't hurt."

No answer from Mama.

Papa: "Who will milk the cows on Tuesday, when you go to the city?"

"Josiah will milk the cows on Tuesdays when I go to the city. If you can afford him to help in the fields, you can afford him to milk the cows so your daughter can have an education."

"You haven't told me yet how she is going to get to New Richmond and back, five days a week."

"I'll find a way. I'll keep *my* promise."

The summer dragged on endlessly. Ginny graduated from the eighth grade that year along with me. Our good friend, Mr. Charlie Green, made me a pretty, simple white dress of crepe de chine. "Snow-Bound" was the poem I chose for my graduation exercise, because it recalled that mystic night of white beauty, when I saw the moonlit snowfall transform the barnyard into a new and never-forgotten place of beauty. Mr. Franz and Miss Behymer gave me a copy of Longfellow's "The Song of Hiawatha." They were married that summer and went away to live in Seattle where he was to teach in a big school like the one I had attended in Cincinnati, with a separate room for every grade. Late in the summer, I received a postcard from him in which he wrote: "Soon you will be in high school and that will be a new and exciting experience. Remember, you can be anything you want to be." But there was no return address.

Rosie and Gertrude, the "colored" girls, had dropped out of our school, in the middle of the term, when their father died. They had not owned the farm on which they lived; so they left with their mother to live in Cincinnati. Mama told me at the time to find out about the funeral so we could go, but there was no funeral on Dunham's Hill; they took their father's body to Cincinnati. It all seemed very sad, and Mama gave me some of her best jam to take to them. Ginny was fifteen and was "keeping company" seriously with the nephew of Mr. Perkins of the general store. She would be officially engaged at sixteen, and was not interested in going to high school. So much was changing, changing, changing. I was uncertain of what my fate would be.

I picked berries for Mr. Lumley, with the other children and women, as though that summer was like any other. But it was not the same at all. When Papa said I could keep all the money I earned to buy a new dress, if I went to high school, my heart pounded so hard that I could hardly breathe. It was the "if" that did it. I guess I looked the way I felt, because he added, "Don't look so scared. Your mama said she would find a way, didn't she?" I developed fears that I had never known before. On Tuesdays, when Mama was in the city and Papa was in the fields, and I had to go into an empty house, I carried a piece of wood as a weapon and made my way, shaking with fear, first to the attic, then to the upstairs bedrooms, closing the door of each room as it proved to be unoccupied by dragons, and so on all the way, room after room, until I found myself at last in the kitchen, to heat up the midday dinner for Papa.

One Tuesday I had to take a family of goslings out to feast in the meadow of red clover. On the other side of the barbed-wire fence was a field of young corn, tiny, succulent little plants that showed promise of making a fine crop. I was so lost in despair that I lay in the sweet-scented meadow, face pressed against the soft red blossoms and the clover leaves, and wept. When I suddenly remembered why I was there, I jumped to my feet and ran to find the goslings. They had left the meadow and devastated a whole row of corn. I crawled under the fence, herding them back into the meadow, and my tears started again, this time at the prospect of Papa's wrath when he discovered what had happened. When he came in for dinner I knew I had to tell him, and I knew, too, that no story I might make up would save me. He would see through my fib, and it would only make matters worse. To my amazement, after he heard my *mea culpa*, he just sat staring at me for a moment or two, and then he sighed and said, "So! Can I have my dinner now?" I couldn't believe he had said it. I stared, open-mouthed.

"Go on, now. I'm hungry," he said. As I started to put food on the kitchen table he said, "Maybe Mama will bring good news when she comes home today."

But there was no good news that day, nor the following Tuesday. Finally, a week before Labor Day—the day before school would start—Mama announced, "I have found a way. But you will start just a little late."

Supper was quickly assembled and on the table; there was cold *schav* (a soup of sorrel and sour cream), blintzes made up the day before, now fried to a golden crispness and topped with sour cream, canned tomatoes brought from the cellar, and late apples, which I had been instructed to bake in the afternoon. Papa glanced over the latest *Forward* as he ate. Finally Mama spoke: "You will listen now, please—you, Mendel, and you, my child." She often reverted to Papa's Jewish name when she had something momentous to say.

Through one of her customers, she had learned that a young Jewish couple lived in New Richmond and might be willing to provide lodging, and maybe board, for a schoolgirl. That week the young wife, whose name was Sarah Lutzky, was in Cincinnati visiting her sister, and Mama's customer arranged for her and Mama to meet. Mr. Lutzky was a shoemaker. He had a shop on the main

street, which was called Front Street because it looked out on the
Ohio River. They had their living quarters behind the store and
were putting up a partition in the one large bedroom to make two
rooms, and I could have one as soon as it was ready. Mama would
trade a dozen eggs, a pound of butter, and a pound of cheese every
week for my room. I would get my own meals, mostly prepared
by Mama and placed in the Lutzkys' icebox. I could use any of the
rest of the space behind the store to do my homework. Papa would
drive me over early Monday mornings and come for me on Friday
afternoons, about three or four o'clock. I would bring my own
pillow, sheets, blankets, and towels, and take everything home on
Fridays to be laundered. All I could think of in response was, in
a rather choked voice, "When?"

"They won't be ready until about the end of September. They
have to put up the partition."

"I'll never catch up!" I cried.

"You will catch up," Papa said, very quietly, for him. "If Mr.
Franz was here he would say, 'You will catch up,' and you would
believe him. So now I say it for him: You will catch up."

"Yes, Papa," I whispered, close to tears. "I will catch up."


"Uncle Charlie" had promised to make me a very special dress
and coat to wear when I was ready to start high school. But unfortunately he had to be rushed to the hospital with a ruptured
appendix, and he was a long time recovering enough to work again.

True to his word, Papa turned over to me the money I had
earned picking berries, but it didn't go very far toward outfitting
me for my entry into the world of higher learning. For the last
time, Mama resorted to barter with her customer who carried "like-
new garments worn briefly and outgrown by children of rich parents." The result was startling: I made my first appearance in New
Richmond High School on Friday, October 4, 1912, in a red sailor

suit, a short black-and-white–checked coat, and a rather absurd red-and-black velvet hat.

The schoolhouse was a drab, three-story building that housed both the high school and the elementary grades. I went directly to the office of Mr. Turnipseed, the superintendent. He was a very large man with a large paunch. He wore a black suit, shoes with elastic sides, and steel-rimmed glasses. I carried my grade school diploma, still tied with a blue ribbon, and my hand trembled as I held it out to him. He took it from me, glancing over the rims of his glasses at me rather than at the document that attested to my completion of the seventh grade. He finally turned his attention to the precious scroll, and I offered him the certificate of satisfactory grades in the Boxwell examination. When he finished his scrutiny of this as well, he turned his attention back to me.

"You're such a little girl," he said.

"Yes, sir. It's just that I'm small for my age. My mama says she was slow growing up, too," I assured him earnestly. Mr. Turnipseed said something like "harrumph," but he almost smiled. He asked me why I didn't start at the beginning of the school year. I tried to explain, but I got rather hopelessly bogged down in the attempt. I promised I would catch up. He said "harrumph" again and asked me if I knew what books I needed. I named them: First-year Latin, algebra, ancient history, English. Mr. Turnipseed told me where to go get them second-hand and save money. And then he stood up and came around to shake hands with me, and now he really smiled.

I walked back to the Lutzkys' on a cloud. I was finally, actually going to high school. Papa had brought me on Friday so I could get settled in my new home-away-from-home before taking on my new career. Then he waited for me until I returned from school. My provisions were already in Mrs. Lutzky's icebox, my bed made up. Mrs. Lutzky put her arms around me, and told me that that first evening I would be their guest for supper. She was a short, plump, pretty woman, a lady who was "in charge." Mr. Lutzky came from the shop and shook hands with me. He was tall and heavy-set, jovial and easygoing. I could see it in the way he responded to his wife's more authoritative manner. He assured Papa they would take good care of me, not to worry. Then Papa kissed me on the forehead and left. I was excited, frightened, already a little homesick, and deliriously happy at the same time. I asked Mrs. Lutzky if I could go out and walk around a little and see the Ohio River, and maybe look at the schoolhouse again. She said of course I could go, but not to get lost.

I walked across the street and found an open space between two buildings where the bank sloped down to the river. The Ohio was before me—mighty, tranquil, awesome. The sun was moving toward the horizon, flinging a broad, jeweled ribbon from Ohio to the Kentucky shore. I felt a little as I had when we were almost snowbound. I would see the river when the surface was so solidly frozen that a team of horses could walk safely across to the opposite shore. And I would know it when it was a rampaging beast rising to devour the town. But at that moment, in the late afternoon of Friday, October 4, 1912, the river was my friend. I was no longer frightened nor homesick. I was there. I was going to high school. I could be anything I wanted to be.

# 21

# *"Veni, Vidi, Vici"*

Like Caesar, I came, I saw, I conquered, if not all Gaul, at least my first-year Latin textbook. Thanks to Miss Florence Allen, who taught the subject, I caught up with the class in Latin before I did with algebra. Miss Allen stayed after school with me four days out of the school week (Fridays were skipped because I couldn't keep Papa waiting). She was a warm and reassuring lady who instilled in me the same kind of confidence that Mr. Franz had given me.

"What do you think, my dear? Have you caught up?"

"Yes, Miss Allen. Thank you. I think so."

"*I know* you have! I want *you* to know!"

"Veni, vidi, vici," I declared. We both laughed and shook hands, and she patted my cheek.

Algebra was harder, but I had help there, too. A handsome, blond freshman, who blushed when he made the offer, just as I blushed when I accepted, helped me with that formidable subject during recess periods. English and History held no terrors for me, and within a month I could say "vici" to everything.

To fit in socially was not so easily done. I was smaller, younger, more shy than anyone. From a fashion magazine that Mama had picked up on the "black car" I had learned a new word that I felt, unhappily, described me. The word was "gauche." Worst of all, perhaps, was not being able to invite other girls to come home with me as I was sometimes invited to their homes. Not that the

Lutzkys would have objected, but I was afraid that the girls of the town would scorn the way I lived, and I would end up being condemned to live farther outside the charmed circle than I already felt.

I had lived in Boston and in Cincinnati, but those cities had not intimidated me as did this little river town with its population of about 1,700. The girls in the high school who lived in town, as well as those from surrounding farms, seemed sophisticated beyond anyone I had known. If course, I had been very young when I had lived in those large cities. They had not challenged me. My world had been a tiny corner of those cities; my world here was the whole town and everyone and everything in it.

Still, I was where I wanted to be, doing what I wanted to do. I was not without friends. And the world, I felt certain, was spread before me to probe, to taste, to encompass, to conquer. All I had to do was find the right books, and all the world's beauty, secrets, pain, and joy would be revealed to me. If I could only find a way to "belong."

My classmates spoke a language within a language, which was as foreign to me as Latin. They were, in a word, at home in the use of slang. I studied the current slang as diligently as I studied my Latin declensions—studied but never used until, one day as we were dismissed and running down the stairway, someone made a teasing remark to me in slang. I do not remember what it was, but I suddenly heard myself replying, loud and clear, "Ne' mind the side-glances, ne' mind!" I don't know whether it was an appropriate rejoinder, but it was current, and it created a sensation. Goldie, the proper, correct little kid from Dunham's Hill, had arrived!

Mr. Utterback replaced Mr. Turnipseed as our superintendent in my sophomore year. He looked not unlike his predecessor in bulk and general appearance; he also wore black suits, but his were alpaca and the truly distinctive feature of his usual attire was, instead of a shirt, a stiff white dickey with a wing collar attached, and stiff white cuffs completely unattached to anything. During Geometry he would assign theorems to several students at a time, watch as we lined up at the blackboard, then sit down, begin to doze, and often end up asleep with his head resting on his arms on the desk. At such times his coat would fall into some disarray, and that is how we discovered his free-floating cuffs and shirtfront.

A weekly class in Current Events was added to the curriculum, and Miss King, an attractive, cool blonde—always smartly dressed, but lacking in the warmth and generosity of spirit of Miss Allen— had charge of that period. Momentous events were happening in the world: rumors of wars and Armageddon; famine around the world; and the winning of the State Association of Garden Clubs' prize for the best arrangement of irises by a lady from Cincinnati. Perhaps Miss King was being ironic, offering a contrasting picture of the events that jostled for our attention in the public press. It did not seem so to me at the time; to my mind, she seemed really to think one as important as the other.

In any case, for me all this paled before my personal event of the year. Uncle Charlie Green had fully recovered form his serious illness, and had made for me a beautiful coat of imitation black astrakhan, with a little collar of white rabbit fur and a lining of lavender sateen. I walked tall; I felt no longer gauche—or, if a little gauche, still, at least, a gaucherie garbed in resplendence.

But I was still deficient in the more arcane elements of the English language. A junior stopped me in the hall one day. "Do you have a pony yet?" she asked. I wondered how she knew about me and ponies. Quite innocently, I told her that I had outgrown ponies but I had a saddle horse. "Ha-ha!" she laughed. "Cute! You know what I mean! A Latin pony for Caesar! I've got one for sale, cheap."

She saw the bewildered look on my face and realized I wasn't
being clever.

"Never mind! Never mind! Just wise up, kiddo!"

I wised up, but I never used a pony. I didn't dare!

Through the four years of our "higher education" a nucleus of
the student body remained to graduate. One of those was Blanche
Dixon, a pretty, very bright black girl. Blanche was a girl of great
pride. She made no effort at close friendships and held aloof even
if they were offered, because she assumed, I suppose, that such
advances were condescending. She was determined to continue her
education after high school and to become a doctor. She was
capable of doing it and, I am sure, would have done it, but a tragic
automobile accident, some years later, ended her dreams and her
life.

Fifteen of us went the course and graduated. Several others,
transferred from different districts, transferred again or dropped
out altogether. One dropout was Horace Lumley, who had come
in as a freshman when I was a sophomore, giving me a chance to
play big sister. Another was a girl named Lillie, who stayed only
through junior year. She was a tall, blonde girl who lived on a
farm a stop or two away from ours. Once Lillie invited me to come
home with her for the weekend. I telephoned home and, much to
my surprise, got permission to go for Friday and Saturday nights,
but was told to come home Sunday on the "black car." Papa even
said he had to go into New Richmond anyway, so he would pick
up my laundry as usual.

Lillie and I took the interurban to her stop, and were met by
her older sister with a horse and buggy. We were also met by a
band of boys in their early teens—one of whom, I later learned,
was Lillie's young brother. As soon as I appeared they shouted,
"Hi, Miss Shew! Pleased to meetcha, Miss Shew! Howdyadew,

howdyadew, howdyadew, Miss Shew!" Lillie laughed and led the way to the buggy, where her sister was waiting.

"What are they saying?" I asked. "It sounded like they were saying it to me, yelling 'Miss Shew'!"

"Don't you know?" Lillie giggled.

"No, how should I know? Who is Miss Shew?"

"Think about it! It'll come to you. But don't let it bother you. They're just a bunch of silly billies. Think they're smart."

I did think about it, and I did let it bother me, and it did come to me. "Shew" meant "Jew," and Lillie had thought it was funny! She had told her parents, I decided, that she wanted to invite a Jewish girl for the weekend; she must have done that.

Her family was nice enough. Her sister left after supper (she was keeping steady company) and the kid brother at the supper table did not speak to me a single time, but cast an occasional sly glance in my direction. It was my first experience of the kind. I was miserable and tried not to show it. I would like to have returned home the following morning instead of waiting for Sunday. I felt shame, fear, anger, and I didn't know how to handle any of it.

Lillie walked me to the interurban station Sunday morning, and I scarcely spoke the whole time. I heard the train pulling in; I breathed a sigh of relief, thanked Lillie and hurried to get on board. From out of nowhere some of the same kids appeared, shouting, "Goodbye, Miss Shew! Come back soon, Miss Shew!" I heard Lillie shouting at her brother that she would tell their Pop, and he'd beat the hide off him. I managed not to cry on the train, but on the mile-long walk from Ten-Mile Stop to our house I let the tears come. One resolution I made as I hurried along: I was not going back to Sunday school anymore. It was, however, a resolution not strictly kept.

Once during the summer Lillie telephoned and invited me to

come to the Fourth of July ice cream social and fireworks display that their church was having. I tried to make excuses, but she sensed the reason for my reluctance and said she hoped it wasn't because of those dumb kids from the last visit, and not to worry, they would be too busy about the fireworks to bother me, and besides it didn't mean anything anyway. I finally agreed to come but said I'd have to ask my parents. I hoped they would say "no," but they disappointed me. I was to take the early evening train on Friday, and return on Sunday afternoon.

I set out Friday in a less than festive mood. I carried my good slippers, wearing my already scuffed everyday shoes to walk to Ten-Mile Stop. Pond Run Road, which led to the stop, was lined on either side with lush sycamores, oaks, and even some evergreens, but I was not aware that afternoon of its loveliness. As I drew near the tracks the sun was already sinking behind the hills, and dusk was falling. I heard the interurban train approaching and then stopping to take on or discharge passengers. The end of the line was New Richmond, where the train turned for the return trip, so I had plenty of time to cover the remaining distance to the tracks.

I walked slowly, and suddenly saw two familiar figures approaching: Moishele Platt and Landa were making a surprise visit. They were even more surprised to see me. I longed to go back with them to the farm; I offered to do so. But Moishele would not hear of it when he found out I was on my way to a party. Of course I must go, he said, and be with young people. I was too embarrassed to assure him that I welcomed an excuse to turn back. I promised to see them on Sunday, and we went our separate ways. I was steps away from Ten-Mile Stop. I stood waiting for the train to stop for me. I heard it drawing closer—then I heard something else. The train was saying, "Miss Shew, Miss Shew, Miss Shew, Shew, Shew, Shew, Shew!" I turned and ran. When I came abreast of the big house on the hill where my friend, Mrs. Jessie Moonlight Haus-sermann, lived, I stopped, confused and uncertain about what to do next. If I hurried I could catch up with Moishele and Landa. I might persuade *them* that I had missed the train, but I would never fool Papa, and the whole story would come out. I could not face that.

I climbed the path to the house. No lights were visible from the front. I went around to the back, and saw the lighted windows of the caretakers' cottage. Mr. and Mrs. Jedediah Bundy had been with the Haussermanns for many years. They knew me; they, too, were my friends. I knocked on the door. I told them I had missed the train, and that it was too dark to go home. I joined them at supper, but I could not eat. I looked up at Mrs. Bundy's gentle face, and told her I had fibbed. The whole story came out. Mrs. Bundy put her arms around me and told me I must not grieve because some fool boys had acted stupidly; they were not worth a moment's thought, let alone tears. She made me sit down again and eat my supper. Then she called Lillie's house and told them I had missed the train and wouldn't be able to come. As she talked she turned her head, winked at me, and held up crossed fingers. Then she made up a bed for me to spend the night. She tucked me in and sat on the side of my bed and talked to me.

"Child," she said, holding my hand, "you are young, and you took this business very hard. I know it has been painful for you. But I'm going to tell you something. As you grow older you'll find there's a lot of pain around, enough for every livin' creature to have a share. For your people, Jewish people, maybe a bigger share than most, except for colored folks. You'll just have to hold your head high and do the best you can, and do all you can to put an end to the hate that poisons so many hearts. Comfort others, and you will be comforted."

She rose, still holding my hand.

"Did you know, child, that Jesus was a Jew?" She nodded as she saw the disbelief in my face. Then she kissed me on the forehead and went out. I knew that when I came home I would tell the whole wretched truth, just as I had told it to Mr. and Mrs. Bundy. I fell asleep.

# 22

# *Ordeal by Flood*

There was no nonsense about winter my freshman year, no dal-
lying with the wanton colors of Indian summer, no battle in the
skies between sun and clouds. In November of that year snow
began to fall, heavily, almost without intermission. The hills of
Kentucky were first capped, then cloaked, in dazzling whiteness.
As for our shabby Front Street, it was like a reenactment of the
well-remembered transformation of our barnyard that winter night.
The river was tranquil and lovely, unruffled under the gentle bom-
bardment of the falling snow.

By December the snow had diminished, and the merchants were
able to keep their sidewalks clear for whole days at a time. Finally
no snow fell at all; instead the weather became intensely cold. The
river froze. Sledders crowded the open space from which I had
first gazed at the Ohio. The snow was packed hard on the sloped
river bank, and the sleds almost soared onto the firm ice, accompanied by shouts of triumph and shrieks of delight and fear.

By the end of 1912, ushering in the new year, the rains came,
not only in New Richmond, but in Pittsburgh, and along the
Indiana River. The snow melted, and river ice began to break up,
as the intense cold gave way to an incursion of warm air.

Early in March, rains on the upper Ohio increased. The very
color and voice of the river grew threatening, and during the second
week fear of high water dominated all thoughts and conversations.

Miss King's Current Events class was almost totally confined to weather reports and speculation as to the imminence of a flood. Three shifts of men kept an around-the-clock vigil, as the Beautiful Ohio no longer left any doubt about her intentions. The only questions were—when would she overflow, and where would she crest?

On the early morning of March 13, it was determined that there would be no safe cresting of the Ohio. The Front Street merchants began to take what measures they could to protect their stocks. Those who had second stories started to move goods and supplies to the upper levels. Others rented space. It was a school day, and classes were in session as usual—hardly quite as usual, really. Everyone went through the motions, but excitement and apprehension hung over the classrooms like final examinations for which you are not prepared. Many of us had never witnessed a flood, especially those who had been inland dwellers. But the others had grown up with accounts of high water that reached even the second stories in the lower parts of the town, sending occupants fleeing to the hills. As for me, it was to be an entirely new experience.

We had been briefed on our behavior: "Stay in your seats, or at the blackboard; attend to your teachers as you would on any other school day. But if the church bells begin to toll, gather up your books and your coats, and leave for your homes in orderly fashion."

I was at the blackboard to demonstrate that the sum of the angles of any triangle was equal to 180°. Suddenly the bells began to toll. I did not reach the goal of Q.E.D. We followed instructions; we left the room in orderly fashion. In the hall other doors opened, and other students spilled from their rooms. Nobody spoke. The familiar march of dismissal was pealing from the organ on the first floor. We descended the stairs as though it were any day at closing time. Once in the street we ran.

Along the streets people hurried—some aimlessly, with pale faces

and frightened eyes, sometimes stopping as if unsure of where they were going, others, grim of countenance but steady of step, walking purposefully. As one, we took off for Front Street. From the direction of the woolen mills a lanky boy came running. He tripped over a crack in the sidewalk and fell, and rose without missing a beat of his message. "Backwater's into the mill basement!" he shouted. We scattered for our homes.

I found Mr. and Mrs. Lutzky frantically pulling boxes and tools from shelves to counters, then moving them from the counters to the floor. It was their first flood, as it was mine. But where, for me, it promised adventure, to them it threatened disaster. There was a vacant two-room apartment above the store. They had hoped one day to afford it; now they had no choice. In anticipation of the imminent ordeal they rented it from the owners, who lived in a two-story building next door. I set about helping them, carrying piles of thread and wax and shoe leather to the room upstairs, humming all the while a tune, then popular, that will always be associated in my mind with high water. It was a silly tune about a young man who urged his sweetheart not to be afraid, that when he got her alone they would sit by the window and pull down the shade, etcetera.

Front Street was crowded with small boys and their express wagons, racing to the grocery stores for supplies—flour, rice, coffee, beans, canned milk, crackers, bacon. From the upstairs window, I saw a young man dash by with a pair of oars and run headlong into a boy with a box of eggs. They bumped, fell, rose, glared, salvaged what they could of the wreckage, all without a word, and dashed on. The church bells tolled again. It meant that the river was still rising. Up and down the stairs we toiled, dragging bedding, food, clothing—and cockroach powder, against the certain invasion of those pests, like ourselves struggling for survival. Occasionally the long, tense silences were broken by half-whispered remarks. "They say this was the kind of spring they had the year it reached seventy—maybe more." "That would mean—the hills! Not many houses in town tall enough to keep that out!" And all the time, under my breath, I hummed the foolish tune.

By dusk we had moved everything possible to the cramped quarters upstairs. At regular intervals the church bells tolled their terrifying, exciting, somehow exhilarating warning. When we had done all we could, we set out to see the progress of the water. The back streets, lower than Front, had already received a sample of the yellowish, rubbish-infested belchings of the mighty Ohio. We turned and retraced our steps. We walked close to the walls of the buildings when we returned to Front Street. It was even more crowded than when we had left the schoolhouse. People were no longer rushing along in silence; instead they were shouting reports to one another, exchanging questions, giving advice—all without stopping for a moment. We were almost back at the Lutzkys' store, when I saw a familiar horse and a two-wheeled rig. The horse was Ol' Belle, and inside the store was Papa.

Word had spread to Dunham's Hill, and he had come to take

me home. I didn't want to go. I told him it was my duty to stay and help the Lutzkys. He wasn't listening; he just told me to get my things together and stop talking like an idiot. Already, he said, he had had to take roundabout ways to get to Front Street; it could be worse going home. The Lutzkys told me Papa was right; besides, they would feel responsible for me, and they'd have enough to worry about without that.

The *Cincinnati Post* became our liaison with the river's rampaging throughout the flood plains: the Indiana, too, had risen. In New Richmond, the more venturesome people were lowering small boats from windows and roofs to row down the streets. Many had, indeed, taken to the hills. I feared for the safety of my classmates, of the Lutzkys, of our school. The *Post* told of small houses torn from their foundations, floating down the streets, and uprooted trees smashing through walls.

When I saw New Richmond again, it was a pathetic, tragic, and—strangely enough—even comical sight. A tobacco barn from Kentucky was planted in front of the drug store, and an outhouse from the poorest section of the town leaned tipsily against the front door of the home of the owner of the woolen mills. Everywhere was dirt, destruction, debris. The river had crested at seventy-two feet before it began to recede. Our schoolhouse was uninhabitable.

But the people were not defeated. Patiently, doggedly, tirelessly they set to work, as they had done time after time before, to restore the life of the town. Our classes resumed in parts of the municipal building and in other makeshift quarters. The Lutzkys were as valiant as any of their neighbors.

The following year we had a handsome new school building, almost a small replica of Cincinnati's Hughes High School, which I thought very beautiful.

Our school library had been swept away by the flood; the students in turn flooded the county, the cities, the state, with letters asking for contributions of books. Some of us even ventured out of the state. I was very proud of an autographed copy of President Woodrow Wilson's *Life of Washington*, which his secretary sent me, but which I never found time to read though I pointed it out with pride to every visitor. We had achieved a place in history. In the World Almanac, under "Disasters, Floods," there is this entry: "1913, March 25–27, Ohio, Indiana Deaths 732." We are not listed by name, but we were part of that great flood. None of the deaths occurred in New Richmond.

# 23

# *A Son Is Born*

Bubbie came that autumn to stay with us. We had expected her, and Mama had prepared the downstairs spare bedroom next to mine for her use. What we had not expected was that Uncle Max, Tante Sadie, and their two children, Goldie and Michael, aged about five and three, would decide to move from Boston to Cincinnati. Tante Sadie, we learned, was pregnant again and she craved, not some exotic food, but to be near her sister when "her time" came. For Mama it was a joyous reunion.

In November they joined us on the farm. I was moved to one of the two upstairs bedrooms. Bubbie got my room, and her room, which was the larger, was prepared for Uncle Max and Tante Sadie. The two children shared my room. Beds were no problem; we still had all the furniture which we had bought for the summer boarders. Dr. John was notified of the coming event, in which he would be next to the most important participant. He came to examine Tante Sadie and said everything looked fine.

On December 3, 1913, a second son was born to Uncle Max and Tante Sadie. He was delivered by Dr. John Mott without the slightest complication, in our house on Dunham's Hill. He was named Hyman, and everyone rejoiced and prepared for the *Bris Milah*, the ritual of the circumcision. Uncle Max went to the city to arrange, with the aid of the Mishkins, for a *mohel* to come to the farm on the eighth day. The Mishkins, the Greens, Moishele,

215

and Landa came for the auspicious occasion. So did Mr. and Mrs. Goldschmidt, Mr. and Mrs. Kullman (Mr. Kullman was Mama's friend from the "black car"), and another Jewish family from Six-Mile Stop, the Abraham Goodmans—who, like the Kullmans, were not "real" farmers yet in the way we were.

On the eighth day after Hyman's birth, Papa and Uncle Max met the Reverend Silver, and accredited *mohel*, at the interurban train stop. The first step had been taken toward preparing the little blond, blue-eyed baby for the ritual of the Covenant "between God and Abraham and all his seed."

Mama, with my help and Bubbie's, was in the meantime preparing a table loaded with sweets and beverages for the celebration in the dining room. In the parlor a small table had been covered with a freshly laundered cloth, on which the Reverend Silver would lay out his instruments.

Uncle Max and Tante Sadie had honored Papa with the role of *sandek* and named Mama as *kwater*. Mama's privilege was to take the baby from his mother, place him on a small pillow, bring him to Papa, who was seated next to the Reverend Silver's table, and place her precious burden gently on Papa's knees. Papa held the child tenderly and looked down at him, but not before I saw his eyes fill with tears. I think he must have felt what it would have been like to hold his own son in his arms. As for me, I fled to Tante Sadie's bedroom to escape the surgical part of the ceremony. I heard one wail from the baby, then happy cries of "Mazel Tov! Mazel Tov!" from the gallery, and Hyman was a certified son of the Covenant.

Tante Sadie, the children, and Bubbie stayed with us while Uncle Max went to Cincinnati to look for work. He was a master mason by trade and had transferred his union membership to Cincinnati. He found employment in construction in a short time, and rented a house on Price Hill, a suburb popular with middle-class Jews at the time. When the family left us, Bubbie went with them to help Tante Sadie with the baby and the house until she was strong enough again to do everything herself. Bubbie's old room was again set aside to be ready for her whenever she wanted to return. I continued to occupy the upstairs room next to the one where the sacks of corn husks were stored. I enjoyed the isolation from the rest of the house. Its privacy made me feel grown up, more my own person, and besides, since I was home only for weekends, it was hardly worth the task of moving my personal things downstairs again.

As it turned out, what had been my little room downstairs was soon to be needed for another very special guest. We had received word that Papa's brother, Herschel, was coming to America. Unlike Papa, his education had been religious and vocational. He was both a student of Talmud and an expert watchmaker. In America his study of the Talmud gave way to the first priority on his agenda: to work and earn enough money to bring his wife and five children to America. He was the luckiest of immigrants. A job was waiting for him when he arrived in Cincinnati! This miracle happened because a prosperous jeweler named Levy knew the value of European-trained watchmakers. An endangered species today, they had been taught how to make the parts needed for repairs; it was never necessary to order them from a manufacturer. Mr. Levy had written about this to a friend in Rowne, and the result was a job for Uncle Herschel (who lost no time, when he arrived, in becoming "Harry")—a ready-made job for the "greenhorn," and only a few hours away from his brother!

So Herschel came to America, and stayed with us on Dunham's Hill. Soon after his arrival, he was able to write home that he was already earning "eighteen half-rubles a week." It sounded, he thought, more impressive than "nine rubles a week." He was also allowed to try his hand at salesmanship with Yiddish-speaking customers. He saved money, but he did not hoard it. After several years he made a down payment on a large if somewhat decrepit house on Price Hill. His wife, Tante Gittel, waiting in Russia for the precious *shiff's-carten*, began to despair of ever receiving them, and probably did not believe his news about buying a fine house to bring them to.

How she managed it I never learned, but she finally refused to wait any longer and set sail, with her five children, for America. By that time Papa, Mama, and I had already left Ohio. But we received word that they *had* arrived, that Uncle Harry had risen to the occasion. She wrote to us that the house *was* finer than anything they had had in the old country. We kept in touch by mail and exchanged pictures, but we never learned by what leg-erdemain, miracle or luck, or combination of all three, they made their way to America without help from Uncle Harry. If he knew, he never told us.

# 24

## *Trial by Fire*

It was a Saturday in January, 1914, early evening, the first weekend in a long time without friends or family sharing our house.
The following day, Papa was to take a new load of sacked corn
husks to Mr. Goldschmidt's plant on Eastern Avenue in Cincinnati.
He planned to leave no later than five o'clock on Sunday morning,
so we would load the spring wagon now and have everything ready
for an early start. Before supper Papa had brought the wagon close
to the house, unhitched the team, and let them get some exercise
in the barnyard while we ate supper.

Now he took them back to their stalls, gave them an extra portion
of hay, and filled their nose bags with grain for the next day's
journey. On Monday Josiah would come early so Mama could drive
me to New Richmond and school. While Papa was in the barn,
Mama and I prepared to get the sacks of corn husks down from
the upstairs bedroom where they were stored. Those rooms were
already growing dark, so I started to light a kerosene lamp to take
with us. Mama said that would be dangerous; it might be acci-
dentally knocked over. "Better take a lantern," she said.

We hung the lantern on a hook near the head of the stairs,
propped the door open, and went to work. Mama tossed sack after
sack down the stairs. I picked them up and threw them through
the parlor door and out into the side yard. Papa had joined us
now, and I helped him pile the sacks into a wheelbarrow, then

throw them into the wagon. Papa climbed into the wagon to ar-range the sacks properly, and I took the wheelbarrow back for another load. I never made it. I had just lifted a sack when an air-shattering scream seemed to knock it from my hands. I screamed "Mama!" and ran back to the parlor, followed by Papa.

Mama was lying at the foot of the stairs, still screaming. The lantern, its glass chimney broken, its kerosene ablaze, was lying no more than a foot or two away from her. Papa and I lifted her to her feet and almost dragged her outside. By the time we had her safely in the yard and steadied on her feet, the lace curtains were curtains of fire. All the time she kept repeating, "I tripped on the stairs! I tripped on the stairs! I tripped on the stairs!"

Suddenly Papa remembered something. "Your mother's trunk!" he cried and ran back to the bedroom, followed by Mama. And over his shoulder he shouted to me, "The bell! The bell! Ring the bell!" As I ran to the back of the house, I remembered that tolling bells had alerted New Richmond to rising water. Now our dinner bell would warn of blazing fire.

It was Saturday night, and most of the members of the Modern Woodmen of America were on their way to attend the monthly lodge meeting in the hall above Mr. Perkins' general store. The members, especially the younger men, looked forward to this event. It was a break from the hard work and rather humdrum quality of most of their days. They met for ceremony first, and then for "man talk" and companionship, and jokes reserved exclusively for all-male gatherings. And then there were the bologna sandwiches and crackers and cheese from the store, washed down with sar-saparilla and perhaps something stronger.

On this night, they were on their way in their horse-and-buggy conveyances, or buckboards, or on horseback. They heard the bell and saw the fire, the "pillar of fire by night"—and they turned their horses around and sped off in the direction of the blaze and the sound.

One or two had already reached the general store; Mr. Perkins was standing out front, a tall stack of new pails by his side. He greeted the first arrivals, we were told later, before they could get out of their rigs and pointed to the buckets. "Better take these," he said. "Likely you'll need 'em. Looks like it might be the Motts or the Weisbergs." And so they came, from every direction, these young men, and older men who had remained at home, and young boys and women, too.

There was no hope for the house. It was tinder-dry. The older part, the two-story and attic section, where the fire had started, was ablaze in what seemed like seconds. A rising wind directed the flames from the burning roof to the tall, ancient cedars and turned them into towering torches, lighting up the sky. We managed to throw most of the sacks of corn husks, still lying in the yard outside the parlor, to relative safety, from which they could be loaded into the wagon, if the wagon survived the falling, flaming pieces of roof and wall. Beyond that, until the first of the neighbors arrived, we were working to little purpose.

Between intervals of ringing the bell I helped drag things from the newer part of the house, the one-story part: the bedding from Mama's and Papa's bed, my school books, and a few other books from the kitchen table. With no plan, with little sense, we seized anything at hand and dragged it out of imminent danger.

In the stables, sensing danger, the horses whinnied in alarm; soon the cows were lowing in chorus with them. My little dog, Prince, had crept under the spring wagon for safety and lay there, whimpering. The smokehouse, the woodshed, and the chicken house were the closest outbuildings to the fire-breathing dragon the house had become. I remembered that a large can of kerosene was kept in the smokehouse. I found Papa leaning against that small building fighting for breath, coughing. He had inhaled smoke. He tried to tell me something, pointing to the smokehouse.

"I know, Papa! Kerosene! Come away!" He kept shaking his head and coughing.

By that time help had begun to arrive—the men from the lodge, the neighbors. One man came running when he saw me trying to get Papa to come with me. I yelled, "There's kerosene in there!" He dashed into the building and emerged at once, carrying the five-gallon can, and ran with it to a safe place by the well. Only then did Papa let me lead him to safety.

In the front, other men were moving the spring wagon out of danger, two in front between the shafts, like a team of horses, others at the back and sides, pushing. Prince emerged from under the wagon and came running to me. I picked him up and comforted him. The men had tied their horses to the fence on the far side of the barnyard fence, to keep them out of the way. There was no hope now of saving any part of the house, or any more of its contents. The men concentrated on saving the other buildings. Almost everyone had brought at least one bucket, and the lodge members had brought a dozen sent by Mr. Perkins. Now a water brigade was formed to save the smaller buildings, and even to protect the barn if the wind should rise enough to endanger that most distant and most important structure. There were enough buckets for two lines from the well—one to the smokehouse, and the other to the woodshed. The wind was a little stronger now, and sparks were flying freely. The cream separator was bolted to a wooden platform cemented to the woodshed's earthen floor. While the water brigade was wetting down the walls and roof, three men were trying to unbolt the separator, using a wrench that they had found on a shelf. It was the wrong size—they threw it aside in exasperation. I said I'd run get a proper wrench.

"All right, fellows, heave ho!" one of them cried. Before I was fairly out of the shed, I heard the sound of splintering wood. I looked around; they were carrying out the separator, with part of the wooden platform still attached.

The din in the barnyard was deafening: the frightened chickens cackling shrilly behind the closed door of their house; the horses in the stables kicking against their stalls and whinnying, answered by the neighbors' horses tied to the fence; the lowing of the cows, and the shouting of men to one another.

It was over. The house was a pile of smoking and smoldering ashes and charred wood. Even the cedar torches had burned themselves out and now stood like very tall black candles at a witches' Sabbath. All the other buildings had been saved. Now the weary water brigade worked to put out little pockets of glowing ashes, to insure that no sudden wind might stir them to new life.

All the women except Mrs. Licht had gone home to bring coffee, food, and blankets. The rest of us were in the barn, out of the cold. Mrs. Licht sat beside Mama, her arms about her, comforting her, stroking her hair.

"Come home with us tonight," she said. "We have plenty of room. You will have a good night's rest, and tomorrow the sun will shine, and God will bring you peace."

Mama said she wanted to stay and look to the animals in the morning. They were so frightened, and they needed to know we were there to take care of them. And Papa said he had to take the load of corn husks to the city.

"We lost part of the sacks," he said, "but thanks to you fellows the wagon was saved, and I had it almost loaded."

"Max," George Lumley said, "let me go into the city with you. You look pretty tuckered out, coughing and all, and I reckon you are; I could spell you with the horses, and you could get some sleep." Papa said he'd be glad of the company, and it was settled. The women returned with hot coffee, bread and butter, and doughnuts. Others had brought blankets and warm coats for Mama and me.

"And tomorrow," said Ollie Lumley, "you come to the house, and we'll see what else you need." We could have gone to any house that night, but we needed to be by ourselves and together—together as we had not been together for a long time. The men threw down more of the fragrant hay from the loft and built it into beds, and with the bedding we had saved and the blankets of our good neighbors we would not fare too badly.

"Well, folks," one of the men said, "if you're ready to hit the hay, the hay's ready to be hit." Everyone laughed a little. George Lumley said, "Now don't you go off without me, Max. I'll be here before five in the morning." Mrs. Licht laid her strong, firm, healing hands on Mama's head and mine.

"The Lord bless you and keep you," she said in her lovely voice. "The Lord make his countenance to shine upon you, and bring you peace." Then she added with a gentle smile, "That's from the Old Testament, Becky." She kissed us both, and everybody went home. For a few moments the three of us sat with our arms about one another. None of us said a word. Then we crawled under the blankets. I let Prince snuggle in beside me. He licked my face in gratitude. And in a little while, exhausted physically and emotionally, we slept.

One of the farms on which Papa had undertaken to plant and harvest grain on shares had an absentee owner. The last tenant had left some time before Papa took over the farming. There was a house on the grounds, a one-story, white-plastered, long, narrow, rectangular structure without an ounce of grace, or a single concession to any attribute besides utility. But it stood on a low knoll that would be green in the summer, shaded by two great sycamores, and it was furnished with the simple necessities for living and working. There were stables for horses and cows, a chicken house and a woodshed, a cellar and a well. And, of course, an outdoor "facility" complete with last year's Sears, Roebuck catalogue. There was even a pigsty, but we were not fattening pigs at this time, so Mama decided that, if we had to live in this place through the summer, it could be converted to the planting of a kitchen garden.

Papa made a deal with the owner: Papa would exchange his share of the grain that he would harvest on this land for the use of the farmhouse and all the buildings until we were able to restore and return to our own home.

We lived in this almost primitive house for several months, and when the season for baking matzos at the Manischewitz plant was over, Zayde came to stay with us.

There had been a five-hundred-dollar policy on the house and all its contents. Some of the money went for essential clothes for all of us; since I had to return to school, I was the first to be outfitted—with a wardrobe as utilitarian as the simple house we occupied. I grieved only for my lovely imitation astrakhan coat, but Uncle Charlie Green promised to make me another, and he kept his word. Mama came next, because she had to be adequately dressed for her weekly trips to the city. Then it was Papa's turn. Fortunately he had laid out, in the kitchen, his felt boots and fleece-lined coat, and everything else he would need for the pre-dawn trip to the city with his load of corn husks. Everything had been in one place, so we had picked them up by the armful and carried them to safety. What was left of the insurance money and the payment for the last load of corn husks was put away for the soon-to-be-due mortgage payment. There remained the problem of funds for clearing the debris left by the fire, and for building a new house. Mr. Benjamin Lumley, from whom we had bought the farm, and who carried the mortgage, offered to postpone the payment or co-sign a note at the bank. Papa thanked him and said he would think about it. His decision was announced to Mama and me one Friday evening, when I had come home for the weekend. As usual, Papa did not ask Mama what she thought about his plan. There was nothing to discuss; there was simply an announcement.

"I want you, Goldele," he said, "to write to Mr. Teitlebaum from the Baron de Hirsch Society. I will tell you what I want him to know, and you put it in good English." The letter related our unfortunate situation, and inquired about a loan and the terms we would have to meet to obtain it. Mr. Teitlebaum replied promptly. He would not need to come to discuss Papa's request. Papa's letter convinced him of our urgent need. An interest-free loan to be paid off in easy installments would be arranged promptly.

There was a footnote to the letter: "Have you given any thought, Mr. Weisberg, to building a silo when you are able to return to your own farm? I am sending you, under separate cover, information about silos and ensilage. . . . " Papa, as always, was interested in new projects, but his interest in silos would remain academic until we again had our own roof over our heads.

Everybody on Dunham's Hill, I am sure, had ordered something from the Sears, Roebuck catalogue at one time or another. We had never used it except for its utilitarian function, placing it where everybody's old catalogue wound up when the new ones arrived. Now we chose something beyond any purchase ever made from this "farmers' friend" by any customer on Dunham's Hill, or in surrounding towns. We ordered a new house! It was one of Sears, Roebuck's "Redi-Cut Houses." It was shipped by freight, "knocked down." Every piece was numbered and lettered, in ways that made it quite easy to put together. With it came just the right amount of paint—white, with green for trim, together with brushes, thinner, everything necessary to erect a dwelling from the ground up! It was to create almost as much of a sensation as the telephone.

Barn-raisings were not uncommon in farming communities. Almost every farmer's ambition was to have a fine barn, and many barns were better and handsomer structures than the houses with which they shared land space. Thus house-raisings usually came about when the family grew and additions were needed or because of a disaster such as ours. So the Weisberg house-raising was an event in which everyone wanted to participate. Every man in the area contributed as much time as he could. Josiah Crane insisted on joining as a volunteer, but the painting was left to him on Papa's established "dollar-a-day-and-found" basis. In a matter of days we had a new house, completely ready except for the outside. The women had their own role in the house-raising; they provided food for the volunteers.

Uncle Max came up on a Sunday to observe the work with the eye of an expert. He took Mama and Papa and me aside and told us he wanted to do something, build something for us, because building was what he knew best—and what would we like? Mama didn't have to think long for her answer.

"I know what I want!" she said. "I want a brick oven like we had in the old country. And there's room for it in the woodshed. You couldn't give me anything I'd like more. I'd bake the big round loaves of pumpernickel and I could make *cholent*. What do you think, Mendel?" When she began talking about the old country, she almost always reverted automatically to calling Papa by his old-country name. Papa shrugged. "Why should I not say yes? I like *cholent*, too!"

Uncle Max built the brick oven, coming up from the city over a succession of Sundays. He and his family shared the first food prepared in it. Within another year he, Tante Sadie, the children, and Bubbie were back in Boston. He had been asked to form a partnership to build commercial property for the small forerunners of today's supermarkets. Their plan was to find available lots in towns surrounding Boston, in locations they considered perfect for the Atlantic and Pacific chain of markets. Once having obtained a contract with A & P, they could attract others to join the group of which A & P formed the nucleus. Uncle Max and his partners prospered and went on to more diversified building, such as schools and warehouses.

Papa accepted Uncle Max's gift gratefully and graciously. But when a letter came from Uncle Mike with a receipt for the money Papa still owed him, and with it a money order for a hundred dollars to buy a housewarming gift, Papa crumpled both the receipt and the money order and tossed them on the floor. He couldn't forget Uncle Mike's sudden decision to abandon us after he had persuaded us to join him in the Ohio farming venture because *he* wanted to "return to the land."

"I want nothing from him!" Papa shouted with his old vigor.

"*I* do!" cried Mama. "He's still ashamed of what he did. He's asking to be forgiven. That's the best way he knows how to do it. Are you God, to say 'No! Never! No forgiveness!'?" She gathered up the two precious balls of paper and smoothed them carefully. "Besides," she added in a matter-of-fact tone, "I need a new stove." Papa stared at her for a moment, open-mouthed. For a long time now Mama's rare moments of self-assertiveness had left him speechless. He shrugged and walked out.

We had the housewarming before we had beds. We slept on borrowed cots, sat on borrowed chairs, ate on borrowed tables. But Uncle Mike's money order had paid for a good secondhand stove, and there was money left over. Everybody came to the housewarming, even some of the Jewish farmers whom we had come to know through the good offices of Mr. Kullman, Mama's "black car" friend. Mr. Kullman himself and his wife and the Gold-schmidts came, too. Our neighbors came, bringing practical gifts, and from the city the Mishkins, Moishele Platt, Landa, the Greens, and Uncle Harry. The Greens brought an elegant parlor lamp with a china globe; the lower half that held the kerosene was also of china, with roses of deeper pink painted on the pale background. These, I thought, were the kind of roses Mama would have pre-ferred to the very bright red ones on her so-briefly-possessed Ax-minster rug.

Moishele's gift, presented jointly with Landa, was a wooden swing for the porch. It would come by freight. The Mishkins brought a gilt-framed painting of a platter of fish backed by a bowl of fruit, for the dining room—a work of art that quite overwhelmed the small room for which it was meant. Clearly, whatever else we might lack, we would have a touch of elegance we had never had before.

Uncle Harry announced that his gift, too, would arrive by freight, and it would be a great surprise. He was sure there was nothing like it on Dunham's Hill, nor anywhere for miles around. It was, he declared, one of the first ones to arrive in Cincinnati. And that was all he would tell us.

There would be no room now for friends or relatives to come and go at will. At least there would be no *rooms*. The new house was erected on the site of the old one, with the same access to the cellar as before; but it probably could have fitted into half of the smaller wing of the rambling old structure that had sheltered us and so many boarders, friends, and family over the years. The new house was just big enough for the three of us. Through the center, using about a third of the space, was the largest room, the parlor. On either side were two rooms—the dining room and the kitchen on one side, and two bedrooms on the other. A front porch ran the length of the house. Now when visitors came from the city, the men would have to sleep in the hayloft and the women on makeshift beds indoors.

Miraculously, the lilac bushes had survived, but not the yellow rose. Mama talked wistfully of planting grass on the lawn, and more flowers, and maybe, finally, putting a white picket fence around the yard. None of that ever happened, but the lilacs bloomed more luxuriously and, it seemed, more fragrantly than ever before. When telephone service was restored, we felt we could really put the tragedy of the fire behind us.

Two months after the housewarming, a notice came informing us that a freight shipment waited for us in New Richmond. It was six weeks after the porch swing had come. We called Uncle Harry at Mr. Levy's jewelry store and asked if it was his present.

"How should I know?" he replied. "Go pick it up and you'll find out!"

He was determined to keep us in suspense, so we played the game of speculation.

# 25

# *Dunham's Hill Is Alive with Mama's Music*

Uncle Harry's housewarming gift had indeed arrived! And was picked up. And unpacked. And gazed upon with wonder and with awe.

Even on Dunham's Hill we had heard of gramophones. Everybody had seen pictures of "talking machines." Even the Sears, Roebuck catalogue pictured one. Two or three prosperous farmers in the county, one in our own Pierce Township, were known to own "contraptions" with cylindrical devices that made tinkly music when you wound up the box into which they were built. In New Richmond, someone had a handsome square gramophone that played music on flat discs, and was topped with a large horn through which the sound came forth. But this gift from Uncle Harry was different. There was no horn; whatever magic was offered was within a handsome mahogany-stained cabinet that was tall enough to stand on the floor, and was equipped with casters that made it easy to move around.

After Papa had unpacked separate parts, which no one could identify, he telephone Uncle Harry at Mr. Levy's jewelry store. It was the first time we had made a long-distance call, and Mama and I stood by as though ready to catch Papa if the telephone on the wall should suddenly attack him. Someone answered.

"Is Mr. Harry Weisberg there?" shouted Papa. Somebody must

have told him not to yell. He repeated in a lower voice, "Mr. Harry Weisberg. Is he there? I have to talk to him."

Uncle Harry came to the phone in a few minutes. Papa would take no chances; he was determined to be heard. Again he shouted: "Herschel, can you hear me?" Uncle Harry could hear him; when he came to visit later, he told us he had had a report from his wife in Rowne that she had heard him, too! Papa went on at the top of his voice, telling Uncle Harry that the surprise had come, but what should we do with it? We should wait until Sunday, Uncle Harry told him. He was coming to visit on Sunday, and he would explain everything.

On Sunday Uncle Harry showed Papa where the turntable went, inserted the handle that would start and stop the turntable, and installed the needle that would magically bring music from the grooves in the record that he had brought from the city. After it was all put together, he stood beside it as though it were a lectern and enlightened us on the history of the phonograph, of which ours was the most advanced model. As early as 1906, a German inventor had developed a phonograph with the horn inside the cabinet, a machine that played discs on a turntable and proved musically better than earlier machines—a thing of beauty, as well. This handsome cabinet, four feet high, was a fine example of that Victor Talking Machine.

Uncle Harry's boss, Mr. Levy, had taken a chance on introducing it to his clientele. He had ordered three; Uncle Harry had immediately taken one off his hands at only 10 percent above cost, to be paid off at a dollar a week.

"And now," he said, bringing the lecture to an end, "I want you to go into the dining room until I tell you to come back here." He had brought a suitcase with him and kept it at his side throughout the lecture. Uncle Harry, I could see, was enjoying himself.

We went into the dining room. We heard Uncle Harry busily at work. And then—a voice of great beauty, a lyric tenor, was singing a liturgical melody in Hebrew. We did not wait until Uncle Harry summoned us; with the first soaring notes of the beautiful music we were back in the living room, speechless, entranced.

Mama finally asked, "A *hazzan?*"

"Not just *a* hazzan!" Uncle Harry reproached her. "*The* hazzan! Hazzan Yossele Rosenblatt!" His name, of course, was Joseph Rosenblatt, but his great following called him Yossele, the affectionate diminutive usually reserved for children and granted to only a few chosen adults who were loved. It was said that the Metropolitan Opera Association had offered him a contract but that he had turned it down, because he would have had to sing secular music on the Sabbath.

Uncle Harry showed us how to start and stop the turntable, how to put the record on, and how to remove it without scratching the surface.

All the records that he had brought were either liturgical music in Hebrew or secular songs in Yiddish—some that Mama sometimes sang. But the voice of Yossele Rosenblatt made great music of them all.

Uncle Harry had to be back at work early Monday morning, so Papa drove him to the interurban at Ten-Mile Stop to make the late afternoon train. They no sooner had left than Mama started the music again, playing a Yiddish lullaby. Suddenly she stopped, chose a Hebrew record of Yossele Rosenblatt's and rang up Ollie Lumley.

"Ollie, my friend," she said, "I want you should listen to something. Just wait for a minute and listen!" And she turned the earpiece of the telephone toward the phonograph and waited. When the record came to an end, she stopped the machine and turned back to the mouthpiece.

"You heard, Ollie, you heard the music?" She was beaming when

Ollie answered, so I knew Ollie's reaction had been up to Mama's expectations. "Yes, beautiful," Mama said. "Our present from my brother-in-law. You must come over with George if you think he will like it. Yes, a big surprise. Come soon."

Yossele Rosenblatt and the voices on the Yiddish records became as well known to the subscribers on the telephone line as the singers in the choir whom they heard on Sundays at the Methodist church. Mama became an impresario, with more or less regularly scheduled concerts at odd hours when she found herself with a little time to spare. She would ring Ollie, or someone else on the line, and others quickly lifted their receivers and became an audience. They learned to prop their earphones so that they could do their ironing or mending or other chores and attend the concert at the same time. From time to time some of the ladies would request a favorite hymn, or an English song, like "Juanita" or "Love's Old Sweet Song." They would give Mama money to buy the records when she went to the city and, with Uncle Harry's help, she was able to find many of them. Just as the telephone had opened new avenues of communication on Dunham's Hill, so Mama's concerts brought a new dimension to the lives of these hard-working women, who loved even the songs in Hebrew and Yiddish, which they could not understand—except with their hearts.

First Alexander Graham Bell had come to Dunham's Hill, and after him—Yossele Rosenblatt.

# 26

## *The Year of the Silo*

The summer of my fifteenth year was the beginning of Papa's chronic illness, though it wasn't diagnosed as chronic at the time. He had developed a dry cough, and when he overexerted himself or shouted in anger he began to wheeze and gasp for breath. Dr. John stopped by one day to visit, on his way to see his sister-in-law, Mrs. Charlie Mott, and Mama told him about it. Papa was somewhere out in the field, so Mama asked Dr. John if he thought it was because of the smoke Papa had inhaled the night of the fire.

"Maybe," Dr. John pondered. "Maybe, a little. He couldn't have inhaled very much and gone on doing all he did that night, and then drive the team into the city early in the morning. Of course, it didn't do him any good," he concluded. "But I don't think it brought on this breathing business all by itself." Then he added, "One thing you should make him do is quit smoking all those coffin nails you stuff for him. Anyway, watch how he gets along, and if there's any change for the worse, let me know."

Papa woke up one morning before dawn, fighting for breath in a most frightening way. Mama awakened me. She was shaking and almost hysterical. "Call Dr. John!" she cried. "Quick! Call the doctor!" She followed as I ran to the telephone, saying over and over, "It's my fault! His sickness is from the fire, and the fire was my fault! From the smoke! The smoke!"

I got Dr. John on the phone and told him what had happened.

"Get your papa out of bed, and sit him up in a chair," he instructed. "He's probably scared, which makes it all the harder. Try to calm him down. I'll get there as fast as I can make it."

Dr. John had a "Tin Lizzie," but he drove it only for emergencies because, he said, it "scared the livin' daylights" out of the horses he encountered on the road. This call he answered with the Lizzie.

"Your breathing machinery is kind of clogged up, Max," Dr. John told Papa after he had checked him over. "I'm going to give you something to open up the pipes." He took an atomizer from his bag and poured some liquid into it from a sealed bottle. He gave what was left in the bottle to Mama, and told her to put it away in a cool place. He showed Papa how to use the atomizer.

"Now I don't want you to wait till you have another attack to use it," said Dr. John. "I want you to use it three times a day: when you get up in the morning, between dinner and supper, and just before you go to bed. And I want you to cut down on those cigarettes Becky makes for you. Now there *is* something else I could use on you. I could use a drug that I'd have to inject into your arm with a hypodermic needle; it's something called 'adrenalin.' Still kind of new; only been around a few years. But I don't want to use it, because I don't know enough about it. If you don't improve, I'll send you to a doctor in the city who does know about it. In the meantime, farm your own land. Don't try to work every idle acre on Dunham's Hill. Let up on the heavy work. And *don't get excited* about things, any more'n you can help. Then maybe I won't have to send you to Dr. Ullery in Cincinnati."

Papa went back to bed and to sleep. The sun was well up when he awoke, and he started to yell at Mama and me for letting him oversleep. Mama reminded him that he wasn't supposed to get excited. The chores were done; Josiah was already in the field working. "So use your medicine and come eat your breakfast,"

Mama said with a note of authority in her voice. "Unless you'd rather get sick again and go to the specialist in the city!"

Papa assured her he had no intention of seeing any specialist. He would use the atomizer and practice being calm, but he had more important things to worry about than a little shortness of breath. For instance, he never could find the time to study for his citizenship test, let alone go to Cincinnati and go through the whole naturalization business. And the war in Europe! Now that was something to worry about! All of Papa's sisters were still in Russia, and so were Uncle Harry's wife and children, and who knew how it would all end? Besides, he had an important project to get under way. He was going to install a silo! He had planted an extra field of corn that spring, but he hadn't told us why. Now we knew: it was for the silo.

The corn would be cut while it was still green, and it would become ensilage. The other fields would be allowed to ripen. Part of the crop, if it turned out to be good, would be husked and stored in the crib for seed corn. The rest would be feed for the horses. The ensilage, served up with a little cottonseed meal, would provide succulent green feed for the cows in the winter when there was no grazing in the pastures for them. If the cows produced on this diet the way Mr. Teitlebaum's literature promised, he would build more stables and buy more cows.

Throughout the hot summer Papa seemed much better. The silo was under construction, and Papa watched with pride as the red-painted cylindrical structure rose, section by section, to its full height. A free-standing metal ladder was hooked over the top on the side next to the barn; at the bottom a removable metal-handled door provided the means to remove the ensilage.

Papa welcomed neighbors, and more distant farmers, who came to watch the silo's progress. I had never before seen him glowing with such pride over any of the innovations he had introduced to Dunham's Hill—the cream separator, crop rotation, the planting of legumes to restore worn-out soil, the binder. All those had been practical means of making the farm pay for itself, providing us with a living. He had proved, at the same time, that he could be a better farmer than the old-timers around him who were born to the role. But only the telephone line came close to this new achievement of which he was so proud.

The silo was a special thing. It was his sonnet, his symphony, his sculpture. Rising grandly amid its drab surroundings, it was indeed a work of art.

The cutting of the still-green corn became a sort of athletic contest. The three young men who had been hired for the job approached it as though training for track events—if not for the next Olympics, then at least for the next county fair. The late-summer sun spilled golden waves of heat upon the fields like hot mulled wine. The men's cutting knives were honed to razor sharpness. Their shirts clung to their bodies. They pushed their wide-brimmed straw hats to the backs of their heads, sweat pouring from their faces. I stood at the ends of the rows, waiting for them with a pail of cold water and a dipper; I knew they would not stop to drink until they reached the ends of the rows.

I watched them get ready. They used the formula of their childhood: "One for the money, two for the show, three to get ready—and four to GO!" When they reached me they stopped, splashed water over their faces, gulped dippersful, turned around, repeated the jingle, and were off again. There was no bonus, no medal at the end of the day's work, but the winner was hailed all over Dunham's Hill as the *champion*—a new star was born!

*        *        *

The threshing of grain in the autumn was an event well known to all and eagerly anticipated by everyone. But the ensilage cutter was making its debut, and it drew a great "house." The stalks of tender corn were fed into the great maw of the beast, where they were cut up and blown into the silo from the top, through a large galvanized iron pipe. But there was one thing no part of the machine could accomplish; it was important that the cut-up fodder be firmly packed, so that no air could get into the ensilage. The intrusion of air would cause the juicy green feed to spoil instead of fermenting, and it would smell of mold instead of beer. To achieve the necessary tightness, the heaviest man in Dunham's Hill was hired to do the packing. Stripped to the waist and barefooted, he climbed the metal ladder and was lowered to the bottom of the silo just before the cutting began. From that moment on, he "tromped." 'Round and 'round he went, rising as the ensilage rose, bearing down, bearing down—and tromping. When he finally emerged at the top, his sweat-soaked torso was completely covered with ensilage, and he looked like a part of Birnam Wood on its way to Dunsinane. He was greeted with shouts and applause as he climbed down the ladder. His friends waited with pails of water, and he was met with a welcome deluge.

The final touch was carrying buckets of moist, rich soil up the metal ladder, spreading it across the ensilage at the top, and sowing grass seed upon it. The miniature meadow thus created was an added precaution against air getting into the ensilage.

For Papa the event was somewhat marred because he could not be in the thick of the action when the ensilage began blowing through the great pipe into the silo. Though the delivery end of the pipe was bent to about sixty degrees at the top, some of the fragments, together with a fine dust, would inevitably escape into the atmosphere; and Papa would start to sneeze, and then to wheeze. Finally he retreated to the corn crib and followed the activity from there. It was his shining hour.

Mama and I watched from the porch. Mama remarked dryly that it was very nice; she hoped that some day Papa would put a picket fence around the yard so she, too, could sow grass, and have a little meadow, in the front yard.

"But then," she added, with a touch of irony I had never detected in her before, "who would come from miles around to look at a picket fence?"

# 27

## "...And Not to Yield"

In September of 1915, I returned to school as a junior. It was a year of many changes. We had a new superintendent, Mr. George L. Borders. He was totally unlike either Mr. Turnipseed or Mr. Utterback in every possible way—in appearance, in dress, in style. He was tall, slender, attractive, with a ready smile. I was sure he would never fall asleep at his desk. There was a quality about him that reminded me of Mr. Frank Franz, which was the greatest accolade I could bestow on any man. He was married to an attractive woman who joined the faculty as music teacher for the elementary grades.

From time to time, the Borders would invite a class from the high school to their home for informal sessions of talk, singing around their piano, and eating popcorn or homemade fudge. If Mr. Borders' two predecessors had had wives, I had never heard of them; it was hard for me, at least, to envision either one of them coming home to a fond spouse—or any spouse at all—especially he of the unattached dickey and cuffs. So the year started well, and for me, in some ways, it was a crucial year.

I remembered that Mr. Franz had said to Papa in my presence, "At sixteen she will be ready for college." But I could not wait until that day to talk to Papa about my ongoing education. Some of my classmates were already making plans. Not all of them would go to college; not all of them wanted to go to college. Most of my classmates who planned on college as a matter of course knew that Miami University at Oxford, Ohio, was their destination. Older sisters and brothers, parents, and even grandparents had gone there. For us, Miami was the most prestigious school in Ohio. It had a beautiful campus, a long and honorable history, and it was the birthplace of Sigma Chi! Who could ask for more?

I would have been happy to make Miami my alma mater as well; but the college I planned to introduce casually at the supper table on a Friday or Saturday night would be a school with a very different philosophy of education—Antioch College in Yellow Springs. I would explain its unique system: students could work and study at the same time, thus paying for their education even as they learned.

I rehearsed my speech in my mind. I would emphasize the financial savings. I wondered if I dared suggest that it would pay for itself by preparing me to earn a living, and thus would make as profitable an investment as the silo, which was designed to increase the output of the cows. I quickly put out of my mind that reckless notion. I thought, "I am really growing up—I am planning to be crafty!"

We were reading Tennyson, and the closing lines of the poem "Ulysses" charted my course. Ulysses is talking to his comrades— he tells them they will "... sail beyond the sunset and the western stars ... to strive, to seek, to find and not to yield."

"Not to yield"—that must be my key to victory. But there were times when I faced reality. What would it avail me "not to yield?" To threaten Papa into submission? To leave home and strike out on my own? At sixteen I would not be a free agent. The law was on the grown-ups' side. And, most insurmountable, what would I use for money? At such times, when I was yielding to despair even before I confronted Papa, I realized that I must stop those depressing fantasies and get on with my life, before I became so mired in a "slough of despond" that I wouldn't even graduate. Then I would recklessly spend my entire weekly allowance on a banana split and face the world.

The Lutzkys had restored their store and living quarters to the functional level of the pre-flood period. Mr. Lutzky had introduced a small stock of new shoes to augment his income from the repair of footwear. They had permanently rented the upstairs apartment and, as a tangible mark of their faith in the future, they had bought a handsome brass bed, the delight of Sarah Lutzky's heart. It stood in solitary splendor in the center of the larger of the two rooms, waiting for the day when a mattress and companion pieces of furniture should create a proper environment for it—a harbinger of better days to come. To me they granted the privacy of the smaller of the two rooms. It held a large wooden bed, a bedside table, two chairs and a table, a walnut wardrobe—all left behind, the landlady told us, by the former tenant in payment of accumulated rent. This room opened directly on a stairway that led to a courtyard at the rear of the building. The arrangement reawakened in me the period of fear and insecurity that had dominated my life for a time on the farm. Just as on the days when Mama was in the city and Papa away in the fields, and I had been driven to search the old house from attic to kitchen before facing the day, I now, before retiring for the night, would first check the large room and its empty closet, then the wardrobe and every shadowed corner of my room before latching the outside door and going to bed. I had thought I had slain the old dragon long ago, but now I knew he had only been sleeping until I should again be vulnerable.

I never spoke about this to anyone, but a possible solution to my problem was presented quite unexpectedly. Two of my classmates, who obviously felt that my living arrangements were less than perfect, suggested that there was a way I could improve them.

They knew a widow who lived alone in a pleasant house on a tree-shaded street. She had a spacious, attractive room with a private entrance that she liked to rent to teachers or young students for a modest sum, because she enjoyed the presence of another person in her house. It was available at the time, and my friends persuaded me to look at it.

The room was indeed superior in every way to the gloomy upstairs bedroom I shared with a dragon. It was airy, carpeted, brightly curtained. It had a gas plate, a small icebox and a sink with dishes and towels, all behind a screen. And, besides a fairly unobtrusive bed, there were an armchair, a rocker, two straight chairs, and a small, round table for studying and eating. Besides all those attractions, I knew that there was a more subtle advantage to making the change. I would at last be able to invite friends in and even serve refreshments. I knew that the following year all the seniors would take turns at entertaining the class. With this new home I, too, could play the hostess. My new landlady would probably help me. When we left the place I promised to discuss the change with my parents. I knew that my friends believed that the move would greatly improve what today we would call my "quality of life." It was also, I believed, an effort on their part to make me socially more—I guess the word would be "flexible"—better able to fit in.

That night I lay awake a long time thinking about what had transpired, about what I should do, about how Mama and Papa would respond to such a suggestion. One thing I was *not* thinking about was my nightly ritual of checking all the haunts where danger might be lying in wait for me—I had forgotten to be afraid! Then, before I fell asleep, I made my decision about moving: I knew I would not leave the Lutzkys, however socially attractive the other place might be. Sarah and Morris Lutzky had been good to me. But for them I might not have gone to high school at all. I never

told my parents about this incident. The next day I met my friends after school and told them it would not be possible for me to make the change. I lived with the Lutzkys until I graduated.

When I came home that weekend Papa had a surprise for me. Even before he unhitched Ol' Belle he led me to the cow stables, where I heard a gentle lowing from Daisy's stall. Daisy was pure white, larger and heavier than any cow we—or anyone else, to my knowledge—had ever had. Big-boned and angular, conforming to no known breed, she was a "sport"— an anomaly—and the producer of the most and richest milk of any cow in the herd. Before I reached her stall I caught sight of a short, white tail switching briskly against flies.

"Daisy calved!" I cried.

"Last night," Papa said, beaming. "Right after supper. She's the best and the most considerate cow we've got. Rosie always chose daybreak; all of them seem to make it as hard on us as possible, but not Daisy!" I was standing at her stall now and saw a beautiful little calf with light and dark brown and black patches on a Daisy-white body, greedily at work on first one, then another of the mother cow's teats. Daisy kept lowing gently, turning her head to look at her beautiful offspring.

"You like it?" Papa asked.

"Of course! She's a little beauty!"

"Yes. Well, she's yours." I looked at him, open-mouthed. "You look after her as much as you can," he continued. "By the time you graduate next year she'll be ready to sell or breed, and you can keep her as a milk cow. That will be my graduation present to you: you can do what you like with her. If you want, you can sell her back to me."

"Thank you, Papa," I cried. "She's a little beauty and that's what I'll call her—Beauty. I probably *will* sell her back to you. I'll need all the money I can earn for college."

Papa's mood changed abruptly. He started out of the stable, putting an end to our happy discussion.

"Better go into the house," he said, all the warmth gone from his voice. "Your mama will be calling us to supper soon."

My reference to college had evoked no response. The very thought, it seemed, was repugnant to Papa. I did not speak of Antioch College that evening, as I had planned to do. Supper was eaten in almost total silence. Sensing something wrong, Mama tried to make conversation. Did I know that Daisy had calved? Did I see her little spotted calf?

"Yes, and she's beautiful." I thought: "She's trying hard to brighten the corner where she's at. I mustn't spoil the evening for her." I looked at Papa. He had stopped eating and was staring at me. I went on: "She's beautiful, and she's mine." I managed a smile. Papa relaxed. It was Mama's turn to stare.

"Yours?" she marveled.

"Yes, Papa gave her to me. At least, she will be mine when I graduate next year. She will be my graduation present, and he will buy her from me if I decide to sell her."

"True, Max?"

"Of course." Papa was eating again.

"Nice," said Mama. "Very nice! What will you do with so much money, my dear capitalist?"

"I will buy a rope of pearls for you, Mama, and a watch and chain for Papa, and a fur coat and a little Cossack hat for me. And now I am going to say good night to my Beauty." My little dog, Prince, who had been lying at my feet, followed me. I didn't cry until I got to Daisy's stall in the stable. My little piebald lovely was asleep, snuggled against her mother. I knelt beside her and smoothed her soft coat of many colors. Then I let the tears come. Prince tried to comfort me by licking my face.

When Papa drove me back to school on Monday morning, it was he who broke the silence which we had each drawn about ourselves like armor. He spoke as though he were just now responding to what I had said in Daisy's stall on Friday—as though no time had elapsed from that moment until now, on Monday morning.

"You're still only fifteen years old. Do you have to rush into college right now? Can't you even wait until you graduate?"

"That's not the way it's done. You can't just go up to a college on the last day, and say well, here I am, you lucky college, you. You have to apply. Maybe they won't want you if you wait too long. Maybe by that time they're all filled up."

"I didn't say wait till the last minute." Then I told him about Antioch. He wasn't sure that that was such a good idea. "Either you get an education, or you get a job. You can't do both at the same time."

"You mean I *can* go to college? A different college? Is that what you're saying, Papa?"

Suddenly he was wheezing, fighting for breath. I was frightened. "Papa," I cried. "Turn around! Let's go home!" He shook his head, handed me the reins, took his atomizer from his pocket, exhaled, and then breathed deeply of the fine spray of his medicine. I drove the rest of the way to New Richmond. Soon Papa was breathing normally. We did not return to the conversation about college.

There was a busy year ahead for us juniors. We were the heirs-apparent to the senior throne. Soon they would abdicate in our favor. We were practicing benign authority, mostly at the expense of the freshmen and sophomores.

Other things happened. A "nickel show" had opened in New Richmond, and Papa had dictated to me a note for Mr. Borders, asking if he thought it would be proper, at my age, to attend this new-fangled (and possibly demoralizing?) contraption. He signed it and I hand-delivered it, greatly embarrassed, to my favorite school superintendent. Mr. Borders looked up and said, straight-faced, "I am going to give my approval, because I am sure you are a very trustworthy and moral young lady." Then his eyes twinkled and he grinned, and I knew he was "making fun," just as I remembered watching eagerly for a sign that Papa was "making fun," in uncertain situations. Mr. Borders sent back with me a note of approval, and my allowance was duly increased by five cents. I still remember a little about my very first movie—*King René's Daughter*. She was blind and beautiful; I remember nothing more.

Miss King, my least favorite teacher, had left to get married and Miss Helen Colvill from Circleville, Ohio, had joined our faculty. She turned out to be the most progressive and interesting of our teachers, and she also coached the girl's basketball team, of which I was not a member. She created a sensation by coming to practice in the same kind of bloomers worn by the girls. Miss Colvill, as I write, is in her nineties and has been for many years Mrs. John C.

Lincoln, widow of a Cleveland philanthropist who, having settled with his family in Phoenix, Arizona, gave the city a hospital, among other gifts.

I was named by my peers as class poet, jointly with Dorothy McFarland. Neither of us ever appeared in any poetry anthologies, but we took ourselves quite seriously at the time.

Another teacher, Miss Nellie Overholtz, who had been on the faculty throughout my high school years, introduced us to her favorite author, Gene Stratton Porter, whose works she considered suitable for young people. She urged us to read everything by this author, but the only title I remember is *A Girl of the Limberlost*. And I remember, too, the subject, if not the title, of another of Miss Porter's novels. The subject was syphilis; this book was discussed in a special session with only the girls present, and its moral was the importance of living a clean, virtuous life. Another and more dramatic event occasioned a similar session convened by Miss Overholtz, "for girls only." One of the boys in our class "got a sophomore in trouble." They both had to drop out of school and get married. The theme of Miss Overholtz's address this time was: "Judge not that ye be not judged." The two young people had sinned, but they had paid for their weakness, and we must forgive, and visit our errant sister when her child was born and extend the hand of friendship and love. The bottom line went like this: we, as women, must be the strong ones; we must not yield to urgencies of the male sex, the latter being really the weaker, even if the more aggressive, of the sexes. We must keep the bright flame of purity and honor eternally glowing.

It was the year of our junior-senior banquet and we were the hosts. A committee of the socially most knowledgeable girls was appointed to plan the menu and the entertainment. It would be held, of course, at the town's only hotel, called the Curry House.

The committee returned with its report, which was unanimously approved. The menu would feature Waldorf salad, chicken à la king, and creamed peas in patty shells, a menu that was to become the blueprint for endless chains of banquets on the lecture circuit for years to come. The banquet was a great success. Every member of the junior and senior classes was there except Blanche Dixon, our brilliant, proud, pretty black student, who was to become salutatorian of the Class of '16. In the midst of the festivities, I wondered why she had not come. Hadn't she been invited? I dared not ask.

Then the talk of college went on apace.

# 28

## "... Over All Mischance"

Mr. Teitlebaum's prediction proved correct: the cows did produce more and richer milk on their new winter diet. The stables at milking time smelled somewhat like a brewery, and I wondered if our cows would ever again be content with their summer sustenance, even if the pasture was sweet clover. Papa began talking seriously about adding to the stables and buying more cows. Mama, with rare courage, said she hoped his plans included an additional milker to go with the increased herd.

Papa was exceedingly talkative that autumn. At mealtimes he was full of jovial anecdotes and forecasts of growing prosperity, repeating the joke about pearls and furs and gold watches.

The seed corn had been very good, and the crib was filled to capacity. The field that had been planted with corn for the horses' feed had turned out well, too. There were lots of corn husks for the *hatamalchick's* tamale business. During the week Mama and Papa stuffed the sacks; on weekends I helped. At such times Papa returned to his old habit of reading aloud to us from the *Jewish Forward*, and Mama and I would clean the silks from the corn husks and do the packing. There was something unreal, unhealthy about Papa's determination to fill the weekends with words that in the end seemed to "signify nothing." Mama told me once when we were alone that this flow of incessant chatter dwindled to a trickle during the days I was in New Richmond, and I suddenly and fearfully sensed the reason: he wanted to leave no time for *me* to talk, for *me* to change the subject—to speak of college again.

We had formed our closest ties with the Jewish farmers—"necktie farmers," Papa called them, afraid to soil their hands with real work. Nevertheless he enjoyed their occasional Sunday visits, enjoyed showing off his improvements and talking about them in Yiddish, enjoyed having me play records for them, enjoyed hitching up Ol' Belle to the surrey and going to their homes on other Sundays. When it was suggested once, at a gathering at the Kullmans', who had a large house and swings for the children, that we plan a seder for all of us together, he did not object, and plans were laid at once for a joyous Passover dinner.

The Greens came one week and told me with ill-concealed excitement that they had a surprise for me. I was to receive my graduation present—at least one part of it—ahead of time. Would I approve? I told them about Papa's present a year ahead of time, so why not? They revealed their plan: during the Christmas school vacation I would come to visit them, and they would introduce me to the world of theatre.

It proved to be one of the most thrilling experiences of my life. We saw the great team of Julia Sanderson, Donald Brian, and Joseph Cawthorn in *The Girl From Utah*. I thought her the most beautiful woman I had ever seen. We saw *Katinka*, with the magic of white doves turned loose on the stage and what seemed to be real snow falling outside the window of the stage set. It was pure enchantment for the little country girl, who had seen the people of the theatre only in discarded magazines that her mother had picked up on the seats of the "black car," where they were left by departing travelers.

We saw *The Man Who Came Back*, in which the protagonist eventually "came back" from a life of drink and brutality to an honorable life, all because of the love of a good woman. And we saw a holiday show on the Keith-Orpheum vaudeville circuit, with dancers, singers, actors, and comedians performing their hearts out, while they dreamed of the day when they would "play the Palace." But perhaps the loveliest of all was a performance by the Vilna Troupe, a Yiddish repertory company from Russia that was touring Canada when the Archduke Ferdinand was assissinated. They did not return to Russia, but continued their tour into the United States. The play that the Greens had chosen for my closing adventure in theatre was the Vilna Troupe's production in Yiddish of Perez Hirshbein's play, *Green Fields*, a tender, moving love story, perfect to touch the heart of an impressionable sixteen-year-old. I was in love again. First it had been with learning and teaching; then it was the art of writing; now the theatre. In some measure, I mastered all three.

We had a small newspaper now at school, and I was the editor; but what I think was most instrumental in granting me a substantial measure of popularity was a basketful of Mama's doughnuts. Pauline White's parents had built a new house, a "Hollywood bungalow," a showplace to which we were all invited. It had polished floors and window seats which, when raised, provided storage space for things that were frequently used. And when it was decided that we seniors should have a fund-raising event, the White house was, of course, the perfect place to hold it. What the funds were being raised for I do not remember, but the event was a great success. The affair was open to the public for a small admission fee. Once inside, guests could buy refreshments—coffee, pie, and doughnuts.

Each of us had been asked to bring doughnuts or pies, while Mrs. White provided coffee, her house, her fine linens and china— and her supervision. I knew that Mama had never mastered the art of pie-making, so I telephoned her and asked if she could make doughnuts, and told her why I needed them. She said, "Of course, what a question!" To my knowledge she had never made them, but she had said yes, so I assumed it was one more of Mama's hidden talents that I had not previously discovered.

On the afternoon of the fund-raising "social," our rural mailman delivered—not in a package properly prepared for stamping and delivery, but as a favor to Mama, who had met him at the mailbox— a large basket of doughnuts covered with her best kitchen towels.

They were magnificent, all six dozen of them—plump, perfectly formed, generously sugared. When I came home and found them waiting for me, Mr. and Mrs. Lutzky broke one into three parts and we all said, "M-m-m." They were the hit of the evening— jand, vicariously, so was I. My job was to sit at the door and collect the twenty-five-cent price of admission. From time to time someone would come up to me, flushed with the success of our venture, bringing bulletins about the smash hit of Mama's doughnuts.

When I came home again, I told Mama of my pride in her newest culinary achievement. I asked her why she had never made doughnuts before.

"I wanted to many times, but I was always afraid I might fail," she replied. "So I'd end up with strudel or *mandel brot* instead."

"Weren't you afraid this time?" I marveled.

"Of course, but this time I had no choice. So I did it." I was to remember this simple philosophy for many years. But now I asked how she had learned what to do.

"You remember after the fire when we were in the barn, and our neighbor ladies brought doughnuts and coffee? The best ones were Ollie Lumley's cousin Emma's. So after things settled down I asked her how she made them. She told me very slowly, and I wrote it down in Yiddish. She said it was her grandmother's 'receipt.' It was the first time I ever cooked anything from a piece of paper!

But," she repeated, "it's what you needed, so I had no choice." I put my arms around her and declared, "Mama, you are the wonder of the world!"

"Don't talk foolish," she said. But she blushed with pleasure.

The round of class parties had started, and they were almost always held on Saturday evenings. Papa never refused to bring me back to New Richmond on Saturday. I would return on Sunday morning on the earliest "black car" and walk home along Pond Run Road. I longed to take my turn at being a hostess. I thought I might find a way to have a party unlike any of the others. One Saturday evening, as Papa was driving me into town for one of the festivities, I hinted at an idea that would be fun and easy: a hayride followed by a box supper or maybe just dessert—one of Mama's special desserts. Papa's response was totally negative, so I never gave a party. Nevertheless, I was invited to everybody else's affairs.

One of the most elegant dinners was that given by Pauline White in the new house. The table was beautifully set, and there was a place card with a name and a quotation at each plate. My quote was from Shakespeare's *King Henry VI, Part III*, and this is what it said:

> Yield not thy neck
> To fortune's yoke, but let thy dauntless mind
> Still ride in triumph over all mischance.

I thought of Papa and college, and wondered if I would ever be dauntless enough to follow the advice of France's Louis XI to England's distressed Queen Margaret.

# 29

# *" . . . The Winter of My Discontent"*

Papa gave me no opportunity to discuss again the subject of college. His growing concern for his sisters in Russia—a Russia now caught up in World War I—dominated all the conversations, and I could not challenge that, even if I had dared. It was indeed a serious situation. He had sent passage money for his sister, Rivka, who was then unmarried, and for Braindele, the revolutionary. Braindele refused even to try for a passport. She would, she felt, at last have a part in a true revolution. Rivka did make the effort, but she had waited too long, torn between leaving her father and sisters and seeking her own safety. When she finally was ready to make the break, it was too late. She was turned back from her first attempt to cross the border, and all hope of coming to America was lost.

It was just about this time that I began having a recurrent dream that I believe Dr. Freud would have been delighted to interpret. It invariably occurred during my weekend at home. I would be arriving at a hospital to visit a friend, and would get lost in a maze of corridors always crowded with doctors, nurses, patients in wheelchairs or on stretchers. When I tried to ask a doctor or nurse for directions to the room I was seeking, they answered brusquely as they hurried past me, gesturing in different directions. I gave up asking, wandering from corridor to corridor, from floor to floor, and then I would suddenly find myself in a totally different section. The halls were quiet and empty. The oppressive silence was suddenly shattered by a cry of anguish from the ward. It was then that I saw a sign that read: Psychopathic Ward.

I ran blindly, finding at length an exit to the grounds. I could see that it was not the way I had come in. The landscape had changed: the hospital was surrounded now by low, grassy, steep hills. I climbed one which had a small building at its crest—sometimes I climbed on all fours. When I reached the small building, I saw a sign over the door: Admissions. I knocked. A gray-haired woman with an impassive face opened the door and stared at me, waiting.

"Yes?" she finally asked.

"Please, help me," I pleaded. "I am trapped in a dream, you see. If you'll just direct me to the road out of the dream, I'll be all right." At that moment I would wake up, shivering, wishing the day would come. The dream, which took possession of my life in sleep, recurred in every detail, but only when I was at home. Once back in school I was caught up in the excitement of being a senior, of being with my friends, of being accepted in spite of the ways in which I was different: different because of my life-style; different because on Friday afternoons I vanished from the life of the town; different because I was the only Jewish student in the entire school. This last difference was one that caused me, once, to react in a manner that surprised me as much as it surprised everyone else.

It happened in the Current Events class, now conducted by Miss Colvill. The subject under discussion was Louis D. Brandeis, who had been appointed to the United States Supreme Court by President Wilson—an appointment that was proving to be very controversial.

"Why," asked Miss Colvill, "do you think there is so much opposition to Mr. Brandeis?"

I didn't even raise my hand. My answer burst not so much from from my lips as from the pit of my stomach.

"Because," I said harshly, "he's a Jew!"

There was stunned silence. Nobody said anything—not even Miss Colvill. She went on to another topic.

I believe it was not so much the substance of my outburst that shocked the class and the teacher. I believe it was the manner— explosive, accusatory—in which the words were spoken. It was as though I were charging *them* as part of a conspiracy because Brandeis was a Jew. In fact, what I had said was the truth, but not the whole truth. Brandeis's record as a labor attorney was also at issue, and I knew that. I was ashamed of my loss of control. I looked down at my trembling hands and moved them to my lap. I wondered what had possessed me to act almost irrationally—but I knew the answer. I was, in fact, at last getting rid of the anger I had suppressed ever since this "difference" had allowed a group of rowdy boys to greet me as "Miss Shew"—my first encounter with anti-Semitism, albeit in one of its sillier forms. The Brandeis incident was my catharsis. It was never again referred to by classmates or teacher. For myself, I was both ashamed and relieved.

The social highlight of our senior year was the reception at the home of Mr. and Mrs. Borders, for the junior and senior classes. All of our class was there except Blanche Dixon. I dared not ask my hostess whether she was coming. I was afraid I might learn that she had not been invited, and if that were true I could no longer admire Mr. George Borders, who shared a place beside Mr. Frank Franz in my pantheon of special gods. So I kept silent. Long afterward I learned that she *had* been invited but had declined.

A dramatic and unplanned climax to this party ended the event literally in a blaze of glory. The New Richmond weekly newspaper gave this account of the affair:

> On leaving Mr. Borders' Junior-Senior reception Tuesday, February 22, about midnight, Harry Few saw a dark red glare against the

sky. On looking down the street, he saw a huge blaze. "Fire," he
yelled, and he, Edwin Carnes and Newel Clark started for the Town
Hall fire alarm.

William Voelkel, Helen Roberts and Pauline White, who were just
behind Harry, started for the fire, which proved to be in the barn
of Bogart and Powers where the C. & O. Transfer horses are
kept.... William Voelkel and Ruric Wiggins, who had just arrived,
succeeded in knocking down the [stable] door with a log. In the
meantime, Dorothy McFarland, Jean Clark, Daisy Davis, Goldie
Weisberg, Dale Nichols, John McNamara and Donald McMurchy
arrived.... Through the smoke and flame [of the hay] Dale, William
and Ruric, each with a knife, started to cut the halters of the horses.
They brought each of the horses to the door where they were taken
to a place of safety by Dorothy, Goldie, Pauline, Jean and
Daisy.... [Dale Nichols got the last two horses out, cut his thumb
and burned his hand. Donald, John, Ruric and Dale went back]...
into the burning building and, amid flying sparks, flaming timbers
and stifling smoke, they [got] every piece of harness out....

The fire companies arrived and after several hours...the flames
were extinguished.... There was no loss of livestock or harness,
owing to the heroic efforts of the boys and girls....

Pauline left both her slippers in the mud. I left one of mine. It
was the most successful party of the year.

I lay awake a long time that night, thinking about the unexpected
drama of the evening. We were a bunch of young people. We had
been faced with a dangerous situation, a high-risk situation. We
had faced it, and we had handled it. We had faced more danger
than the newspaper described; the boys had brought the horses
to us and we, the girls, had led them to safety. But "led" is the
wrong word. The horses were terrified; they screamed and reared,
lifting us off the ground as they tried to break away from us. But
we hung on. We did what we had to do. We did not yield. I believed,
at that moment, that I could face anything, any obstacle, and

overcome it, and I was ready " . . . to strive, to seek, to find, and not to yield."

Not long after this, my second encounter with "trial by fire," Mr. Borders called me into his office.

"I have two things to tell you," he said. "First, you are going to be valedictorian. I am telling you now because I would like your valedictory address to be in the form of poetry, and you should have plenty of time to prepare." I must have looked utterly stunned. He smiled broadly. "Are you surprised?" he asked.

"I thought it would be Blanche," I replied, my voice not quite steady. "I think she's the smartest one in our class."

"Blanche is salutatorian," he replied. "And if you are harboring any notion that she is in second place because of her color, please put that out of your mind. I hope you respect me more than to think me capable of such prejudice."

We stared at each other for a moment.

"Blanche *is* very bright," he continued. "She is going on to college, and she plans to go to medical school. She already has a grant from a foundation to assist black students. You have gifts, talents, beyond just being bright. My decision is an honest one. I hope you believe me."

My eyes filled. I smiled. He held out his hand and we shook firmly.

"Now, I told you I have *two* things to tell you. The other thing I am telling you because you need time to talk to your parents, so they will know what lies ahead for you, and help you prepare for it." I waited.

"Ohio Wesleyan University, a very good college, has offered a scholarship to our school. The scholarship is for four years. It covers almost everything. The faculty of New Richmond High School has voted to offer it to you."

The rest of the school week I was in a daze. Mr. Borders had asked me not to make public what he had told me—not yet. Only my parents should know and, if I wished, the Lutzkys. Tradition required that awards and honors be announced at the graduation ceremonies.

Driving home that Friday afternoon, I was bursting to tell Papa, but I wanted Mama to hear it at the same time.

Papa seemed to be in a better frame of mind than he had been for some time. He made jokes, made me laugh, did not even speak of his anxiety about his sisters. We were almost home when he said, with an enthusiasm that seemed to be somehow overdone, "I have something to tell you, daughter, that I think will make you as happy as it has made me and Mama. But it will keep until after supper."

"And I have something to tell you and Mama," I said, "and I hope it will make you both as happy as it has made me! But I'll wait so Mama can hear it, too."

"Well, well, happiness on all sides! Moses and the Israelites must have felt like that when the Red Sea parted!"

My own excitement was somehow tinged with apprehension; I had a feeling that Papa's good news was not going to make me as happy as he said it had made him and Mama.

There was a special supper that night: chopped herring salad for an appetizer, a soup of barley and split peas and a *cholent*, the special dish baked overnight in the brick oven that Uncle Max had built for us. *Cholent* was a delectable combination of richly browned pot roast surrounded by deep-crusted golden-brown potatoes, fragrant with onions, and surrounded with butterbeans that melted in the mouth from the long, slow cooking. There was also a fresh baked twist loaf, and a compote of dried fruits, with sponge cake for dessert. I waited anxiously, and not without dread, to hear Papa's news. I helped Mama clear the table, helped her bring glasses of hot tea, and a dish of cherry preserves to make the tea more than an ordinary beverage. Mama smiled but seemed a little nervous. My apprehension mounted. We sat down to our tea.

"Now," Papa finally said, "you have some news for us, daughter?"

"Yes, Papa, but you have something nice to tell *me*, you said!"

"True," he replied, "but you go first." I told them first about being chosen valedictorian and explained what it meant. They beamed and expressed their pride in me, and Papa declared that that was indeed good news.

"But that's only part of it, Papa!" I cried. "What's *really* important is the scholarship!" There was a moment's silence. Mama's face reflected mixed feelings. She didn't quite know what that meant. I was sure that Papa knew; there was no mistake about how *he* felt, and what I saw chilled me to the bone. I explained it to Mama. She glowed with pride.

"Mendel," she exclaimed. "That changes everything!"

"It changes nothing," Papa replied. "She hasn't even heard my news. . . . You want to hear it, don't you?" he turned to me.

"Of course, Papa."

"Good." He relaxed, smiling. "It's like this. I was in Kegtown this week, and in the general store I ran into Mr. Wentzeler, the president of the school board. Did you know that Kegtown School is an independent district? All the others pay only forty dollars a month, but this one is special. It pays fifty!"

Under the table I clenched my fists to stop my hands from trembling. My apprehension mounted. Papa stopped to sip some of his tea, then quickly put the glass down. Maybe he was a little uneasy, too, or ashamed. Maybe his hands were shaking like mine.

"Well, the long and the short of it is, they need a teacher for next year, and he offered you the job!"

"How could he offer it to me?" I cried. "I wasn't even there!"

"But I was there! I am your father, and I could speak for you. I accepted for you."

"I'd rather go to college!" I exclaimed. "I've got the scholarship! It pays for almost everything. When I sell Beauty to you I'll have enough. You could at least have asked me first! You could have—"

"I could have! I could have! I could have!" His voice was rising. Mama looked at me pleadingly. "I made the right decision for you, because you are still a child. You're not even sixteen yet—not until April. And this summer, after you graduate, before you start teaching, you *will* go to college! You didn't give me a chance to tell you that!"

"I don't understand."

"It's the law! For six weeks you have to go to a normal school. That's what it's called. But it's college! Something like in Russia the Normalne Utilitze. And I will give you top money for Beauty, and extra, so you can go to school and buy clothes like for a college girl!"

I stared in stony silence. Papa continued in a more conciliatory tone.

"Is that so terrible? And this year, teaching in Kegtown, you'll have all this wonderful experience, and when the school year ends in the spring, you'll still be only seventeen. How will it hurt you to stay home one more year?"

"You mean after I teach one year I can really go to college?" There was a long pause. Finally he spoke, and I knew it was perhaps the hardest thing he ever said.

"Yes."

"I won't have my scholarship then."

"No matter."

Mama reached over and touched me. "You see, dear heart? It won't be so bad." Her voice was urgent, pleading.

Papa said, "My tea got cold."

"I'll go make fresh tea," Mama said, reverting to her old speech for peace and harmony. I had not heard it from her for a long time.

I had a minute alone with Mama in the kitchen when Papa went out to check on the stock.

"Mama," I said, "you helped me go to high school. Why can't you help me now?"

She shook her head. "It's different now. He won't give in to it; he's a sick man. He needs you near, and that's the truth. I'm sorry, my child. Forgive me."

That night I dreamed my dream again.

# 30

# "Ave Atque Vale"

Mr. Borders sat for what seemed a long time, just looking at my stricken face.

"I would like to talk to your father," he said finally.

I shook my head. I told him it would do no good, only make it harder on me and on Mama. And it might bring on an attack.

Two things absorbed my total attention and left me very little time to brood. One was my valedictory poem. The other was the class play.

I believe the play was a romantic comedy called *The Elopement of Ellen*, and a young woman came up from Cincinnati to direct. I was cast as the grandmother of the young lovers. My hair was made up white, and dressed in a manner apparently fashionable for old ladies somewhere, sometime: short, corkscrew curls on either side of my face, and bushy gray eyebrows to match. I recall only one line of my part, and I believe it may have been the only one, repeated many times throughout the three-act opus. The line was: "Things never was [*sic*] like this when I was a gal!" delivered in a quavery voice worthy of a feeble one-hundred-year-old survivor. But I was delighted just to be in the play, to be in "show business."

The second project, and the more important one, was the writing of my valedictory, which I had planned to call "Ave Atque Vale," but it was going in a direction away from the classical "hail and farewell" theme. I spoke to Mr. Borders about it, and he told me to write what I felt, say what I wanted to say, and not worry about conforming to any established pattern. The speaker of the evening, he said, would surely say everything that could be said, or ever had been said, about standing on the threshold of a new and challenging world, and about the New Richmond Class of '16 dedicating itself to meet that challenge, etcetera, etcetera.

"You have my permission," said Mr. Borders, "to write what your heart and your mind dictate." So I wrote a long poem in blank verse called "The Hall of Fame." I remember only the first lines: "Up to the portals of the Hall of Fame, the young man made his way." He was met by the angel who guarded the hallowed door. I remember that he asked her what he must accomplish to earn a place in the temple. The angel told him something to the effect that she could offer no formula. The years of his life, she said, lay before him, and he must use his life as he thought would merit his place in the Hall of Fame. He and only he could make the choice.

The young man decides to become a man of great wealth, a great philanthropist. When he makes his next visit, the angel asks him why he thinks that he who has amassed such wealth . . . who has been lauded by press and from pulpit for giving so generously to numerous charities . . . is worthier than an obscure laborer who, when he had a loaf of bread, shared it with someone even less fortunate than he. The supplicant goes back to the city and decides at last to win fame as a military genius. He enlists in the army of his native land, distinguishes himself in battles, reaches the highest rank, and is retired in a blaze of glory, bedecked with medals and ribbons of every kind. He is a gray-haired figure now when he appears again before the angel, who, of course, is ageless. Again she shakes her head. The Hall, she says, is already overflowing with military heroes. The only space left is for a hero of peace. What has he done, she asks, to advance peace?

Greatly discouraged, he seeks a mountain peak, which he climbs. He communes with the stars, the wind and all the elements of nature and "whatever gods there be." He realizes that he must live as a man and pursue those virtues that a true man should cultivate, and let fame come to him if he earns it. My poem, alas, did not clarify what those virtues should be and I, myself, was apparently ignorant of the fact that wealth and philanthropy and military prowess were, in fact, among the most acceptable of all achievements. But naive and pompous as my "Hall of Fame" was, it won the acclaim of my peers and even of my teachers.

The last social function of the Class of '16 was to display the graduation gifts at the homes of the graduates. Mine, of course, were not on display. But I did pass around a picture of Beauty taken with a box camera, which was also a gift. The others I had to tell about. One of them I wore—a white lace "fascinator," a head scarf guaranteed to enhance the appearance of the wearer to the extent of making her utterly fascinating. Mama had traded some of her rose preserves for a lovely piece of lace which she bound with white satin ribbon to make the gift. Mama's rose preserves had become, over the years, her private negotiable currency, and she had gained considerable skill in its use.

We wore caps and gowns for our graduation, and dresses of our choice for the baccalaureate. Mr. Charlie Green had made me a lovely, simple dress of peach-colored crepe de chine to wear under my black robe. It doubled as my baccalaureate dress, and served me for all the parties.

We met in the church chosen for the baccalaureate service to rehearse the processional. We were fifteen graduates—four young men and eleven young women. Four of the girls had arranged to march with the four boys, with whom they had already been more or less keeping company. For the rest, the girls were to be paired two-by-two. The arrangement had been unofficially planned by the girls before the rehearsal. Now, before the choices could be announced, Blanche Dixon spoke up: "Who am I supposed to march with?"

"Since we are an odd number," Miss Colvill pointed out, smiling, "one of you will have to condescend to march with a teacher."

Impulsively I spoke up. "I'll be your partner, Blanche, if you want me."

"All right," she replied.

I looked at the girl I had left in the lurch—I believe it was Dot McFarland. My look carried an appeal for forgiveness. She shrugged and looked at Miss Colvill. They smiled at each other. Nobody smiled at me. Not even Blanche.

It was over: the parties, the baccalaureate, the vows of friendship; the writing in one another's memory books; the high-flown speeches; the class song; the class motto, *To be rather than to seem*, engraved in Latin on our class rings; the tearful embraces; the congratulations from proud parents; and finally, in some cases, "See you at Miami in the fall."

# 31

# *A Log with Me at One End*

I did not see any of the Class of '16 at Miami in the fall or at any other time. But I *was* at Miami in the summer of 1916, to learn in six weeks to teach any child who came before me at any age from six on, in any grade from one to eight. The prospect before me seemed as dreary as Macbeth's view of the dread future that was to be his: "Tomorrow, and tomorrow, and tomorrow, / Creeps in this petty pace from day to day...."

But I explored the lovely campus, which at that time merged with the grounds of two other colleges—Oxford College for Women and Western College for Women. All of us in my cottage shared packages from home, had midnight snacks sneaked into our rooms in giggling secret—patterned, I suppose, after the stories about the halcyon days of college life. We learned that the newest trends in the teaching of reading discarded the introduction of the alphabet at the very beginning. The two favored methods were the synthetic and the analytic. Neither was recommended. It was a case of "you pays your money and you takes your chance." The use of flash cards was highly recommended. The rest of the curriculum was equally indecisive and confusing. After six weeks we received certificates qualifying us to teach at the lowest level of the public school system of Ohio: one teacher, one room, grades one to eight.

Later in the summer there was a teachers' institute at our own county seat, during which we were entertained and instructed by role models who demonstrated techniques and projects which could enhance the teaching process in the one-room school.

One of these was a storytelling session. It was the one idea I carried away with me, and the only thing I used in an unorthodox method of stimulating the children's *desire* to read. I believed that if the desire was there, the learning would follow.

In September, on the Monday after Labor Day, in the year 1916, at the age of sixteen years, five months and five days, I met my eight grades in the Mount Pisgah Elementary School. (Nothing about the village was called anything but Kegtown except the church and the school: they were dignified by use of the proper name, Mount Pisgah.) My eight grades contained twenty-odd boys and girls ranging in age from six to seventeen. Some of them were children I had played with before I went off to high school. Two of the boys were older than I was. I tried to look at them with an air of authority. They grinned and giggled when they greeted me with "Good morning, Miss Goldie." At least they did not try to lock me in the woodshed!

The schoolroom was almost a replica of the one in which I had spent so many years on Dunham's Hill—the same round-bellied cast-iron stove in the center of the room, the same cloakroom, the desktops carved with initials and hearts pierced by arrows. Graffiti as we know it today had not yet been invented. But in two respects this new school was wanting: it had no flag, and no library—with the exception of a tattered volume of *Uncle Tom's Cabin* and the ubiquitous *In His Steps* by the Reverend Dr. Sheldon. Not even Horatio Alger, Jr.!

One of our martyred presidents, James Garfield, is said to have remarked in a speech at a banquet in 1871 that " . . . a university is a log with me at one end and Mark Hopkins at the other." There are other versions of the quote, but this seems the most succinct. I was no Mark Hopkins, but I could supply the figurative log and try to instill in the children an interest in learning in the best way I knew.

I had subscribed in the spring to the *Ohio Teacher*, and in it I found a variety of fund-raising plans to meet such school needs as the district board could not, or would not, supply. With the approval of the parents, we undertook a pencil-selling project, the children acting as salespeople. The response of the Kegtowners enabled us to win a handsome flag. We held a flag-raising ceremony, and sang "My Country 'Tis of Thee" because it was much easier to handle for our combined voices than "The Star-Spangled Banner," which had not yet been made the official national anthem.

Money for books for the library was harder to come by. I realized that I must first inspire in the children a genuine desire for books beyond their texts, which most of them would have happily done without. At this point I drew on the storytelling demonstration that I had found interesting at the teachers' institute that summer. The tale that the "story lady" had used was *Peter Pan*, and I decided to experiment with that one.

One rainy morning I told the children we were going to have something new during reading period—something I hoped the whole school would enjoy. I was going to tell them a story.

To my delight the children were completely captivated by *Peter Pan*. Even the two seventeen-year-old boys, pretending to be asleep, listened intermittently. At a crucial point in James Barrie's fantasy about a boy who refused to grow up, when one of Peter's boys shoots an arrow that fells Wendy, I looked at the clock. The rain had stopped, and I announced that it was time for recess. The children set up a clamor. They offered to forego recess if I would finish the story. I said I could not do that because recess was important—it offered time for fresh air and exercise through games. The older boys loudly agreed; the others wanted to stay and learn what happened to Wendy. I compromised. I told them

I would lend my copy of *Peter Pan* to a seventh-grade child to take home. The next day the child would read the rest of the story aloud—or tell it, if she preferred.

My stratagem worked. The children were discovering the fun to be found in books.

One day I decided it was time to talk about a new project. I told them that if we had a library to fill the empty shelves of the bookcase that stood in the corner, they could borrow all kinds of wonderful stories and take them home to read in private. I asked for a show of hands: "Who would like a library?" All raised hands, even the oldest boys, making a joke of it, and the one six-year-old who didn't quite know what he was voting for, but followed the lead of the others. This, accompanied by cries of loud approval, gave me my consensus. It was time to think of ways and means.

The last story we had read on our weekly special reading day was *Rip Van Winkle*. I was ready to apply my recently inspired passion for the theatre to our present need. The Washington Irving story seemed ideal. I could adapt it so that every child could be involved in some way. When I revealed my plan for producing a play to raise money for our library, the enthusiasm was boundless. I set about preparing a dramatization of the story.

Friday afternoons were traditionally set aside for "speaking pieces." Now we used the time for studying the play, the children taking turns reading different parts. Finally I started the casting. Every child had a part, either in the play itself or on the production staff. We made wigs of cotton batting, and mothers helped with the costumes. The Modern Woodmen of America allowed us to use their hall over the general store. The hall had a sizable platform at one end, which served as a stage. As we progressed, we began to come back on Saturday afternoons to rehearse, and become accustomed to working in that facility. The last three rehearsals were held there in the evenings in full dress, and with a few parents present to accustom the children to performing in the "theatre" before our audience.

While the mothers helped with costumes, the fathers helped improvise crude, basic scenery, hanging a curtain of colored sheets on a heavy wire rod, practicing opening and closing it; they also set up chairs for the audience. Mr. Wentzeler offered to take tickets at the door. Admission was fifty cents.

We presented *Rip Van Winkle* on a Saturday evening in February. It was a rousing success. After the final curtain was drawn and the final bows taken, Mr. Wentzeler, a parent and I checked the receipts. We announced to the waiting parents and the members of our acting company that we had taken in fifty dollars. I doubt if an announcement that the national debt had been paid would have elicited a more resounding "Hip, hip, hooray!" Mama and Papa, waiting for me to go home, were beaming with pride like all the others. Mr. Wentzeler suggested that he keep the money over Sunday, as he lived so close by and it would be safe. He would meet me on Monday, after the post office branch in the general store opened. He would buy a money order and bring it to me at the schoolhouse.

The children crowded around me for one last assurance of my pride in their achievement. At last everyone went home, reluctant to end the evening, to miss one last grain of praise—to sleep, "perchance to dream"—more likely to stay awake as long as possible, reliving the wonderful experience of creating a fine thing.

I came to school early on Monday. Mr. Wentzeler was already inside, out of the cold. As president of the board, he had his own key to the building. He had even built a fire in the potbellied stove, saving me the disagreeable task, and I was grateful.

"Was the post office open so early?" I asked.

"No, it will be soon."

"Oh, I thought maybe you had the money order for me. I have my list of books all made out." I started to read it to him: "*Little Women*, Hawthrone's *Tales from Grandfather's Chair*—" He interrupted me.

"I need to talk to you, Goldie." I sensed trouble. I put away my list, and waited.

"You know, all the board members were there Saturday night and they all thought it was fine, just fine."

"I'm glad."

"There's one thing, though, and I hope you won't get upset. We're short of funds this month, and we're going to have to use the play receipts to pay your salary."

I jumped up.

"You're *what*?" I yelled.

"Keep your voice down now, *Miss* Goldie. 'Tain't nice for a schoolmarm to yell like that."

"I won't stand for it!"

"Then there won't be any money to pay your salary this month."

"Suppose we hadn't had a play—hadn't made fifty dollars— how would you have paid me?"

"Oh, I reckon we'd have scrounged around, maybe gone to the bank, maybe told you you'd have to wait."

"Well, you can start scrounging now, or going to the bank, and just forget about telling me to wait! Because you can't have that money! I worked many a night to put on that play. The parents worked hard. The kids worked hard—"

"That's right!" he interrupted. "They worked on a fool play instead of doin' homework. That didn't set so well with the board."

"Then get another teacher!"

"Don't threaten me, Goldie. There *are* folks say you're not so good at discipline."

"You mean because I never used a switch?"

"Don't tell me there ain't a single young'un didn't need it!"

"I don't beat children. And I want that money we earned and you're holding out."

"You're pretty tough for a little gal run barefoot around here in the summer not so long ago gettin' the soles of your feet so tough she could walk on oat stubble!"

"I'm tough all over now!" I was beginning to hear children's voices in the schoolyard. I spoke more quietly.

"I'll get a petition out against you," I said. "Every parent will sign it and other teachers in the district, too, I'll bet. We'll get what we earned—you'll see!"

I walked toward the door and began ringing the first bell—the warning bell for stragglers. Mr. Wentzeler walked out without another word. Suddenly I was overcome by the enormity of my daring. I clung to the bell rope to steady my shaking hands.

The next morning, I walked into the schoolroom and straight to my desk. I intended, as the first of the day's business, to draft a petition to send home with the children. An envelope addressed to me was lying on my desk. It was in Mr. Wentzeler's handwriting. I thought, with surprising detachment, "What will Papa say when I tell him I was fired for insubordination?"

I opened the envelope. In it was a money order for fifty dollars. I was stunned for a moment. Then I let out a most unladylike whoop. I cried to the walls, to the blackboard, to the round-bellied stove, "I did it! I did it! I stood up to him, and I did—not—yield!" Then I looked heavenward. "How about that, Ulysses?"

I sat down at my desk for a few minutes, savoring my newfound power. "And now," I thought to myself, "I can remind Papa about his promise, and begin planning my college future."

# 32

# *"The Best Laid Plans . . ."*

I did not go home that Tuesday after school. Mama, as usual, had needed Ol' Belle for her weekly trip to the city, and I often walked the mile in good weather. But this evening I had been invited to have supper and spend the night at the home of two pupils, Flora and Michelle Laing. Entertaining the teacher in this way was an accepted and pleasant extracurricular part of the school year, and promoted a cooperative relationship with the parents. Tuesday was my best day for such amenities, as everybody knew, because on that day I did not have a horse at my disposal.

The meal at the Laings was eaten against an excited recapitulation of "the theatrical event of the season," full of the children's "Do you remember's?" and "Do you think anybody noticed when my wig almost fell off?" and—above all—"Do we have to wait until next year to do it again?" I did not tell them that next year I hoped to be elsewhere. It was neither the time nor the place for such an announcement. Besides, it was premature; I felt brave but, where Papa was concerned, not yet invincible.

In the morning the two little girls and I, holding hands, walked the quarter of a mile from their home to the schoolhouse. I was startled to see Dr. John's horse and buggy hitched to the post in front of the yard. Dr. John himself was chatting with Mr. Gillespie, on his way to open his blacksmith shop. The men greeted me, and the children ran off the join some of their classmates approaching down the road.

"I have something for you, Goldie," said Dr. John as he joined me. "It's a little present for the library of the Mount Pisgah Elementary School. Oh, I know you have lots of money now, and you'll raise more, but I hope you will allow me to present you with the very first volume. It's one that I loved as a boy—Robert Louis Stevenson's *Treasure Island*. And, without your permission, I made so bold as to inscribe in it...." He opened it to the flyleaf and handed it to me. I finished reading it aloud: "... To the fine actors and actresses and their inspired director and teacher, Miss Goldie, and the boys and girls of the Mount Pisgah Elementary School. (Signed) John Mott, M.D."

I looked up at this man who had so enhanced my childhood and said, "If it wasn't so public, I'd kiss you. The children will be proud of this—and so am I."

"Well, I want to talk to you anyway, so come inside and you can kiss me in private."

His manner was grave. I became apprehensive. We went inside and sat down by my desk.

"I had to go and see your papa again last night. Josiah was there helpin' your mama, doin' the chores, but Max insisted on gettin' into the middle of things. I think ensilage may be one of the things he can't tolerate. Anyway, he had a real bad spell. So bad that he finally agreed to go to Cincinnati and see Dr. Ullery. I'd say your papa has developed a deep-seated chronic bronchial asthma. Dr. Ullery is a specialist in respiratory problems. I called him and made an appointment for him to see your papa on Saturday morning. And I want you to go with him."

I could not trust myself to speak. I nodded.

"I'm going out to see him this evening again," he continued. "I told your folks I'd pick you up and bring you home at the same time. And now," he rose, "I'll collect that kiss and be on my way." He hugged me for a moment and left. I managed to regain my composure, and turned to the job of starting the fire in the stove.

\*     \*     \*

Papa made light of the attack when Dr. John brought me home in the "Tin Lizzie." He told me the doctor just bullied him into agreeing to see Dr. Ullery. He finally said "yes" to stop Dr. John's nagging. But even now, after he had come through the worst of the episode, his speech got increasingly wheezy as he talked.

"Well," I said, "don't try to nag *me* out of it. I'm counting on a day in the big city. Maybe we'll go and have a soda at Mr. Goldenstern's Confectionery and Cultural Center. It won't hurt two hayseeds like us to get a little polish."

Every day seemed endless before we reached Saturday. Papa and I drove Ol' Belle to the place where we had left her for years when we went to the city. We took an early train to Cincinnati. We talked about many things, but not about promises and colleges. At ten o'clock in the morning, we were admitted to Dr. Ullery's consulting room by his nurse-receptionist, a gray-haired, motherly-looking woman in a white uniform and nurse's cap.

I had expected a city doctor to have an aura of grandeur, to wear pince-nez on a black silk ribbon, to look grave and stroke his chin. Dr. Ullery was totally unlike that image. He was short, stocky, with tousled gray hair and quizzical eyes. He was wearing black alpaca trousers, a rumpled but clean white coat, a stethoscope, and carpet slippers. He also had a warm, engaging smile which was reassuring. He stuck his head into the reception room.

"I'll need you in ten minutes, Maggie," he said. Then he and Papa disappeared into the examination room. I looked at my watch. In exactly ten minutes Maggie appeared, gave me a warm smile in passing, and disappeared to join Dr. Ullery and Papa. I picked up a well-worn, year-old copy of the *Saturday Evening Post*, and tried to read. I closed my eyes and dozed. When I woke up an hour had passed. A few minutes later Dr. Ullery, followed by Maggie, came in.

"He's getting dressed," he told me.

Dr. John's diagnosis, it turned out, was correct—"right on the nose," Dr. Ullery said. Papa needed a change of climate; another winter on the farm could do him in. The doctor suggested Arizona—either Tucson, which he pronounced "Tuckson," or Phoenix. In the meantime, he was to use the atomizer with the medication that Dr. John had prescribed. If he felt a bad attack coming on, he was to use adrenalin. All the talk about a radical change in his life, of pulling up roots, going to Arizona, the danger of another winter in Ohio, brought on the very attack that Dr. Ullery had warned him against. The doctor called Maggie to prepare an injection of adrenalin. We watched as he squeezed between two fingers a muscular part of Papa's arm. Maggie swabbed it with alcohol, and Dr. Ullery quickly and deftly injected the adrenalin. He told me he would give me a syringe with a needle that I could use to practice on an orange, and another with sterile needles to use on Papa if necessary. And I must teach Mama, too. He dictated to Maggie detailed instructions for me, and wrote a prescription for the adrenalin. He told Papa if he were alone and having an attack, he could give himself an injection into his thigh or even a muscular part of his belly. He would call Dr. John and also send him a complete report of his examination and findings.

The relief afforded Papa by the adrenalin was so complete and so rapid that it worried him. Perhaps it was too soon, like morphine? Dr. Ullery reassured him, but warned him to use it only when a bad attack was coming on.

How did it all happen? I asked. Dr. Ullery said it was difficult to pinpoint. Papa was probably allergic to a number of things, including extreme cold. There was also the emotional element. Yes, Dr. John had told him about the mild smoke inhalation. It was probably much less damaging than all the cigarettes he smoked, and he'd better do something about that. In any case, rather than spend weeks, maybe months, trying to pin down the exact genesis of his asthma, Dr. Ullery's advice was definitely, unequivocally, "Go west, young man," and the sooner the better. We shook hands.

"Your Dr. Mott is a good man, a good doctor," said Dr. Ullery.

"I know," I replied. "None better."

We left with our sheet of directions and our prescription, which we filled in the pharmacy in the same building. Papa was frightened, discouraged, on the verge of breaking down, like a child. Finally he spoke, his voice husky with emotion.

"You'll come with us, with Mama and me, to Arizona?" I was astounded. He had humbled himself to *ask*, almost to plead.

"Yes, I will come," I said. I managed to smile as I made the commitment. He smiled back, relaxed. He took my arm, and we walked slowly to Mr. Goldenstern's store for a soda and a smidgin of culture.

It was almost dark when Papa and I drove into our own barnyard. Dr. John's Model T was parked near the house. The sign of it frightened Papa.

"Why is *he* here? Maybe Mama took sick?" he demanded.

"I'm sure he's here because Dr. Ullery called him. You know he said he would," I reassured him. "And you know it's just like Dr. John to be here when we come home."

"Just the same," he insisted, "you go on into the house and see is everything all right. I'll stable Ol' Belle and be in in a little while."

I found Mama sitting by the kitchen table, her head in her hands. Dr. John was standing over her, patting her on the back.

"All right, now, Becky, you've done your crying," he was saying. "And you had a right to cry. But that's over. You've got to show a good face to Max when he comes in." He turned to me. "Where *is* your papa?"

"He's taking care of Ol' Belle. When he saw your machine he thought something was wrong with Mama."

"Mama's fine, ain't you, Mama?"

"Sure, I'm fine! We're going to make a new beginning again." She dried her eyes. "You're so late. I was worried."

"We went to Mr. Goldenstern's for a few minutes." I took off my coat, scarf, and hat and put them aside as I talked. "Then we stopped in to see Uncle Harry. Papa wanted him to know what was happening. After that we went up to Tante Freidel Mishkin's and she insisted we stay for dinner. We called Frumcha and Charlie Green from there, but they weren't home. Papa seemed to want to talk about what happened to us. Anyway we missed the next interurban, and lost an hour that way." To Dr. John I said, "I take it Dr. Ullery talked to you." He nodded. Mama asked him to stay for supper, but he said Velma, his niece, and "Doc" Leeds were expecting him. He had come over to talk to Mama, he said, so she'd be prepared for the news she would hear from us. He took Mama's hand and patted it.

"You call me now, Becky, if you need me." I walked out to the porch with him. We saw Papa approaching. I went back into the house and helped Mama put supper on the table.

After the shock of the first few days, we faced the reality of our situation. We tossed a coin to deecide our choice of destination. It fell "heads" for Phoenix. The farm was put up for sale and, unless someone came along who wanted everything—the land, the stock, the whole "shootin' match"—we would hold a public auction. George Lumley and other neighbors told Papa he ought to plan on two days for the sale. The seed corn alone would bring people from all over the county. On Sundays neighbors came to visit, to say how sorry they were, to lend support.

It was a painful time, especially for Mama and Papa. I had my days filled with the schoolroom and the children. In the middle of March our books arrived. Because they were ordered from a school supplies house, we got a lot of books for our money. Our fifty dollars bought thirty-eight books—*Little Women, Little Men*, Hans Christian Anderson, *A Child's Garden of Verses, Black Beauty, The Little Lame Prince, Tales from Grandfather's Chair, Hans Brinker and the Silver Skates*, Lamb's *Tales From Shakespeare*, books about other children and other lands. We made bookplates and inscribed them:

FROM THE LIBRARY
OF THE
MT. PISGAH ELEMENTARY SCHOOL

We had a special showing for parents and the board. A few days later, on a Friday afternoon, shortly before the close of the school day, Mr. Wentzeler came in near the end of our "recitation" period and sat down at the back of the room. One of the seventh-grade girls was delivering Lincoln's Gettysburg Address. When she finished he applauded and she returned to her seat, blushing and smiling.

I dismissed the class. We all wished one another a pleasant weekend. I reminded them of their homework and we said good-bye until Monday.

When the last child was gone, Mr. Wentzeler came over to my desk. I rose.

"I'm real sorry to hear about your pa," he said.

"Thank you, Mr. Wentzeler." I sat down again, suddenly very tired. He perched on one of the children's desks, facing me.

"Goin' out west, are they?"

"Yes, to Arizona."

"What do *you* figure on doin', Goldie?"

"Going along with them. What else can I do?"

"Well, I figured you might let them go, and you stay on here for another year, till they got settled. And then, if it worked out for your pa, and you wanted to, you could join them." I waited. I felt there was something else that he wanted to say.

"What I'm tryin' to say, Goldie, is, if you want it, the school job's yours."

I felt my eyes filling up. It took me a moment to recover my voice.

"Mr. Wentzeler, I appreciate that. It means a lot that you'd want me back. But I must go with them. They need me."

Early in March, 1917, Mr. Sam Romberg, one of the group that Papa called "necktie farmers," sold our farm. Mr. Romberg was a salesman for a Cincinnati real estate firm, and we were pleased that someone we knew would benefit from the transaction. The buyers were James and Ada Gribben, a young couple with little or no experience in farming, who harbored a romantic fantasy about the idyllic, pastoral life they would lead when he, James, would be able to leave his job as bookkeeper in Cincinnati and would no longer have to commute, but could settle down with his wife and raise a family. They reminded me of Uncle Mike and his vision of a rustic paradise. I could only hope that their dreams were made of sterner stuff, that they could withstand the assaults of reality.

The Gribbens had owned their home on Walnut Hills in Cincinnati, and Mr. Romberg had found a buyer for them, too. That deal, they told us, was in escrow and due to be closed in a matter of days. They could not wait, they said, to get their hands deep into God's beautiful earth, to be awakened by birdsong in the morning, and go to sleep to the chirping of crickets at night.

Papers were drawn up. The Gribbens assumed our mortgage and paid us part of our equity at once as earnest money. They promised the balance as soon as the money from the sale of their house was released. In the meantime they gave us a note co-signed by Mr. Romberg.

They wanted to buy all the cows, the two draft horses, and their two beautiful foals. They would not need a buggy horse because they had a Ford, which Ada could use, since James did not really need it in the city. Papa suggested they wait until the auction, since they would have their money then. He also advised them to start with two cows—enough for their personal needs—until they gained more experience. That, they said, was no problem; they planned to hire a full-time "hand" to keep things going until James could take over. Papa introduced Josiah to them. They were definitely looking at their future through rose-colored glasses.

The Greens came to stay with us in order to help us through this transition period with affection and moral support, as well as in more practical ways. It was then decided that I should finish out the school year boarding with Mrs. Belle Green, a widow who lived with her mother in a cottage across the way from the schoolhouse. I would come home for the weekends, just as I had when I was going to high school.

The auction would offer for sale just about all our possessions. There were three major exceptions. One was the Victrola, which we felt should be returned to Uncle Harry for the enjoyment of his family when they finally arrived from Russia. The second exception was the pair of heavy brass candlesticks which Bubbie (my grandmother) had handed down to Mama. The third was the feather bed that Mama had brought from Russia to Boston, then transported from Boston to Cincinnati and from there to Dunham's Hill, where it kept me deliciously warm in the winter. She was insistent about taking it to Phoenix, but I never needed it there. It was eventually transformed into lovely goose down pillows.

We scheduled the auction for the twenty-fourth and twenty-fifth of August. We needed that much time to make a date with Mr. Von Dundee, a very busy auctioneer, to post the notices all around Clermont County and to give Josiah plenty of time to check all the machinery and see that everything was in good shape and clean, and that the harness was polished and mended if necessary.

September would be devoted to making all the preparations for our departure. In October the Gribbens' notes would fall due; we would accept payment and give the new owners possession, and we would be on our way to a new and strange world.

The Ladies' Aid of the Mount Pisgah Methodist Church, as was their custom whenever an auction took place in territory within their purview, asked for and received our permission to set up tables from which to serve the anticipated large crowds. The ladies stored food in our cellar, and commandeered the help of everyone within their organization and as many as possible out of it.

Three days before the sale, Mr. Romberg came with bad news. The sale of the Gribbens' home in Walnut Hills had been stalled until there could be further search of the title, which at the moment seemed slightly clouded. But not to worry. We had the note and, if necessary, the Gribbens were prepared to raise a small second mortgage on the farm to pay all they owed us. Everything was going to be fine. Papa hoped so, because, he reminded Mr. Romberg, *he* was co-signer on the note. Mr. Romberg remembered, but Papa was understandably worried. And worry, next to anger, was bad for a man with chronic bronchial asthma.

On April 6, 1917 on my seventeenth birthday, I started to cross the street from Mrs. Green's house to the schoolhouse. It was an early spring morning, balmy and sunny, and we no longer needed fires in the stove. I stood looking up at the clear blue sky, and thought how helpless we humans are in the face of circumstances. I had believed last year, when I had yielded to Papa and agreed to wait another year for college, that I had only his promise to worry about. Still I had been confident. By this time, I had been sure, I would have picked my college, have sent in my application and be waiting only for the notice of acceptance.

It is written in Ecclesiastes: "There is . . . a time to every purpose under heaven." Shakespeare puts it another way: "There is a tide in the affairs of men, / Which, taken at the flood, leads on to Fortune; . . . " Well, I acknowledged, time and tide and had passed me by—or perhaps it was I myself who had done the passing.

My ruminating was interrupted by a youth trotting from the direction of the general store.

"You hear the news?" he shouted. "We've joined the war! I'm going home to tell my folks I'm enlisting!"

I was too stunned for a moment to move. Then I crossed the street slowly and took out my key to the schoolhouse. I was turning it in the lock when, from around the corner of the building, came a rush of children shouting "Surprise! Happy Birthday!" I pushed to the back of my mind the tragic news that I had just heard. I could not shatter the children's festive mood with the announcement that our country was now at war.

Soon after school opened, I had ordered, through the *Ohio Teacher*, stencils for a monthly blackboard calendar with an appropriate seasonal design for each month. I had let the children fill in the outlines of the scenes with crayon colors of their choice. The dates of the established holidays and the dates of the children's birthdays were outlined in red, and they insisted that my birthday should also be shown on the calendar. Each birthday child had special privileges on his or her day, and the children whose birthdays fell during vacation were distributed among the sparser school months. This day it was my turn. The April calendar was bright with yellow jonquils and a robin on the wing, and mine was the birthday of the month.

My privileges, they announced, were a promise that they would be good all day. No whispering, no passing of notes, no hiding contraband behind the large open geography books. And would I please tell them a story? Not a story, really, only about myself whan I was little, before I ever came to Dunham's Hill.

I told them about the swan boats in Boston, and about the zoo in Cincinnati, and about the heat in the crowded streets, where children would run after the ice wagons and grab the slivers of ice that were chipped away when the drivers stopped to make deliveries. And then I told them about the news I had heard early in the morning: "Our country is at war!"

Their first reaction was one of excitement. They had heard phrases from their elders' comments as they read the newspaper accounts. One of the boys shouted, "Yay! Now we'll kill the Kaiser!" Others took up the cry. I restored order and told them how I felt about war.

"You are all excited about it. You think about war as though it were some glory game where young men march and sing. Maybe there are wars that *have* to be fought. I don't know. But they are not glory games. And I think maybe they could be avoided, if people really gave more thought to that. But there is one thing I want you to remember. War is not something to cheer about, and nobody ever really wins. So let's all hope and pray that this war will be over soon, and maybe for once do some good."

I don't know what they told their parents that night about Miss Goldie's dissertation on the subject of war. I never found out, and I never was charged by any parent with being unpatriotic or corrupting their children's minds. The "war to end all wars" was off and running. Gold stars in memory of those killed in battle would soon be appearing in windows throughout the land. Songs were written about this war, to be sung by school children, and at rallies, and by marching men. I don't think there is much singing at wars anymore.

School was out in the middle of May. The spring work on the farms was beginning, and the call was out for the sons to help the fathers.

The last day of school ended with tearful good-byes and going-away presents for Teacher. I, in turn, had gotten bookmarks for the children, and I explained how much better it was to use them to mark one's place in a book than to dog-ear a corner of the page. I said that books should be treated like friends, and to remember always to return a book they had borrowed, whether from school or from a friend. If they did that, I told them, whoever their new teacher might be she would be proud of her new pupils, who understood how to take care of books. I promised to send each one of them a postcard from Arizona, and I kept my word.

Mr. Wentzeler, much to my surprise, came to pick me up at Mrs. Green's and take me home. He hoped I didn't mind. He had called my folks so they wouldn't have to bother to come for me.

When we arrived at our place, before we shook hands and I got out of his buggy, he gave me an envelope and handed down my suitcase at the same time. I looked up questioningly.

"You can open it when you get in the house. Good luck—*Miss* Goldie," he grinned, and then turned his horse and drove away. I opened the envelope. In it were three crisp, new five-dollar bills, and a note that read:

A small bonus for being a good teacher and a good friend to the children of the Mt. Pisgah Elementary School.

Sincerely yours,
District School Board
Floyd Wentzeler, Pres.

# 33

## *Going Once . . . Going Twice . . .*

The auction began as scheduled at six o'clock in the morning of August 24, 1917. The early hour was chosen to take advantage of the cooler part of the day. It was no hardship for farmers; they were usually in the fields even earlier during the summer. They began arriving for the auction by five o'clock, with horses and buggies, buckboards, and two-wheel traps and rigs. Some came on horseback, families in surreys, even in Model T's, but the latter had to park well down the road or risk creating panic among the horses.

The Ladies' Aid women were ready with large graniteware coffee pots kept hot on our kitchen stove, and milk and lemonade kept cold in our cellar.

The day was ideal. The sky was clear blue, the surrounding meadows green. Pear and cherry trees were decked out in fragrant white blossoms; the blooms on the early apple trees were a delicate, pink-edged white, while peach trees wore more a flamboyant deep pink.

Mr. Von Dundee, a portly man with a gray-fringed bald head and a commanding nose, took his place on his traveling platform and tried the firmness of the stand on which his gavel rested. Then, in a stentorian voice, he tested the phrase which would be heard many times that day and the next: "Going once . . . going twice . . ." He started the morning dressed in a black alpaca suit, a stiff, detachable collar on a white shirt, and a black string tie. As the day wore on he discarded first the coat, then the collar and tie; finally he opened the neck band of his shirt.

At his right, on a lower platform, also part of the auctioneer's traveling equipment, were placed a wooden bench and a table improvised with a large plank on a sawhorse. In front of this table sat Mr. Von Dundee's two assistants. One was a young man with an open ledger in which he would record the names of the winning bidders, a description of the purchase, and the amount of the bid. At his side sat the cashier, a young lady in crisp white dimity and a brown pompadour, both of which miraculously withstood the heat of the day and found her, at five o'clock, looking almost as neat as when the day had started.

At exactly 6:00 A.M., on the instruction of Mr. Von Dundee, I rang the dinner bell to signal that the sale was about to begin.

The Gribbens had driven in early and were eager for the bidding to start. Mr. Von, as the auctioneer was addressed familiarly, opened the proceedings with announcements about procedure and financial arrangements. He also explained that while Ol' Belle, as faithful and gentle a creature as could be found in Clermont County, would be offered for sale, she could not be delivered to the buyer until October 1, when the Weisbergs would leave the farm for Arizona. This, he added, was also true of the furniture, which would "go under the hammer" on the second day.

Josiah and I brought Maudie and Queenie out one at a time. Papa had insisted on taking part in the presentations, though the barnyard with its irritating dust was hardly the place for him to be. He followed us with the two colts. The bidding started for the team, with the first bid by a horse dealer. The Gribbens raised. Others entered the contest, always outbid by James Gribben. The team was finally "knocked down" to him, and Mr. Von introduced him and his wife as the new owners of the Weisberg farm. There was no burst of applause, but those standing near them said "Howdy," and assured them they were getting as good a place as could be found on Dunham's Hill.

Mama and Frumcha Green helped the Ladies' Aid replenish the refreshment tables, and when Mr. Von Dundee announced a thirty-minute break for lunch, Mama was persuaded to play some records to create a festive atmosphere for the Ladies' Aid enterprise.

After lunch the machinery, the harnesses and the hand tools were lined up for bidding. The cows, the furniture, miscellaneous articles, and the seed corn—which, in a year of poor seed, had attracted the most attention—were held over for the second day.

The Gribbens ended up with machinery about which they knew nothing, but they had arrived at an understanding with Josiah, so they felt confident. Papa had ended up with an injection of adrenalin.

The next day the crowd was almost as large as on the previous one. New buyers had arrived for the corn and the cattle. Mr. Romberg had come in from Cincinnati with the Gribbens, and served as somewhat of a brake on their compulsive bidding. Keenly aware of his own signature on the notes, he was determined that they keep their buying more conservative.

The furniture sold first. Interested parties were invited to view it inside the house, after Mr. Von Dundee explained again that it could be bought but not collected until October.

Mama withdrew, and cried a little when her pretty parlor lamp, a gift from the Greens, was bought by a stranger. As each piece of furniture was sold, a tag was attached with the name of the purchaser and other vital information written upon it. So she was already living, she said, in somebody else's house, sleeping in somebody else's bed, eating on somebody else's table. She felt like an intruder, and when the calendar said "Now!" she would have to run as the cat did when she said "Scat!"

\*    \*    \*

Josiah, Charlie Green, and I brought out the cows. I had Daisy and my little Beauty, now a heifer ready to be bred. Josiah held two Jerseys, Charlie Green led two Holsteins and Papa came last with two more. The cows all stood patiently, lowing softly as if in mild annoyance at this unusual break in the routine of their lives. Beauty kept nudging me for a treat. I had an apple ready for her, which she munched while Mr. Von read off her lineage and the astonishing record of Daisy's output, and pointed out the markings of Beauty, inherited from her sire, who had a very impressive pedigree. The Gribbens ended up with Daisy, Beauty, and Rosie, and were persuaded by Mr. Romberg to stop with them.

The liveliest bidding was for the seed corn, offered by the bushel. Mr. Romberg managed to keep the Gribbens out of that contest altogether.

It was over at last. The friends, the neighbors were gone; the buyers who had come from long distances had left, taking with them what they could carry, arranging to return for what they could not. Mr. Von Dundee had settled up with Papa, beaming over the success of the two-day auction. The Gribbens, joined by Mr. Romberg, had a session with Papa and me: Charlie Green sat in as a "friend of the court." They promised that the notes would be met on the due date without fail. In the meantime, they told us magnanimously that we were free to use the milk from the cows, the eggs from the chickens, and the vegetables from the garden, forgetting that none of that had been paid for, that it was not theirs to bestow.

There was a stand of timothy ready to be cut that nominally belonged to the Gribbens, as did everything on the ground or in it. Josiah agreed to cut and store the hay in the hayloft.

Mama told the Gribbens she would leave for them some jars of fruit that she had put up as it ripened. She held back only enough to see us through September, our last month on Dunham's Hill.

Just as I had found Mama crying quietly in the house, I discovered Papa relieving his pent-up feeling in Ol' Belle's stall, where he was currying her and petting her and talking to her, because she was all that was left to him of his pride and his possessions. What he was doing seemed almost suicidal. The dust and loose hair were rising from Ol' Belle's hide, which grew cleaner and glossier with each stroke of the curry comb, while the air grew dirtier and thicker. It was the worst possible place for Papa to be, and the worst possible thing for him to be doing.

"What are you trying to do—kill yourself?" I cried in exasperation.

"I don't know—maybe. Maybe it's not such a bad idea." It was then I discovered that he, too, had been crying. I remembered the last time I had seen him weep, and it brought back that terrible night of my childhood and my despair. I remembered how Mama had wiped his tears with her apron. I pulled a handkerchief from my sleeve and wiped his face.

"Come on, Papa," I said. "You've made Ol' Belle look like a young filly again. Now let's get out of here and give you your medicine and get you cleaned up." He had no breath left for speaking. He pointed to the pocket on the bib of his overalls, and I took out the atomizer and handed it to him. We walked out of the polluted air in the stables into the fresh outdoors. He took a deep breath of the fine spray of the medicine and paused until he could breathe more freely, and we walked back to the house.

# 34

# *The Long Good-bye*

It was early fall, and our Jewish farmer friends were celebrating the festival of *Succoth*, giving thanks for the harvest of the fruits of the earth. The Kullmans had build a *succah*, an arborlike shelter which is the symbol of the festival. Most of the Jewish farmers were there; Mr. Romberg was not among them.

I felt a renewed kinship with all these people—a kinship that I had first experienced when we had joined them in a community seder the year before on Passover. It was a feeling I had never experienced before—a feeling that it was good to be part of such a group. There was shelter there for one another. It gave me a sense of self, a sense of identity. I had grown up confused about my place as a Jewish child in a non-Jewish world; perhaps if I had been more sure of myself in the life space I occupied, I would not have been so devastated by a bunch of unruly boys crying "Miss Shew, Miss Shew!" Perhaps I could have responded to the question about Louis D. Brandeis without the explosive hostility that must have shocked everyone in that high school classroom, in that moment which now seemed so long ago.

It did not take us all of September to prepare to leave Dunham's Hill. To have remained beyond the time needed would have been like participating in an overlong death watch. We would stay with the Greens and the Mishkins while we closed the financial deal with the Gribbens. We called and told them that if they wished to settle the notes at once, they would not have to wait for October to take possession of the farm. They said they would let us know in a day or two.

Instead of hearing from them, we received a call from Mr. Romberg, who said he would like to come out the following day and talk to us. He told us he would drive up, so there was no need to meet him.

Why was he coming? we wondered. Was something wrong?

Mr. Romberg arrived full of apologies, but full of good cheer as well. The title to the Walnut Hills house had finally been cleared, so *that* obstacle was out of the way. But, in the meantime, the buyer of the Gribbens' house had exercised his right to withdraw his offer if the sale were not closed by a certain date. However, not to worry. A new buyer was already waiting, had already paid earnest money, and it was now just a matter of a few weeks before the house on Walnut Hills and the farm on Dunham's Hill would change owners. No need, Mr. Romberg assured us, to alter our plans. For his health's sake Papa should leave for Arizona without delay, and he, Romberg, would take care of everything. Papa suggested that if he, Romberg, were so confident and since he was, after all, as legally obligated as Mr. Gribben himself, why not take up the notes, pay Papa and collect when the two deals were closed?

"Are you going to press me to the wall?" pleaded Mr. Romberg. "I have a wife and children to think of. Have a little patience, a little mercy! I give you my word—"

Charlie Green interposed dryly: "He has your bond, and that isn't doing him much good. Will your word buy tickets for the railroad journey, and will it provide a living in Arizona until they are settled?"

"But it's not as if he's without a penny! All the money from—the—sale—" His voice faded out as Charlie stood up and glared

at him. He shrugged, held out his hands to Papa in appeal, and
repeated, "I give you my word."

Charlie had had some experience in the purchase and sale of
property; it looked to him, he said, like Papa was going to have to
sue the Gribbens and Mr. Romberg. But Papa should get out of
Cincinnati as soon as possible. Charlie would see his own lawyer
and start proceedings after October 1 if that deadline was not met.

"What you have to admit to yourself, Max," Charlie said, "is that
the doctor told you you can't spend another winter here. And it's
not just the cold. Do you realize how much soot you swallow every
time you come to the city because of the soft coal that's burned
here? You've forgotten because all these years you've been burning
good clean wood. I'll bet that the lungs of half the population of
Cincinnati are coated with soft coal dust!"

Papa was strangely silent; we took this to mean he agreed with
Charlie and would follow his advice.

We could not remain in the house at the farm beyond October
1. The buyers of the furniture would take their purchases away;
the man who bought Ol' Belle would claim her. The Victrola had
been crated, and shipped to Uncle Harry for his house on Price
Hill. Even my little dog, Prince, was gone. All through the last
weeks that we still were in our home, he had scarcely left my side,
as though he knew that at any moment I might disappear. Several
neighbors had offered to take him but I had chosen the Brewers,
new neighbors who had a little adopted boy, for Prince's new family.
I left him there, hurrying away from the sound of his plaintive
barking, the bitter taste of my betrayal in my mouth.

We left for Cincinnati near the end of September, 1917, making
Josiah the overseer of the farm until it should be taken over by the
new owners. In the meantime he was to have all the milk from

Daisy and Rosie, and all the chicken and duck eggs, until Papa gave him the word that the Gribbens had paid what they owed and he could turn everything over to them. If this did not take place by October 1, he was not answerable to them for anything, not the fruit on the trees, the vegetables in the ground, nor the chickens or ducks themselves. And we, of course, would pay him for his labor.

Josiah had his own horse and rig now, and on the appointed day he drove us and the Greens to Ten-Mile Stop and we left for Cincinnati.

Papa, by his failure to reject Charlie's advice, seemed to have accepted it. Once settled, I with the Greens, and Mama and Papa with the Mishkins, he let me make an appointment for him with Dr. Ullery. We sat in his consultation room for a few minutes, waiting until he dismissed an earlier patient from the examining room. He came in looking exactly as when we had seen him last, wearing his carpet slippers, his clean but rumpled white coat, and his stethoscope.

"So," he greeted us. "You're finally getting out of the Queen City, the lady with soot all over her face."

"I came in to have you check me over, not to say good-bye," said Papa. "I'm not leaving until I collect what is due me!"

We both stared at him in amazement. Apparently he had never intended to take Charlie Green's advice. He had listened, and then pursued his own counsel.

"Maybe," said Dr. Ullery grimly, "I don't want you for a patient anymore. Maybe I'll just let you go ahead and kill yourself."

Papa rose and started for the exit door, looking back at me and gesturing that I follow.

"Come back here, you stubborn ox!" roared Dr. Ullery. "Get in there in the examining room!" Papa turned, looking just as grim as the doctor. I just sat there, in a daze.

\* \* \*

We went to live in Uncle Harry's house on Price Hill, where the air was better than in the city. Charlie Green called on Romberg and told him he was now acting as Papa's agent, and he was addressing him rather than the Gribbens because he seemed the spokesman for them as well as co-signer on the notes. He warned Mr. Romberg that he would bring suit for repossession of the land, the stock, and everything the Gribbens had bought and not paid for within a reasonable time. I went looking for a job.

What was I qualified for? After a fashion, for teaching children by instinct rather than training. I could ride a horse, bareback or saddled. I could walk barefooted on oat stubble, as attested to by Mr. Wentzeler. I could milk up to eight cows in a row. None of these, nor any other skills I could name, were marketable in Cincinnati; but Uncle Harry found a job for me. He saw a sign in a window that read: "Young woman wanted for payroll clerk. Must be good at figures." And so I found myself sitting in a stuffy, poorly lighted loft, on a high, backless stool, in front of a slanted table-desk. On it rested a ledger in which I was to demonstrate my proficiency with figures. A naked bulb hung from the ceiling over the "desk."

The loft was a pants-pressing and pants-finishing mini-factory. The men were pieceworkers, and the rate of pay differed for the pressers and the finishers. My job was to keep track of the time each worker put in. They were expected to put in a full day, even though they were not paid on a time basis. The payroll that I made up was based strictly on the amount of work checks the foreman turned in for each man.

The first time a new man came in and presented me with a work slip on which was written "Presser starts," I asked, "What is your first name, Mr. Presser?"

"Oo!" he oo-ed, looking around the room. "Here is a real smart lady and she makes jokes, too!"

"I'm sorry," I mumbled. "I saw on here it says 'Presser starts.' I thought your name was Presser."

"My—name—is—Joe—Pincus," he enunciated slowly as if to a small child. "I—am—a—presser. I—press—pants. And I came in at eight o'clock, exactly. Put it down eight o'clock, not—" he looked up at the wall clock "—seven minutes after eight, which you took up making jokes. Thank—you—very—much." He left me speechless and very red-faced.

The loft had some ceiling fans, but they scarcely made a ripple of breeze against the stifling heat augmented by the warmth from the steam irons. I came to work at eight in the morning, had a half-hour for lunch and left at five-thirty. I worked five and a half days a week. I went home to Price Hill by trolley, a thirty minute ride, often standing most of the way. I was making sixteen dollars a week, which came to almost seventy dollars a month. I worked there for ten months and turned over most of the money to Papa.

Well, it was better than picking berries at six cents a basket—financially, that is. And I was very lucky, I was told—a girl with no experience, right off the farm—to do so well. And it served to keep my mind off the war.

The summer was not totally without its rewards. The Greens, the Mishkins, and Moishele and Uncle Harry saw to it that on Sundays I could forget the loft and the steady parade of men arriving with slips of paper bearing the legends "Presser starts" and "Finisher starts," and the almost equally steady exodus of men with slips of paper that read "Presser quits."

On a Sunday that summer a gala event took place in the city— an event that drew even Papa and Mama down from Price Hill. Cantor Yossele Rosenblatt, whose recordings had once opened Mama's concert series on Dunham's Hill, was in town for a Liberty bond drive. The event was not just for music lovers; it was for music lovers who were willing to buy bonds in order to hear the golden-voiced lyric tenor sing their requests.

It was a memorable evening. Rosenblatt walked out on stage to a shouting, clapping, standing ovation. A short, stocky man with a beautiful black-bearded face, he stood nodding and smiling and finally lifting his hands for the crowd to settle down. There was a short fixed program, starting with "America," in which the audience joined. Then he sang a half-dozen favorite cantorial and folk songs and closed with a lovely melody from one of Goldfaden's Yiddish operettas. After that came the bidding—not in dollars but in bonds. He sang as long as the audience was buying. Finally, close to midnight, exhausted, he held out his hands in appeal and left the stage.

Charlie Green kept us informed as to the progress in the prospective case of *Weisberg* vs. *Gribben and Romberg*. Not that it had actually developed into a court battle, but it worried Romberg enough so that he brought pressure on the Gribbens to raise at least part of the money owed us, warning that we would have to get a court order to repossess everything if they did nothing.

In December the Gribbens had come up with the balance they owed on our equity in the farm. The sale of the Walnut Hills house fell through again. I cannot remember the manipulations that went on, the robbing of Peter to pay Paul, the dribble of money that came in from time to time. Papa got through the winter somehow, depending much more on adrenalin than was good for him.

Charlie Green allowed the Gribbens to move to the farm, with the understanding that they would put the most advanced machinery up for sale and, if need be, the team of draft horses. Charlie placed an advertisement in the New Richmond paper and told Josiah to see that a sign was mounted in the general store.

In the loft where I worked, Pressers and Finishers started and Pressers and Finishers quit at the same monotonous pace. At least we did not suffer the heat of the summer, heat that had lasted unseasonably late into autumn, heat that had seemed at times so solid that you could grasp it in your hands. The winter, in fact, was quite mild.

April sixth—my eighteenth birthday—fell on a Saturday, so I had a half day in which to celebrate. I could not believe that I had lived only eighteen years; I felt so much older; I thought, how could so much have happened in only eighteen years? Out of the last payment the Gribbens had made, Papa gave me fifty dollars, the money that my heifer, Beauty, had brought at the auction. I spent it all on clothes; for the first time in my life I had a head-to-toe coordinated costume—a spring suit of shepherd's check, a crepe de chine blouse, a tricorn straw hat with a tiny green feather in the band, new shoes, and a black purse. And I had enough left over to stop off two blocks from the Price Hill house and buy a half gallon of ice cream to bring home.

I said to Papa, as I displayed my purchases, "I am ready to travel. Are you?"

"When I collect some more money," he replied, with grim humor, "so I can buy a new outfit for Mama and a new outfit for myself, we will travel." I knew he meant it, not as a joke, but as an act of unbending will.

On a pleasant Saturday afternoon in June we were surprised by a visit from Dr. Ullery. He had made a house call on Price Hill and stopped by to see Papa.

"This is a social call," he announced. "No charge. How's it going, Max?"

"Well, I'm still here; I'm still alive," replied Papa. But the apprehension created by this unexpected visit brought on a bad asthmatic attack.

Dr. Ullery asked me when Papa had had adrenalin last, and I told him almost three days earlier. So the doctor gave him a shot.

"I'm sorry, Max. Looks like the sight of me made you sick!" Papa managed a weak smile at the joke. Dr. Ullery went on in a more serious tone, "There's something going around that has us worried. Some kind of chest problem that seems to be different from anything we've had experience with. It may not be anything serious, but we're watching it very carefully. And that's really what I stopped by to talk to you about. I don't want you to go out into crowds; don't get overheated and drink ice water; don't do anything that could cause you to catch cold. And you, Mother, take care of yourself, too. Don't go downtown if you can help it." He turned to me. "And you, Daughter: I know you've got this miserable job in the city; the minute you start feeling off your feed, headachy, feverish, walk out and come straight to my office. Understand?" I nodded. He rose to go.

Mama said, "You'll have a glass of tea, Doctor?"

"Of course, Mother, with pleasure." He sat down again. "Now I hope I scared you enough so you'll be sensible, but no so much that you'll be afraid to go on as happily as you can within the limits I just prescribed."

Mama brought tea with preserves and *mandel brot*. When he finished the refreshments he shook hands all around.

"Becky, don't forget to pay the doctor for the visit," said Papa.

"I told you, this was a social call," said Dr. Ullery. "Nobody asked me to come. Thanks for the tea and cookies, Mother. Best tea I ever had." Mama walked him to the door. He turned for one last word.

"You get away from here before winter, Max. If you don't, I'm through with you. This time I mean it."

"I promise," Papa said. "I mean it, too." Dr. Ullery left. Papa looked very tired. "I think I'll go lie down," he said.

Within the next two months we began to hear more about the disease; it was thought to be a new kind of influenza, and it was defying usual treatment. One Sunday evening, when Uncle Harry came home, Papa said, addressing his brother by his Jewish name, "Herschel, I want to go to Arizona. I am going to leave everything in Charlie's hands. I can trust him to do what is best for us." Mama and I looked at each other. It was the first time we had heard of this firm decision. On Monday I gave notice to the foreman of the shop that I would be leaving at the end of the following week.

# 35

## *The West Is Where the Sun Goes Down*

But " . . . the sun also rises," I thought. We were gathered at the Southern Pacific railroad station—Mama, Papa, and I, and friends to see us off: the Mishkins, the Greens, Uncle Harry, Moishele, and Landa. I wasn't listening to the conversation—it was too cheerful, too bent on pretending we were off on a holiday.

Suddenly something that Frumcha was saying stirred a familiar if distant memory. She was speaking softly, for Mama's ear alone: "It's not too late, even now. Goldie could stay with us and go to college right here at the University of Cincinnati. . . ."

I looked at Mama, and it was as though we were at another railroad station, in Boston, waiting for the train to take us to what Tante Sadie perceived as "the wild west and full of Indians," and she was pleading with Mama to let me stay with the family in Boston. I remembered how I had clung to Mama's hand, holding my breath with fear until I heard Mama saying, "I thank you, sister, but the child belongs with me." Now Mama was looking at me with frightened, pleading eyes. We had changed places. She was the child and I the mother.

"Tante Frumcha," I said, "I love you and Uncle Charlie, and I appreciate your offer. But I can't accept it. I belong with Mama—and Papa."

A whistle announced the train's approach. There was no longer a pretense at merriment. The good-byes were tearful. Again there were boxes of food, again dollar bills thrust into my hand by each of the men—"for the train butcher." Again the dining car moved past us, curious diners pausing with a lifted glass or fork to gaze down at us. Finally the day coach section came into view and chugged to a stop. As soon as arrivals were let off, we boarded quickly in order to find good seats. Moishele and Charlie hoisted our luggage on board. It seemed hours before we heard "All aboard!" and the train began to heave into motion. We waved. Our friends waved. We cried. They cried. And then we could scarcely see them through the dirty windows. We were on our way to Arizona.

The train made frequent stops. The details of the journey elude me. In one city—I think it may have been Kansas City, Missouri— we made a long stop, and we were able to get off and move about. I remember that the station was clean and cool, in contrast to the train, which was dusty, dirty, stuffy. Before the journey was over, we discovered that vermin shared our space. Sitting up in our seats, we slept fitfully, of course, though we were offered pillows for our backs. We let Papa have two seats facing each other to himself so that he would rest better and, since the section was not filled, the conductor did not object.

The countryside changed day by day, hour by hour. We were seeing America and it was a sight to behold, even from our poor vantage point. The plains stretched endlessly, the flatness broken by lines of trees serving as windbreakers. We passed fields of golden grain, and Papa remarked that it was ready for harvesting. I detected a wistful note in his voice; after all, he had been a farmer longer than he had been anything in his adult life.

We moved into higher country, passed hills that were brown from the summer's heat, perhaps from drouth. We stopped at towns briefly, or went through without stopping. Always there were idlers lounging on a bench outside the station, watching, perhaps peopling their own fantasies with our faces, creating new adventures for their dull lives. "Train butchers" passed through, offering simple food for sale. We slept off and on, sometimes in the daytime, sometimes in the night. I wondered what the sleeping cars were like. Some day, I vowed, I would know. I would know many things, do many things. I thought of Mr. Frank Franz. What would he have said about my failure to go to college? I imagined he might have said, "Don't let that stop you. You can still be anything you want to be. Don't ever forget that!" I decided I would believe that that was really what he would have said.

We left middle America and entered a new time zone. There were mountains now; it was higher and cooler. We stopped at a New Mexico town called Alamagordo. Indian women with long black hair, dark, broad, smiling faces, ample of figure and dressed in very full calico skirts and blouses, lined up outside the windows of our train. They carried baskets of the most beautiful purple plums I had ever seen, lifting them for us to inspect through the train windows. There were other wares offered for sale, but we three travelers saw only the plums. We raised our windows and exchanged money for the delectable fruit. It was a luscious interlude. I like to remember Alamagordo for this sustenance, its gift to travelers. Later the town would become known for Robert Oppenhimer's terrible words, as the deadly mushroom cloud rose to the sky: "Now I am become Death!"

We moved steadily westward, and eventually we found ourselves in desert country. In Maricopa, Arizona, we discovered that we had reached the end of the main line of the Southern Pacific. We got out to stretch, and learned quickly what desert heat could be like; but for Papa there was a miraculous change. He breathed more freely than he had since the beginning of his illness. We bought cool drinks at the little station and heard the clang of the uncoupling of our car, and its recoupling to a new engine. We heard the familiar call to board. We began the last leg of our journey.

We had come to the end; we were in Phoenix. We followed the luggage into the station. We found nothing to say to one another; we were too tired, too apprehensive. The scene about us was depressing. Men in tall Stetson hats and boots seemed to be everywhere. It was mid-September, and the heat was like that we had encountered in Maricopa. Papa tested the atmosphere, breathing deeply. It was not quite like the first time in Maricopa, but it was better than Cincinnati, better than Dunham's Hill. It gave us something to talk about, to break the silence in which we had been following the luggage.

We took off our suit jackets and entered the waiting room. Papa told me to go to the desk and ask three things: could we check our luggage until we found a place to stay? Was the station far from the town? And were there any Jewish people in Phoenix? The answer to all three questions was "yes." I came back and reported to Papa: the man said if we walked straight up the street when we left the station, we would come to Washington Street. Then, if we turned right, almost every other store was "a Jew store." In Yiddish, which we always spoke to one another, it came out "...a Yiddishe store," which eliminated the crude connotation implied in the stationmaster's choice of words.

We checked our luggage and walked outside. We paused for a moment to survey the prospect before us, a pretty dismal one indeed. One day I would find the desert beautiful, mysterious, haunting; I was to see sunsets turning the hills around the town into muted shades of rose and gray and purple. Against the twilight sky I would see the delicate leaves of the cottonwoods that lined the canals turn to black lace that seemed to float unattached to the swaying trees. But all this would come much later.

We were about to step off the curb when Papa said, "Wait! I

want to say something." He spoke with difficulty, as though what he had to say was necessary but not easy.

"We are going into a place where we know no one. We are going to see some hard times, maybe. I want you know, Brucha, I will try to be a better husband than I maybe have been. You have done your best. I will try my best now, too. I wanted to say this to you before we start our new life. I want us to start clean with one another. If I have not always been kind or patient, I ask you, now, to forgive me."

Mama's voice shook. "I forgive you from my heart," she said. "And as long as we are starting clean, I have something to say. It has been heavy on my heart for a long time. The fire was my fault—"

"Mama!" I cried.

"Let me speak. It will leave the heaviness from my heart. And because of the fire you swallowed some smoke. . . . "

"Mama, both doctors said it's not so."

"I must finish. That day, when we were getting the sacks for the *hatamalchik*, I caught my heel in the hem of my skirt where it was ripped. I didn't know until just before that it was ripped, and I didn't want to stop and fix it then. I thought, I'll be careful. It was all right until it was all finished, and I took the lantern and started down the stairs. I forgot to be careful. My heel caught in the hem again, and I fell. And that how it was."

Neither Papa nor I spoke for a moment. I thought, "Poor Mama. What has she done to herself?"

After a moment Papa spoke, very quietly, without any emotion.

"Never speak of it again. It is over. It is forgotten."

"You forgive me?"

"I know I always told you to hurry, hurry, hurry. I probably told you then the same thing. So, like you said, I forgive you from my heart."

He turned to me.

"I know you think I wronged you, daughter. Maybe I did. I didn't mean to wrong you. I don't have to say more than that. Can you forgive me?"

It took me a moment to find the right words. I could not say what they had just said to each other: "I forgive you from my heart." I was not quite ready for that.

"I forgive you Papa. We must forgive one another, or we perish."

"Yes," he said. "That is true. And now, let us go to this Washington Street and turn to the right."

We stepped off the curb, self-shriven, and walked to whatever lay in store before us.

# 36

# *Postscript*

Washington Street in Phoenix was fully paved, wide and lined on either side with shops. A trolley ran from east to west and back again. We walked slowly, looking into store windows. Different wares were displayed, but the stores all had one thing in common: a sign that bore the strange message: "Aqui se habla Español."

We stopped at a clothing store with "Shapiro Brothers" lettered on the display window. A man who looked like he might be a Shapiro greeted us. He invited us in. He was indeed one of the brothers. We asked if he could recommend a lodging house where we could make a temporary home. It turned out that he and his wife had recently converted a wing of their large house into a furnished apartment—clean, bright, and available. It became our home for nearly two months.

Mr. Shapiro drove us to the station to pick up our luggage and then to our new home. He explained that the signs in the windows meant "Spanish is spoken here."

We met other Jewish families; in each there was at least one health-seeker, and each new acquaintance asked, "What line of business are you in?" And Papa always answered, "I am a farmer."

"A Jewish farmer!" they marveled.

"Why not?" Papa would retort. "Jews were farmers long before they were storekeepers. Is it not written that 'Adam tilled the soil'?"

Papa applied for citizenship. Under his aegis Mama would also become naturalized, but I would have to wait until I was twenty-one, and Papa decided to wait with me, so that I would not be a "furriner" in an American family.

Some money came via Charlie Green, who had thrown himself totally into getting the debt to us paid. Papa promptly bought forty acres of alfalfa, still green with its fourth crop of the year (made possible, of course, by a year-round growing season in this irrigated desert valley). I discovered that Papa had been reading up on Arizona agriculture during the last summer in Cincinnati. He knew that the best thing to do with the last stand of alfalfa was to sell the crop to sheep growers in the fall when they brought their flocks down from the seven-thousand-foot-high mountain country of northern Arizona where they summered. The herders were Basques, who knew everything there was to know about sheep. I learned about "leppies"—newborn lambs whose mothers died or who rejected their offspring out of hand. The foreman gave them to me and I raised them on the bottle. And a generous neighbor across the road from us gave me the use of a retired "cow" pony, which no longer had any cattle to work. In my spare time I explored the desert and the fascinating mountains that surrounded us.

Long staple (Egyptian) cotton had been successfully introduced into the valley, and whole families had been brought in from Mexico as legal alien labor to pick the crop. Dairy farmers and ranchers had sold their cows and plowed up crops to make room for the new cotton. The economy boomed.

We had bought our forty acres from a widow with four children. Her new residence was not yet ready for occupancy, so the family stayed on with us for about a month. The eldest son had a motorcycle, and he and I—I riding on the gas tank—joined the cotton pickers until I was drafted as a substitute teacher in a nearby school.

Papa, in the meantime, was having problems. The moisture generated by irrigation, the life-giving arteries that had turned tens of thousands of desert acres into productive farms, defeated the life-restoring dryness of the air that had been so healing to him.

Eight months after we had bought the "ranch," Papa sold it and became a storekeeper after all. He had paid $300 an acre for the land; he sold it for $380. With the profit we bought a modest house away from all the things we had loved—trees and shrubs and flower beds. Mama was sad; Papa was sad and bitter. I missed the music of the sheepherders at night and the little white "cow" pony.

The twenties were an endless parade of good times. The valley prospered, the town prospered, the imported Mexicans prospered, and the merchants prospered. Then, suddenly, it was October, 1929. Banks failed. Merchants declared bankruptcy. Ranchers began to sell off stock and acreage. But Papa's health improved. He also had to close, but he rejected the bankruptcy route. He sold everything he had in the store at any price he could get. He paid all his bills. Money continued to dribble in from Ohio. We had our house. I became the bread-winner. And I began to write.

Through an incredible series of events I was invited to submit something to H. L. Mencken's *American Mercury*. Almost as incredibly, a door was opened to Hollywood. In 1937 I went there on a three-months' script-writing contract for a studio. I remained for fifteen years. As soon as I got settled, Mama and Papa pulled up stakes and joined me.

The Second World War soon dominated all our lives for a time. I bought a house with a large backyard, a section of it fenced off for a "victory garden." Papa and Mama could work the land again. When a new acquaintance would ask Papa, "What do you do?", he would say, "We are farmers."

"Really! What do you raise on your farm?"

"My wife grows tomatoes," he would reply, "and lettuce and stuff like that. I specialize in sweet corn."

In 1952 I returned to Phoenix and married my husband. Papa had died in 1948 and Mama lived with us in Phoenix until her death in 1958. She never conceded that the best tomatoes in the best markets even approached the ones she grew in her "victory garden."

# 1980

It was June in Ohio, perhaps the loveliest month of the year. It was June on the banks of the Ohio River and on the hills beyond the river in Kentucky and on the lush hills that rose above the left flank of the town, just as the river, a giant moat, protected its right flank.

It was 1980, and I had returned to Ohio after an absence of sixty-two years, broken only by a brief stopover in 1925 on my way elsewhere. This place, of all places and over so many years, had remained more firmly in possession of a part of my heart and of my life than any other. I returned now to discover why I was so bound to the place and the time.

New Richmond itself had changed very little. The most notable difference was the presence of cars on the streets and two service stations on Front Street, the main thoroughfare that looked down upon the river. The one hotel I remembered, the Curry House, was gone, and I was staying at the town's only motel. Our high school building, erected after the great flood of 1913 had destroyed the old one, was now used to store records. All the one-room schools in the district plus a handsome new high school had been consolidated into a fine group of brick-and-glass structures in the hills above the town. I would visit them, I thought, and seek out the few friends who might be there. But that could wait until later.

\* \* \*

I rented a car and drove west on a highway that was wider and better-surfaced than any I recalled. But for some distance the great oaks still rose on either side as I remembered them—or others like them. There'd been rain in the night and the damp earth had that fragrance like no other that rises up through the soil when the roots have been nourished in the dark. Blue spruce mingled with the oaks and small raindrops still bejeweled the flat needles as the sun filtered through and set them alight. I marveled at this; I did not remember the blue spruce.

I approached Mount Pisgah, or "Kegtown," as it was familiarly known. It seemed more changed, more modernized than New Richmond. I recognized only one familiar landmark: the spire of the Methodist church. I turned the corner where once Perkins' General Store had stood and headed for the bend in the road, beyond which lay the very soil into which I had put down roots when I was a child of six.

The way seemed interminable. Had I taken a wrong turn? I considered turning back and starting over, but I moved slowly ahead, past neat houses with well-kept lawns, each with its own mailbox beside the road. Suddenly there loomed ahead of me an abandoned dwelling. It was of brick, painted gray. The paint was worn away and weather-stained. The windows were broken and shutters hung loose. The yard was overgrown with tall grass and weeds. A dead tree, its branches bare and blackened, was the only one left of several I remembered; this one had once yielded a treasure of hickory nuts. It was the old Mott Place, where Dr. John Mott's brother Charlie lived with his family—our nearest neighbors on that side. And beyond, the bend in the road would take me home.

I made the turn and drove through a neat gate that stood hospitably open. Where our barn had been now stood a three-car garage. The house, set in the same position, was almost like the one we had lived in during our last five years on Dunham's Hill. But it was larger, and a storybook white picket fence surrounded the yard. There were hollyhocks against the fence but no lilacs, no yellow rose. Two children were playing on the porch; they ran into the house, no doubt to report a stranger approaching. I turned and drove away.

I had my bearings now and drove to the site of the old schoolhouse that I attended through the seventh grade. I found the building easily, resting firmly on a low rise, painted white and half a story higher. A doghouse stood where the "privies" had been. The woodshed had turned into a garage.

That night I sat on a bench on a strip of grass beside the motel and looked out at the river. The surface was very calm and smooth and a full moon flung a golden carpet between Kentucky and Ohio. I felt completely at peace.

We had arrived in a strange community, aliens in many ways. My parents' English was the speech of aliens; their religion was a religion of aliens; their food was the food of aliens. I was a child who did not know the Lord's Prayer. Yet the people made us welcome. We learned from them and, in time, they learned from us. We respected one another. When I invited some children to my home and included the two black girls who were our classmates, nobody boycotted the party. If they did not embrace those two "aliens," they did not offend them. There was affection at the most and respect at the least on Dunham's Hill.

In those years between 1906 and 1918 I had come to know pain and joy, bewilderment and fear. But I had also learned not to judge. In this community of acceptance I learned to accept and in time to forgive. Watching the moon's bright path on the river, I knew why I had come home.